Edited by
J. F. W. DEAKIN

The Biology of Depression

Proceedings of a meeting of the Biological Group
of the Royal College of Psychiatrists
held at Manchester University, 1985.

GASKELL

ISBN 0 902241 16 8

Gaskell is an imprint of the Royal College of Psychiatrists,
17 Belgrave Square, London SW1

Distributed in North America
by American Psychiatric Press, Inc.

ISBN 0-88048-254-0

Typeset by Dobbie Typesetting Service, Plymouth, Devon
Printed in Britain at the Alden Press, Oxford

Contents

Biology of Antidepressant Drugs

List of Contributors

I. M. Anderson, University Department of Psychiatry Research Unit, Littlemore Hospital, Oxford

C. A. Burke, Wellcome Research Laboratories, Beckenham, Kent

S. W. Burton, Institute of Psychiatry, Denmark Hill, London

C. M. Bradshaw, Department of Psychiatry, University of Manchester

D. R. Chambers, HM Coroner, Inner North London, Camden, London

S. A. Checkley, The Maudsley Hospital, Denmark Hill, London

S. J. Cooper, Department of Mental Health, Queen's University of Belfast

T. H. Corn, Institute of Psychiatry, Denmark Hill, London

P. J. Cowen, MRC Unit of Clinical Pharmacology, Radcliffe Infirmary, Oxford

T. J. Crow, Division of Psychiatry, Northwick Park Hospital, Harrow, Middlesex

Sharon L. Davies, Department of Pharmacology, St. George's Hospital Medical School, Cranmer Terrace, London

J. F. W. Deakin, Department of Psychiatry, University Hospital of South Manchester

I. B. Glass, Institute of Psychiatry, Denmark Hill, London

Guy M. Goodwin, MRC Unit of Clinical Pharmacology, Radcliffe Infirmary, Oxford

A. Richard Green, MRC Unit of Clinical Pharmacology, Radcliffe Infirmary, Oxford

Antony S. Hale, Department of Psychiatry, Guy's Hospital Medical School, London

Roger W. Horton, Department of Pharmacology, St. George's Hospital Medical School, Cranmer Terrace, London

J. Johnson, Division of Psychiatry, Northwick Park Hospital, Harrow, Middlesex

Cornelius L. E. Katona, Department of Psychiatry, Middlesex Hospital Medical School, London

Randy Katz, Institute of Psychiatry, Denmark Hill, London

John J. Kelly, Department of Pharmacology, University of Edinburgh

Peter McGuffin, Institute of Psychiatry, Denmark Hill, London

Graham J. Naylor, University Department of Psychiatry, Ninewells Hospital and Medical School, Dundee

F. Owen, Division of Psychiatry, Northwick Park Hospital, Harrow, Middlesex

M. Poulter, Division of Psychiatry, Northwick Park Hospital, Harrow, Middlesex

Eugene S. Paykel, Department of Psychiatry, Addenbrooke's Hospital, Cambridge

E. Szabadi, Department of Psychiatry, University of Manchester

Andreas E. Theodorou, Department of Pharmacology, St. George's Hospital Medical School, Cranmer Terrace, London

Carol A. Tunnicliffe, Springfield Hospital, London

Keith Wood, MRC Neuropsychiatry Research Laboratory, West Park Hospital, Epsom

Yukiharu Yamaguchi, Department of Pharmacology, St. George's Hospital Medical School, Cranmer Terrace, London

1 Monoamines, rewards and punishments: the anatomy and physiology of the affective disorders

J. F. W. DEAKIN; T. J. CROW

That a deficiency of one or more of the monoamine neurotransmitters is a biological component in the genesis of depression is an idea that has dominated biological views of depression for the last quarter of a century. The continued influence of this hypothesis, up-dated by advances in understanding monoamine mechanisms, is exemplified by the contributions to this volume.

The origins of monoamine deficiency theories lie in clinical observations of drug effects. In the 1950s there were reports of precipitation of depressive illnesses in hypertensive patients being treated with reserpine, a drug which depletes monoamine stores. Soon afterwards, the antidepressant efficacy of imipramine and iproniazid was discovered. These drugs, it was argued, might ameliorate depression by potentiating the synaptic actions of monoamines, imipramine by inhibiting re-uptake and iproniazid by inhibiting monoamine oxidase.

Subsequent attempts to demonstrate reductions in the concentrations of monoamine metabolites in the biological fluids or post-mortem brain of depressed patients have not met with unequivocal success. This is in contrast to studies in Alzheimer's and Parkinson's disease in which decreases in noradrenaline and serotonin, and dopamine metabolites respectively have been demonstrated. Furthermore, antidepressant drug actions are more complex than first conceived. Antidepressant effects require prolonged treatment and in animal experiments such treatment is associated with adaptive changes in receptor mechanisms and monoamine release which would appear to nullify the acute effects. These findings have shifted attention from monoamines to their receptors in the search for the pathogenesis of depression and the site of action of antidepressant therapies. We suggest that one way forward is to understand the normal behavioural functions of monoamine systems and how their dysfunction might result in depression. This is the subject of our chapter, and in the course of it we shall describe some basic concepts relevant to the chapters which follow.

The neuroscience of monoamine systems

History and techniques

Noradrenaline was identified in brain in the early 1950s (Vogt, 1954) and by the end of the decade it was clear that its precursor, dopamine, was also present and had an independent role (Bertler & Rosengren, 1959). Adrenaline, a catecholamine long identified in the periphery, was not conclusively demonstrated in brain until 1974 (Hokfelt *et al*, 1974). The indoleamine 5HT was found to be present both in brain and in the periphery in the early 1950s (Erspamer & Asero, 1953; Twarog & Page, 1953). In the 1960s a remarkable new technique made it possible to visualise monoamine neurones in histological sections of the brain (Dahlstrom & Fuxe, 1964a,b). Formaldehyde produces a fluorescent condensation product with monoamines, and this renders the neuronal stores fluorescent. Refinements of the method and the development of immunohistochemical techniques have produced a detailed knowledge of the origins and distribution of monoamine systems (Lindvall & Bjorklund, 1974).

More recently, monoamine binding sites (loosely called receptors) have been visualised using autoradiographic techniques. Brain sections are incubated with tritiated drugs which bind to 'receptor' sites. Areas of bound radioactivity are revealed by pressing the incubated sections against tritium sensitive photographic emulsion. When the film is developed the density of silver grains reflects the density of binding sites (e.g. Slater & Patel, 1983).

General properties

Monoamine systems are highly divergent. Comparatively few neuronal cell bodies in discrete brain stem nuclei give rise to widespread terminal arborisations and monoamine release probably occurs from varicosities (swellings) widely distributed over the long pre-terminal regions of the axon. Furthermore, there are few specialised postsynaptic structures. Neuronal cell discharge is likely to induce monoamine release over substantial areas of the brain. These anatomical relations imply that monoamine systems are involved in exerting general effects rather than accurate point-to-point transfer of information.

In recent years the discovery of peptide co-transmitters or co-modulators in peripheral monoamine neurones has overturned the principle, articulated by Sir Henry Dale, that each neurone contains a single neurotransmitter in all its branches. Co-localisation of monoamines and peptides is being increasingly recognised in CNS neurones (Hokfelt *et al*, 1980). The functions of peptide co-transmitters remain obscure, but the general principle that

Ascending noradrenergic pathways

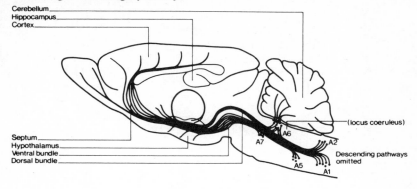

Fig. 1 — Noradrenergic pathways shown on a saggital section of the rat brain.

they modulate postsynaptic responsiveness to classical neurotransmitters may be emerging.

Noradrenergic systems

Pathways

Two major ascending noradrenergic pathways have been described in the brain stem — a dorsal bundle of fibres arising from cells of the locus coeruleus (A6) lying in the floor of the IV ventricle, and a ventral bundle arising from more caudally placed cells (A1, A2, A3 groups — see Fig. 1). Dorsal bundle fibres innervate cerebral cortex and hippocampus. Microinjections of the catecholamine neurotoxin 6-hydroxydopamine (6 OHDA) into the dorsal bundle (dorsal bundle lesions) produce a near total noradrenergic denervation of the cortex. Ventral bundle fibres innervate various hypothalamic nuclei. A more detailed description is to be found in Lindvall & Bjorklund (1974).

Receptors

As in the periphery, alpha and beta adrenergic receptors have been described in CNS. Both types are present in cerebral cortex and are located postsynaptically since they remain after dorsal bundle lesions (U'Prichard & Snyder, 1979; U'Prichard *et al*, 1980). The ability of noradrenaline to increase cyclic AMP formation in cortex is mediated by beta receptors linked

NORADRENERGIC SYNAPSE

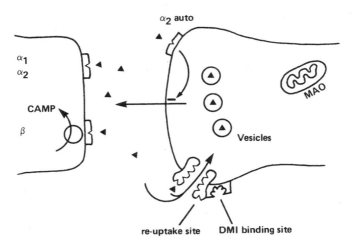

Fig. 2 — Schematic noradrenergic synapse.

to the enzyme adenylate cyclase (Fig. 2). Beta receptors on the outside of the cell membrane are linked to cyclase molecules on the inside.

Alpha receptors have been pharmacologically subdivided into alpha$_1$ and alpha$_2$. Some alpha$_2$ receptors are located on presynaptic noradrenergic nerve terminals (Fig. 2). They may 'sense' the concentration of noradrenaline in the synapse and exert a negative feedback effect on noradrenaline release (Langer, 1978). Thus presynaptic alpha antagonists increase noradrenaline release. Some antidepressant drugs such as mianserin may act in this way. Agonists at presynaptic alpha$_2$ receptors (such as clonidine) mimic noradrenaline and supress further noradrenaline release. Some alpha$_2$ sites appear to be postsynaptic and may mediate the growth hormone response to clonidine infusions (Checkley, see Chapter 6).

Re-uptake sites

Noradrenergic nerve terminals actively take up noradrenaline probably through specialised channels made of protein molecules (Fig. 2). Tricyclic antidepressants, with varying potency, inhibit noradrenaline re-uptake. Desmethylimipramine (DMI) is a selective noradrenaline re-uptake blocker. Dorsal bundle lesions greatly reduce cortical binding sites for ^{3}H-DMI, indicating that these sites are located presynaptically.

Co-transmitters

A variety of peptides (e.g. enkephalin,) are co-localised with noradrenaline in peripheral sympathetic nerves. In the CNS only neuropeptide Y has so far been identified as a noradrenergic co-transmitter (Yamazoe *et al*, 1985).

Dopamine systems

Pathways

In contrast to noradrenaline, dopamine-containing nerve terminals are mainly localised to subcortical structures; the basal ganglia (caudate, putamen), the amygdala—the limbic extension of the caudate in the temporal lobe, and the nucleus accumbens. More recently a restricted dopaminergic innervation of areas of limbic cortex (frontal, cingulate and entorhinal) has been described. These dopamine terminal networks arise from a continuous sheet of dopamine cells in the brain stem. The midline portion is the ventral tegmental area (A10 group) which gives rise to mesolimbic terminals, and the lateral extensions are the zona compacta of the substantia nigra (A9 group) innervating the basal ganglia (Lindvall & Bjorklund, 1974; Fig. 3).

Dopamine neurones in the arcuate nucleus of the hypothalamus release dopamine into the portal veins in the median eminence to inhibit prolactin release from the anterior pituitary.

Receptors

Some dopamine receptors are postsynaptic (D1, D2). D1 receptors are linked to adenylate cyclase. Others receptors are located presynaptically on dendrites

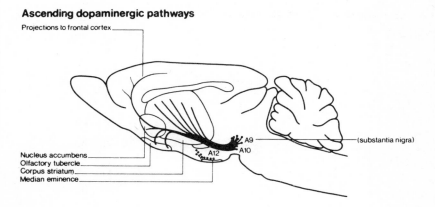

Ascending dopaminergic pathways

Projections to frontal cortex

Nucleus accumbens
Olfactory tubercle
Corpus striatum
Median eminence

A9
A10
A12
(substantia nigra)

Fig. 3 — Dopamine neurones in the rat brain.

and terminals where they may have a negative feedback function on dopamine release (Seeman, 1980).

Re-uptake sites

Tricyclic antidepressants do not inhibit dopamine re-uptake. However, the newer antidepressant nomifensine is a dopamine re-uptake blocker.

Co-transmitters

A proportion of dopaminergic terminals innervating the nucleus accumbens contain cholecystokinin (Hokfelt *et al*, 1980).

5-hydroxytryptamine (5HT, Serotonin) systems

Pathways

Most 5HT cell bodies are located in the midline raphe nuclei of the brain stem. Caudally placed B1–B3 cells innervate the dorsal and ventral horns of the spinal cord. More anteriorly placed cells in the dorsal and median raphe innervate most regions of the forebrain (Fig. 4). The two nuclei project to different areas. The dorsal raphe nucleus distributes 5HT terminals to areas innervated by dopamine; the amygdala, basal ganglia and some cortical areas. In contrast, the median raphe nucleus innervates hippocampus and cortex, a distribution which is parallel to but more limited than that of noradrenaline (Azmitia & Segal, 1978; Bobillier *et al*, 1976). Microinjections

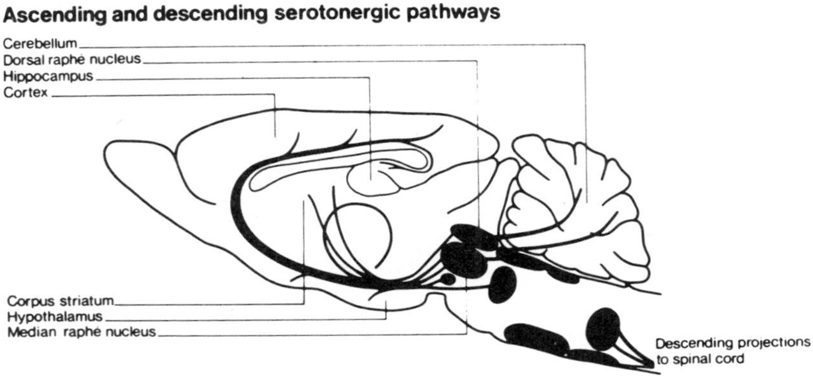

Ascending and descending serotonergic pathways

Cerebellum
Dorsal raphe nucleus
Hippocampus
Cortex

Corpus striatum
Hypothalamus
Median raphe nucleus

Descending projections
to spinal cord

Fig. 4 — 5-hydroxytryptamine containing neurones in the rat brain.

of the 5HT neurotoxin, 5, 7 dihydroxytryptamine (5, 7DHT), into the raphe nuclei substantially deplete forebrain 5HT content.

Receptors

Radioligand binding studies suggest the existence of at least two 5HT receptor subtypes. Tritiated 5HT labels sites which are distinct from those labelled by 5HT antagonists such as ketanserin. These have been designated $5HT_1$ and $5HT_2$ sites respectively (Leysen *et al*, 1983; Peroutka *et al*, 1981). Autoradiographic studies reveal that 3H-ketanserin binding (to $5HT_2$ sites) is selective to the frontal cortex and basal ganglia and parallels the distribution of dopamine terminals and 5HT terminals originating from the DRN (Slater & Patel, 1983). In contast, $5HT_1$ binding sites are concentrated in hippocampus along with MRN 5HT terminals and noradrenaline (Biegon *et al*, 1982).

There is evidence that $5HT_2$ binding sites are postsynaptic (Leysen *et al*, 1983) and mediate some aspects of the behaviours induced by serotonergic drugs, the '5HT syndrome' (Peroutka *et al*, 1981; Green, 1984). 5HT inhibits its own release, an observation that suggests there are autoreceptors on 5HT terminals. Some evidence indicates the existence of presynaptic $5HT_1$ receptors (Martin & Sanders-Bush, 1982). However, $5HT_1$ binding sites in the substantia nigra increase after 5, 7DHT lesions of the raphe, which suggests that these receptors are postsynaptic and develop denervation supersensitivity (Blackburn *et al*, 1984; Fig. 5).

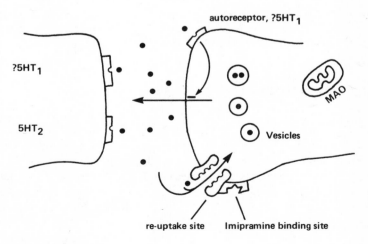

Fig. 5 — Schematic 5HT synapse.

Electrophysiological studies also indicate that different 5HT receptor mechanisms mediate pre- and postsynaptic effects. However, there is as yet no explicit correspondence between electrophysiological and ligand binding 'receptors' (De Montigny *et al*, 1984).

Re-uptake

Tricyclic antidepressants vary in their relative potencies in inhibiting noradrenaline and 5HT re-uptake. Some new compounds (e.g. citalopram, zimelidine, fluvoxamine) are highly selective 5HT re-uptake blockers (Wong *et al*, 1983). High affinity binding of tritiated imipramine is greatly reduced by 5, 7DHT lesions of the raphe nuclei and this binding is probably is probably closely related to the 5HT re-uptake site (Langer *et al*, 1981). There is some evidence that an endogenous substance may modulate 5HT re-uptake by acting at the binding site (Barbaccia *et al*, 1983).

Platelet 5HT markers

Platelets are ultimately derived from the neural crest and have properties in common with 5HT neurones. They store 5HT and have uptake and ^{3}H-imipramine binding sites. They also have $5HT_2$ receptors (Leysen *et al*, 1983). These platelet parameters have been used as peripheral indices of central 5HT function, but there is little evidence that CNS and platelet 5HT parameters co-vary.

Co-transmitters

5HT neurones in the caudal raphe, projecting to spinal cord, also contain the peptides, TRH, enkephalin and substance P. So far, peptide co-transmitters have not been identified in ascending 5HT projections.

Behavioural functions of monoamines

General observations

Brodie & Shore (1957) were the first to speculate on the behavioural functions of the monoamines. They suggested that noradrenaline neurones are an 'ergotrophic' system which mediates behavioural activation and associated activity in the sympathetic nervous system, whereas serotonin neurones mediate 'trophotrophic' behavioural inhibition associated with para-sympathetic activity. The theory was based on a misinterpretation of the effects of reserpine and LSD, but the concept retains some validity. Inhibition of catecholamine synthesis with alphamethyl paratyrosine (AMPT) is indeed associated with behavioural inhibition and sedation, but the amine involved is probably dopamine and not noradrenaline (Rech *et al*, 1966). Dorsal noradrenergic bundle lesions produce no gross change in activity, whereas 6 OHDA-induced damage to dopamine systems is associated with hypo-activity, adipsia and aphagia (Ungerstedt, 1971). In contrast to dopamine depletion, inhibition of 5HT synthesis with parachlorophenylalanine (PCPA) increases activity, reactivity, sexual behaviour and aggression and reduces sleep (Weissman & Harbert, 1972).

These contrasting effects of catecholamine and 5HT depletion suggest that catecholamines facilitate behaviour whereas serotonin has inhibitory effects. It is argued below that similar reciprocal functions are seen at the level of the spinal cord and that catecholamine and serotonin systems that ascend from the brain stem have the functions of facilitating approach to reward associated stimuli and avoidance of aversive stimuli, respectively.

Spinal cord monoamine systems — the 5HT syndrome

In the spinal cord catecholamines and serotonin have opposed motor functions, the former facilitating flexor reflexes and the latter extensor reflexes (Anden *et al*, 1964). L-dopa and clonidine restore integrated patterns of forward locomotion in acutely spinalised animals (Forssberg & Grillner, 1973), whereas serotonergic drugs (Table I) induce a retropulsive syndrome including extension of the hind limbs alongside the trunk and reciprocal forepaw pushing movements (Deakin & Dashwood, 1981). The net effect is that the animals push themselves backwards. These behaviours persist after transections of the hind-brain which indicates that they originate in the spinal cord. The intensity of the 5HT syndrome has been used as a

TABLE I
Drugs eliciting the spinal cord 5HT syndrome

Drugs	Behaviours
Presynaptic	
MAOI + Tryptophan	Reciprocal forepaw treading
Fenfuramine	Head weaving
p-chloroamphetamine	Blind limb extension
	Tremor
	Hyperthermia
	Piloerection
Receptor agonists	
Quipazine	
5-methoxy-N, N-dimethyltryptamine	
(5MeODMT)	
LSD	

quantitative measure of *in vivo* 5HT neurotransmission (e.g. see Green, Chapter 10).

It is suggested that the contrasting spinal actions of catecholamines and noradrenaline reflect phylogenetically primitive unconditioned approach and retreat (escape) mechanisms. With phylogeny and the development of ascending forebrain projections the role of monoamine systems has been elaborated from unconditioned to conditioned, or learned, approach and avoidance behaviour; catecholamines facilitate approach to stimuli predicting reward (food, water, etc.), and serotonin facilitates avoidance of stimuli predicting noxious events.

Catecholamines and reward

Self-stimulation

In 1954 Olds & Milner observed that stimulation of certain brain areas through chronically implanted electrodes appeared to have reward-like properties. Rats could be trained to press a bar for brain stimulation just as hungry rats bar-press for food. Self-stimulation can be rapid, associated with behavioural activation and can persist to the exclusion of other behaviours. The behaviour was shown to be anatomically and neurochemically specific: many brain areas did not support self-stimulation, and reserpine and chlorpromazine potently inhibited the behaviour, whereas other sedatives did not (Olds *et al*, 1956).

The discovery suggested the existence of specific neuronal systems coding for reward (reinforcement), a concept implicit in psychological theories of learning since the turn of the century. The hypothesis that these systems were adrenergic arose from the observed inhibitory effects of reserpine and the enhancement of self-stimulation rates by low doses of amphetamine which were otherwise without behavioural effects (Stein, 1962).

Self-stimulation mapping

High rates of self-stimulation were obtained with electrodes implanted in the medial forebrain bundle, which histochemical techniques later showed contains densely packed catecholamine and indoleamine nerve fibres. With the development of monoamine maps, it became possible to determine which monoamine systems mediate self-stimulation by testing brain stem electrode sites for self-stimulation and observing whether they corresponded to one or more monoamine cell groups.

Crow (1972) demonstrated that self-stimulation was obtained when electrodes were located in the A9/A10 area, the dorsal bundle and the locus coeruleus. He concluded that both dopamine and noradrenaline containing neurones originating in the locus coeruleus might be substrates for self-stimulation behaviour whereas the noradrenergic neurones originating in the caudal brain stem were not.

Many experimental tests of this hypothesis have since been carried out. These include attempts to eliminate the reward component of brain-stimulation with drugs or lesions which disrupt dopaminergic or noradrenergic neurotransmission. The evidence has been reviewed elsewhere (Crow & Deakin, 1978). No convincing refutation of the involvement of dopamine has emerged. Furthermore, animals will bar-press for intravenous infusions of the dopaminergic drugs apomorphine, amphetamine and cocaine (Baxter *et al*, 1974; see Crow & Deakin 1985). The rewarding component of drug-reinforced behaviour is specifically disrupted by neuroleptics and by destruction of mesolimbic dopamine terminals using 6 OHDA (e.g. Goeders & Smith, 1983).

A role for noradrenaline in self-stimulation behaviour is less securely established than that for dopamine. The difficulty is that while drug-induced disruption of noradrenaline systems has the predicted effects, 6 OHDA lesions of noradrenaline pathways have not been shown to do so (Crow & Deakin, 1978). Indeed, other, somewhat implausible theories have been advanced to account for localisation of self-stimulation sites to the locus coeruleus (Van der Kooy & Phillips, 1977).

Self-stimulation pathways and behaviour

The discovery of self-stimulation pathways suggested a neuroanatomical and later a neurochemical substrate for learning theory concepts of reinforcement and incentive. In the operant conditioning tradition reinforcers are stimuli which increase the probability of antecedent behaviour or, in Hulls terms, habit strength. Thus behaviours followed by reinforcement are learned. Thorndike (1911) suggested this occurred by a retroactive action of reinforcement 'stamping in' connections between antecedent stimuli and responses. On subsequently encountering similar stimuli the rewarded behaviour is more likely to occur. Later theories stressed the importance of attractive, energising or incentive properties of reinforcers and the ability of stimuli predictive of reinforcement to acquire 'incentive' through the mechanism of classical conditioning (Bolles, 1967).

Crow has postulated a neuroanatomical and neurochemical substrate for these psychological concepts (Crow, 1973). According to this theory conditioned incentive stimuli attract the organism and guide it to the reinforcer by activating dopaminergic pathways. Dopamine neurones thus function as an incentive, approach or guidance system, homing-in the organism to reinforcers. The consummatory response, Crow suggests, activates the coerulo-cortical noradrenergic pathways and the resulting release of noradrenaline consolidates connections between recently active neurones representing environmental stimuli and the dopamine incentive system. Thus, stimuli predictive of reinforcement acquire the ability to activate the dopamine approach system. In this way dopamine systems are involved in one type (the learning of incentive value) of learning. According to the theory, however, all forms of learning (e.g. motor skills, learning of visual perception) and of memory are mediated by changes in neuronal connectivity brought about by the operation of the coerulo-cortical reinforcement system when a sequence of stimuli and behaviours is followed by a successful outcome (i.e. reinforcement). The locus coeruleus noradrenergic system thus plays a critical role.

Dopamine and incentive

There can be little doubt that dopamine systems have important sensory-motor guidance functions. Experiments with 6 OHDA lesions of different terminal fields of the dopamine system implicate the nigro-striatal systems in determining direction of attention and activity (Marshall & Teitelbaum, 1974). Nucleus accumbens terminals determine the level of locomotor activity and patterns of exploratory behaviour (see Robbins & Everitt, 1982; Kelley *et al*, 1975). These findings are compatible with the proposed guidance function of the dopamine system. That the system is specifically activated by reinforcers and incentives to 'home-in' the organism is compatible with much experimental evidence. Some key findings are as follows:

In operant tasks in which animals traverse a runway or press a bar for food, removing the reinforcer is followed by a gradual decline in responding (extinction). The dopamine receptor antagonist, pimozide, also causes extinction of responding despite the continued presence of the reinforcer (Wise *et al*, 1978). Various controls in these experiments suggest the drug directly interferes with some aspect of the reward quality of the reinforcer rather than causing sensory-motor impairments. Furthermore, other studies suggest that stimuli predictive of reinforcement (classical conditioning) fail to acquire or elicit incentive when animals are treated with neuroleptics (Benninger & Phillips, 1980). Conversely, in thirsty rats, amphetamine or pipradrol-enhancement of dopamine release, greatly accelerates bar-pressing to activate a light (conditioned stimulus) that had previously regularly preceded presentation of water (Robbins, 1978).

These findings are consistent with a role for dopamine in incentive. An even more direct role for dopamine in reinforcement effects has been suggested and is a matter of continuing debate (Wise, 1982; Benninger, 1983).

Noradrenaline and learning

Learning and memory necessarily involve changes in neuronal connectivity. In many species connections are particularly 'plastic' in the early stages of brain development and at this stage they can be influenced by experimental means. In some situations plasticity depends on intact noradrenergic neurones (Kasamatsu & Pettigrew, 1976; Sutherland *et al*, 1982). In the cat, visual cortex neurones are binocular—driven by input from both eyes. Temporary eye closure in infancy results in inputs from the closed eye being taken over by inputs from the eye which remains open. Kasamatsu & Pettigrew (1976) showed that cells remained binocular despite eye closure in animals with 6 OHDA-induced destruction of cortical noradrenergic terminals. Thus, plasticity may depend upon an intact noradrenergic innervation to the cortex.

The involvement of cortical noradrenaline in changes in neuronal connections which are involved in learning new behaviours in adult animals is more controversial. Early reports that lesions of the locus coeruleus disrupted simple runway learning (Anelzark *et al*, 1973) have not been seen with more selective dorsal bundle 6 OHDA lesions. Simple operant tasks are learned despite depletions of cortical noradrenaline by more than 95% (Mason, 1981). However, recent experiments demonstrate that dorsal bundle lesions prevent acquisition of more complex operant tasks at the rate achieved by control animals (Robbins & Everitt, 1982).

Avoidance learning may also involve the operation of reinforcement processes, in this case activated by the 'relieving' offset of punishment. In rats, learning not to step off a platform onto an electrified grid is impaired by drug or lesion-induced disruption of noradrenergic systems. Some of these experiments have suggested a role for noradrenaline in memory consolidation (Crow & Wendlandt, 1976; Hall, 1976; Stein *et al*, 1975).

A new systemically effective neurotoxin, DSP-4, causes a more widespread depletion of noradrelanine than dorsal bundle lesions and this may explain why DSP-4 and not dorsal bundle lesions can produce learning impairments in simple tasks (Archer *et al*, 1982; Archer *et al*, 1983). However, experiments with DSP-4 (Bradshaw *et al*, 1985) cast doubt on the idea that noradrenaline transmits information about changes in the magnitude of reinforcement. No DSP-4 effects on patterns of bar-pressing for changing rates of food reinforcement were seen.

Simple classical conditioning is not impaired by dorsal bundle lesions. However, in 'blocking' experiments, Lorden *et al* (1980) have argued that the unconditioned stimulus remains 'unexpected' in animals with dorsal bundle lesions. Thus animals depleted of brain noradrenaline fail to learn aspects of the predictive nature of conditioned stimuli.

In summary, there is evidence for a role of noradrenaline in neuronal plasticity and learning. Whether cortical noradrenergic synapses are activated by reinforcement has yet to be established. Competing and viable theories hold that noradrenergic neurones are concerned with selective attention (Waterhouse & Woodward, 1980; Pisa & Fibiger, 1983) and arousal (Robbins & Everitt, 1982), but suggestions for their involvement in frustrative non-reward (Gray *et al*, 1975) and anxiety (Redmond & Huang, 1979) are inconsistent with much experimental evidence. For an extended discussion see Crow & Deakin (1985).

Serotonin and punishment

Theoretical aspects

An extensive literature suggests an inhibitory role of 5HT release on the transmission of pain within the spinal cord (Dickenson *et al*, 1979; Jordan *et al*, 1978); activation of this system may be one mechanism by which opiates induce analgesia (Deakin & Dostrovsky, 1978). The normal functions of this system are not clear. Bolles & Fanselow (1980) have suggested that fear inhibits pain to allow escape responses to proceed unhindered by reflexes to tissue damage which are more appropriately released when the organism is safe. There is indeed evidence that stimuli which predict pain (conditioned fear stimuli) induce a preparatory analgesia dependent upon descending pain-inhibiting 5HT systems (Watkins *et al*, 1981). Conditioned fear stimuli also induce freezing and behavioural inhibition and many experiments have shown that drug-induced impairments of 5HT neurotransmission release behaviours suppressed in anticipation of pain (see below). This has given rise to suggestions that the central motive state of fear is mediated by ascending 5HT projections (Wise *et al*, 1970).

Early operant learning theorists conceived of aversive events weakening connections between antecedent stimuli and responses to suppress punished behaviour. Such simple S-R conceptions of learning are certainly inadequate and later theorists emphasised the ability of stimuli predictive of punishment (conditioned fear stimuli) to acquire aversiveness or negative incentive by classical conditioning (Miller, 1948; Mackintosh, 1974).

Deakin (1983) has argued that negative incentive may be subserved the DRN-limbic-striatal 5HT system. 5HT operates in antagonism to dopamine in the control of locomotion (Carter & Pycock, 1979; Mabry & Campbell, 1973; Lyness & Moore, 1981) and aversive activation of 5HT release in these areas would inhibit approach and guide the organism away from conditioned fear stimuli.

The median raphe nucleus innervates hippocampus and cortex and is hypothesised (Deakin, 1983) to function antagonistically to noradrenaline by weakening neuronal connections in aversive situations.

The dorsal raphe nucleus and fear

The conflict test has been widely used to investigate anxiety and anxiolytic drugs. Hungry rats are trained to bar-press for food and then a conflict contingency is introduced when bar-presses also produce footshock. Animals learn to withold bar-pressing during the conflict stage and thus avoid footshock. Benzodiazepines and other anxiolytic agents release bar-pressing from footshock inhibition. So do drugs which interfere with 5HT neurotransmission (Geller & Blum, 1970; Graeff, 1974) and, most impressively, 5, 7DHT lesions to 5HT pathways (Tye *et al*, 1977). Thiebot *et al*, (1980) demonstrated that localised microinjections of benzodiazepines into the DRN reproduced the anti-conflict effect of systemic benzodiazepines. This and other evidence (File *et al*, 1979; Hobbs *et al*, 1984) implicates the DRN in anxiety and as a site of action of benzodiazepines.

More complex forms of aversive learning also seem to involve serotonergic mechanisms, although no studies have sought to implicate the DRN system specifically (Deakin, 1983). It can be seen that a good deal of evidence is compatible with a negative incentive function for serotonergic neurones, particularly those arising from the DRN.

The median raphe disconnection system

There are three experimental situations in which weakening of neuronal connections has been invoked to explain decrements in behaviour. These are (i) the long-term disappearance of behaviours when they are no longer rewarded; (ii) habituation of exploration of novel stimuli or environments; and (iii) latent inhibition — possibly a special case of habituation. There is evidence that disruption of serotonergic mechanisms abolishes or reduces all three phenomena so that behaviours which should disappear are abnormally persistent (Deakin 1983; Benninger & Phillips, 1979; Hole *et al*, 1977; Thornton & Goudie, 1978). In one study the effect was localised to the MRN system (Solomon *et al*, 1980).

In summary, there is evidence that decrements in behaviour which may involve neuronal disconnection are dependent on serotonergic systems. There is as yet little direct evidence for the hypothesis that hippocampal-cortical 5HT projection is the system involved.

Clinical implications

Behavioural and neurochemical formulations of depression

The occurrence of depression in patients treated with reserpine (Muller *et al*, 1955) or tetrabenazine (Lingjaerde, 1963), which deplete all three monoamines, is the initial observation on which neurochemical theories of depression are based. Schildkraut (1965) proposed the more specific noradrenergic deficiency theory on the basis of early pharmacological studies which suggested antidepressants facilitated noradrenergic neurotransmission. Stein (1962) was the first to formulate a noradrenergic deficiency theory based upon the putative behavioural function of noradrenergic neurones as a reward system. An attraction of this behavioural theory is the suggestion that, in addition to endogenous predisposition, loss of environmental sources of reinforcement (bereavement, redundancy) is predicted to reduce transmission in noradrenergic reward systems and might explain the importance of these factors in the genesis of depression. Akiskal & McKinney (1975) have pointed out how various formulations of depression have a common postulate of a lost efficacy of reward. Clinically, a pervasive loss of interest or pleasure is held by many to be at the core of depressive symptomatology.

Symptoms of anxiety are a common feature of depressive illnesses and depression complicates anxiety states. The relationship between the two syndromes is obviously close and, in the neuroses, there is evidence the two cannot be separated in terms of responsiveness to different treatments (Johnstone *et al*, 1980). Evidence discussed earlier suggests that anxiety and fear, preparatory aversive responses, are mediated by serotonergic 'negative incentive' systems. It would follow that inappropriate anxiety could result from excessive activation of serotonergic negative incentive systems. That depression and anxiety are separate dimensions of behaviour may follow from their separate mediation by catecholamine deficiency and serotonin excess; the fact that they are related, from the reciprocal interactions between the two neurochemical systems. Thus diminished catecholamine function (depression) may be primary, or secondary to excessive inhibition from an overactive serotonergic anxiety system. Conversely, excessive serotonergic function (anxiety) could be primary, or secondary to loss of reciprocal inhibition by catecholamine neurones.

Noradrenaline and depression

Although many findings in biological psychiatry are not replicated, two findings in depression are persistent. Firstly, several groups report lowered urinary excretion rates of the noradrenaline metabolite MHPG in depression (see Checkley, Chapter 6). To the extent that urinary MHPG reflects brain metabolism, this finding is consistent with a deficiency of noradrenergic transmission. Secondly, several groups report that hormonal responses to amphetamine and clonidine are blunted in depressed patients indicating a defect at the level of postsynaptic alpha noradrenergic receptors or beyond (see Checkley, Chapter 6).

Dopamine and depression

Reduced CSF levels of the dopamine metabolite homovanillic acid (HVA) have been reported in depression (Van Praag & Korf, 1971). The behavioural functions of dopamine suggest that a reduction in dopamine release would impair incentive aspects of reward mechanisms and explain the presence of apathy, anhedonia and retardation in depression. However, while neuroleptic drugs may induce such symptoms they probably do not precipitate depression, and attempts to treat depression with L-dopa have resulted at most in improvements in retardation (Goodwin *et al*, 1970). Defective dopaminergic neurotransmission may thus account for components of the depressive syndrome, but the complete syndrome may require additional dysfunction elsewhere.

Serotonin and depression

Several studies have reported reduced CSF levels of the 5HT metabolite 5-hydroxyindoleacetic acid (5HIAA) in depression (Asberg *et al*, 1976; Van Praag *et al*, 1973; Sjostrom & Roos, 1972). These findings encourage 5HT deficiency theories of depression. However, the behavioural effects of 5HT depletion in animals (see above) are far more reminiscent of mania than depression. It is conceivable that reduced 5HIAA is a compensatory response to excessive serotonergic activity (e.g. at the postsynaptic level) rather than an indication of reduced serotonergic transmission. The efficacy of 5HT precursors (5 HTP, tryptophan) in the treatment of depression is controversial; they may act through non-specific effects on catecholamine metabolism (Van Praag, 1983). Attempts to assess the functional state of 5HT neurotransmission in depression using neuroendocrine strategies have yielded conflicting evidence (see Cowen, Chapter 4). Thus biological studies in depression have yet to discriminate between 5HT deficiency and 5HT excess theories of depression.

Perhaps the most direct approach to monoamine theory of affective disorder is through post-mortem studies of patients with suicide and depression. That such studies have so far failed to yield evidence of significant disturbances of monoaminergic transmission (Cooper *et al*, Chapter 3) is perhaps the most serious challenge the monoamine hypothesis now faces.

The mechanism of action of antidepressants

Acute effects

The discovery that tricyclic drugs inhibit noradrenaline uptake and thus potentiate its synaptic actions was an early impetus to the monoamine theory of affective disorder. The finding that some tricyclics block 5HT re-uptake lead to suggestion that there are both noradrenaline and 5HT deficiency depressions, differentially responsive to tricyclics active at one or other uptake site. However, more recent studies indicate this is unlikely since many antidepressants (e.g. amitriptyline, doxepin, nortriptyline, mianserin) have 5HT receptor antagonist properties as demonstrated by their ability to antagonise the behavioural effects of 5HTP and to displace ^{3}H-5HT and ^{3}H-LSD binding (Nagayama *et al*, 1981; Fuxe *et al*, 1977). Indeed, for trazodone 5HT antagonism is its main pharmacological action and the only currently available explanation for its antidepressant effects (Al-Yassiri *et al*, 1981).

It is of interest that some clinical studies report antidepressant and anxiolytic effects of 5HT antagonist drugs such as pizotifen (Standal, 1977). Other antidepressants (e.g. viloxazine, maprotiline) lack 5HT antagonism but are potent noradrenaline re-uptake blockers. Therefore, as far as immediate effects are concerned, there is no unified mechanism of antidepressant action. At least two actions may contribute to aspects of therapeutic efficacy: (i) potentiation of noradrenaline — perhaps a direct antidepressant effect reversing defects in catecholamine reward mechanisms; and (ii) antagonism of 5HT — perhaps reversing symptoms of anxiety by antagonising excessive 5HT punishment system activity and thus contributing indirectly to antidepressant actions.

Delayed effects

The acute effects of antidepressants are in contrast to their delayed therapeutic effects. In neurochemical studies of prolonged antidepressant treatment delayed effects which (in contrast to the acute actions) are common to most antidepressants have been described. Sulser and colleagues (1983) demonstrated that all antidepressants, when administered for several days, induced delayed reductions in noradrenaline sensitive adenylate cyclase activity. In many but not all cases there is a corresponding reduction in beta-adrenergic receptor sites in radioligand binding assays. Furthermore, the same effects are produced by repeated electrically-induced seizures (ECS) (Deakin *et al*, 1979). There is evidence that these changes are secondary, adaptive responses to increased noradrenaline release since dorsal bundle lesions prevent antidepressant and ECS-induced down-regulation of beta receptor function (Wolfe *et al*, 1978). However, recent studies indicate that intact 5HT systems are also necessary for this down-regulation to occur. The mechanisms involved are at present obscure (Sulser *et al*, 1983). The overall effect of antidepressants on noradrenergic function net of pre- and postsynaptic actions and of acute and chronic administration remains unclear. The effectiveness of antidepressant drugs with actions on noradrenergic mechanisms cannot be construed as unequivocal support for the noradrenergic deficiency theory of depression.

With the exception of nomifensine and MAOIs, antidepressants do not have acute effects on dopaminergic neurotransmission. However, prolonged administration of some antidepressants and ECS have been associated with potentiated dopaminergic effects. In both cases this is a functional change so far unassociated with changes in ligand binding.

A second delayed property shared by established antidepressant drugs is a down-regulation in $5HT_2$ binding and an associated reduction in behavioural reactions to serotoninergic drugs (Peroutka & Snyder, 1980). Paradoxically, repeated ECS has the opposite effect. It increases 5HT-mediated behaviour and $5HT_2$ receptor binding, and this is a major difficulty for the idea that down-regulation of $5HT_2$ receptors is a common mechanism of action of antidepressant therapies.

Electrophysiological experiments are at variance with receptor binding and behavioural evidence for down-regulated 5HT function following antidepressants. De Montigny *et al*, (1983) found most antidepressants and ECS enhance electrophysiological responsiveness of cells to intophoretically applied 5HT. The mechanism of this effect is unknown.

Several drug companies have developed drugs which are highly selective 5HT re-uptake blockers (citalopram, fluoxetine, fluvoxamine) aimed at reversing a supposed deficit of 5HT in depression. The drugs mentioned (in contrast to zimelidine) do not have 5HT antagonist properties nor do they induce delayed down-regulation of beta or $5HT_2$ receptors. Assuming no other pharmacological properties are discovered, their effectiveness in depression may prove a critical test of the 5HT excess theory of depression and anxiety.

Conclusions

The monoamine hypothesis remains a major stimulus to neurochemical and pharmacological research on the affective disorders.

With increasing knowledge of the physiological functions of monoamine neuronal system the hypothesis retains its attraction. Thus there are strong grounds for believing that these systems mediate general aspects of the organism's responses to rewards and punishments in the environment. Catecholamine systems appear closely related to reward and approach behaviours, and serotonin neurones to punishment and avoidance. Specifically it is suggested that dopamine systems mediate the incentive or activating effects of rewarding stimuli on behaviour, while noradrenergic systems (e.g. the dorsal bundle) may influence the synaptic plasticity in the cortex which underlies learning. Conversely, serotonergic systems are envisaged to mediate the effects of noxious stimuli, including reflex withdrawal (at the spinal level), negative incentive (at the level of the striatum), and perhaps extinction and habituation. The monoamine hypothesis of affective disorder can thus be reformulated: 'Depression results from hypoactivity of catecholaminergic reward systems, and anxiety from hyperactivity of serotonergic punishment systems, the two systems interacting with each other such that anxiety and depression represent separate but correlated dimensions of disturbance.'

The therapeutic effects of antidepressant and anxiolytic drugs can perhaps be understood within this framework — noradrenergic potentiation contributing to the former and serotonin antagonism to the latter — but much concerning these actions, including the time course of the effects, remains obscure. Direct evidence for disturbances of monoaminergic transmission in patients with affective disorder (a major focus of the contributions to this volume) is as yet equivocal. The interpretation of studies on peripheral fluids and on CSF is difficult, and post-mortem studies to date have provided surprisingly little evidence of significant disturbances of monoaminergic transmission. In spite of these difficulties the monoamine hypothesis remains at the centre of attempts to understand the pathophysiology of affective disturbance.

References

AKISKAL, H. S. & MCKINNEY, W. T. (1973) Depressive disorders: towards a unified hypothesis. *Science*, **182**, 20–29.

AL-YASSIRI, M. M., ANKIER, S. I. & BRIDGES, P. K. (1981) Trazodone — a new anti-depressant. *Life Sciences*, **28**, 2449–2458.

ANLEZARK, G. M., CROW, T. J. & GREENWAY, A. P. (1973) Impaired learning and decreased cortical norepinephrine after bilateral locus coeruleus lesions. *Science*, **181**, 682–684.

ARCHER, T., COTIC, T. & JARBE, T. U. C. (1982) Attenuation of the context effect and lack of unconditioned stimulus — pre-exposure effect in taste-aversion learning following treatment with DSP4, the selective noradrenaline neurotoxin. *Behavioural and Neural Biology* **35**, 159–173.

ARCHER, T., MOHAMMED, A. K., ROSS, S. B., & SODERBERG, U. (1983) T-maize learning, spontaneous activity and food intake recovery following systemic administration of the noradrenaline neurotoxin, DSP4. *Pharmacology, Biochemistry and Behaviour*, **19**, 121–130.

ASBERG, M., THONEN, P., TRASKMAN, L., BERTILSSON, L. & RINGBERGER, V. (1976) 'Serotonin depression' a biochemical subgroup within the affective disorders? *Science*, **191**, 478–480.

ANDEN, N. E., JUKES, M. G. M. & LUNDBERG, A. (1964) Spinal reflexes and monoamine liberation. *Nature*, **202**, 1222–1223.

AZMITIA, E. C. & SEGAL, M. (1978) An autoradiographic analysis of the differential ascending projections of the dorsal and median raphe nuclei in the rat. *Journal of Comparative Neurology*, **179**, 641–668.

BARBACCIA, M. L., GANDOFFI, O., CHUANG, D. M. & COSTA, E. (1983) Modulation of serotonin uptake by a putative endogenous ligand of imipramine recognition sites. *Proceedings of the National Academy of Science*, **80**, 5134–5138.

BAXTER, B. L., GLUCKMAN, M. I., STEIN, L. & SCERNI, R. A. (1974) Self-injection of apomorphine in the rat: positive reinforcement by a dopamine receptor stimulant. *Pharmacology, Biochemistry and Behaviour*, **2**, 387–391.

BENNINGER, R. J. & PHILLIPS, A. G. (1979) Possible involvement of serotonin in extinction. *Pharmacology, Biochemistry and Behaviour*, **10**, 37–41.

BENNINGER, R. J. & PHILLIPS, A. G. (1980) The effect of pimozide on the establishment of conditioned reinforcement. *Psychopharmacology*, **68**, 147–153.

BENNINGER, R. J. (1983) The role of dopamine in locomotor activity and learning. *Brain Research Review*, **6**, 173–196.

BERTLER, A. & ROSENGREN, E. (1959) Occurrence and distribution of dopamine in brain and other tissues. *Experientia*, **15**, 10.

BIEGON, A., RAINBOW, T. C. & McEWEN, B. S. (1982) Quantitative autoradiography of serotonin receptors in rat brain. *Brain Research*, **242**, 197–204.

BLACKBURN, T. P., BAVERY, N. G., COX, B., HUDSON, A. L., MARTIN, D. & PRINCE, G. W. (1984) Lesion of the dorsal raphe nucleus increases the nigral concentration of 5HT1 receptors. *British Journal of Pharmacology*, **82**, 293P.

BOBILLIER, P., SEGUIN, S., PETIJEAN, F., SALVERT, D., TOMET, M. & JOUVET, M. (1976) The raphe nuclei of the cat brain stem: a topographical atlas of their efferent projections as revealed by autoradiography. *Brain Research*, **113**, 449–486.

BOLLES, R. C. (1967) *Theory of Motivation*, Harper, New York.

BOLLES, R. C. & FANSELOW, M. S. (1980) A perceptual-defensive model of fear and pain. *Behaviour and Brain Science*, **3**, 291–232.

BRADSHAW, C. M., MORLEY, M. J. & SZABADI, E. (1985) Failure of DSP4 to affect positively reinforced behaviour. *British Journal of Pharmacology* (in press).

BRODIE, B. B. & SHORE, P. A. (1957) A concept for a role of serotonin and norepinephrine as chemical mediators in the brain. *Annals of the New York Academy of Science*, **66**, 631–642.

CARTER, C. J. and PYCOCK, C. J. (1979) The effects of 5, 7-dihydroxytryptamine lesions of extra pyramidal and mesolimbic sites on spontaneous motor behaviour and amphetamine-induced stereotypy. *Naunyn-Schmiedebergs Archives of Pharmacology*, **208**, 31–54.

CROW, T. J. (1972) A map of the rat mesencephalon for electrical self-stimulation. *Brain Research*, **34**, 265–273.

—— (1973) Catecholamine neurones and self-stimulation. II A theoretical interpretation and some psychiatric implications. *Psychological Medicine*, **3**, 66–73.

—— DEAKIN, J. F. W. (1985) The neurochemistry of behaviour, the pharmacology of centrally acting drugs and the mechanism of the disturbance in psychiatric disease. In *Handbook of Psychiatry* Vol. 5, (eds. Shepherd, M. and Zangwill, O. L.) Cambridge University Press.

—— DEAKIN, J. F. W. (1978) Brain reinforcement centres and psychoactive drugs. In *Recent Advances in Alcohol and Drug Problems* Vol. 4. (eds. Israel, Y., Glaser, F. B., Kalant, M., Popham, K. E., Schmidt, W. and Smarr, R. G.) New York, Plenum Press.

—— WENDLANDT, S. (1976) Impaired acquisition of a passive avoidance response after lesions induced in the locus coeruleus by 6-OH-dopamine. *Nature*, **259**, 42–44.

DAHLSTROM, A. & FUXE, K. (1964a) Localisation and morphology of monoamine-containing nerve cells. *Acta Physiologica Scandinavica* (Suppl. **232**), 13–25.

—— (1964b) Evidence for the existence of monoamine containing neurones in the central nervous system I. Demonstration of monoamines in the cell bodies of brain stem neurones. *Acta Physiologica Scandinavica*, **62**, (Suppl. 232), 1–155.

DEAKIN, J. F. W. (1983) Roles of serotonergic systems in escape, avoidance and other behaviours. In *Theory in Psychopharmacology* Vol. II, (ed. Cooper, S. J.), London, Academic Press.

—— DASHWOOD, M. R. (1981) The differential neuro-chemical bases of the behaviours elicited by serotonergic agents and by the combination of a monoamine oxidase inhibitor and L-DOPA. *Neuropharmacology*, **20**, 123–130.

—— DOSTROVSKY, J. O. (1978) Involvement of the periaqueductal grey matter and spinal 5-hydroxytryptaminergic pathways in morphine analgesia: effects of lesions and 5HT depletion. *British Journal of Pharmacology*, **63**, 159–165.

—— OWEN, F. & POULTER, M. (1979) Alpha and beta receptor changes in cerebral cortex after electroconvulsive treatment in rats. *Neuroscience Letters*, Suppl. **3**, 5250.

DE MONTIGNY, C., BLIER, P. & CHAPAT, Y. (1984) Electrophysiologically-identified serotonin receptors in the CNS. *Neuropharmacology*, **23**, 1511–1520.

DICKENSON, A. H., OLIVERAS, J. S. & BESSON, J. M. (1979) Role of the nucleus raphe magnus in opiate analgesia as studied by the microinjection technique in the rat. *Brain Research*, **170**, 95–111.

ERSPAMER, V. & ASERO, B. (1953) Identification of enteramine, the specific hormone of the enterochromaffin cell system, as 5-hydroxytryptophan. *Nature*, **169**, 800.

FILE, S. E., HYDE, J. R. G. and MACLEOD, N. K. (1979) 5, 7-dihyroxytryptamine lesions of dorsal and median raphe nuclei and performance in the social interaction test of anxiety on a home-cage aggression test. *Journal of Affective Disorders*, **1**, 115–122.

FORSSBERG, H. & GRILLNER, S. (1973) The locomotion of the acute spinal cat injected with clonidine i.v. *Brain Research*, **90**, 184–186.

FUXE, K., OGREN, S-O., AGNATI, J.A., GUSTAFSON & HANSSEN, G. (1977) On the mechanism of action of the antidepressant drugs amitryptyline and nortriptyline. Evidence for 5-hydroxytryptamine blocking activity. *Neuroscience Letters*, **6**, 339–343.

GELLER, I. & BLUM, K. (1970) The effects of 5-HTP on parachlorophenylalanine (P-CPA) attenuation of conflict behaviour. *European Journal of Pharmacology*, **9**, 319–324.

GOEDERS, N. E. & SMITH, J. G. (1983) Cortical dopaminergic involvement in cocaine reinforcement. *Science*, **221**, 773–775.

GOODWIN, F. K., BRODIE, H. K. H., MURPHY, D. L. & BUNNEY, W. E. (1970) L-Dopa, catacholamines and behaviour: a clinical and biochemical study in depressed patients. *Biological Psychiatry*, **2**, 341–366.

GRAEFF, F. G. (1974) Tryptamine antagonists and punished behaviour. *Journal of Pharmacology and Experimental Therapeutics*, **189**, 344–350.

GRAY, J. A., McNAUGHTON, N., JAMES, D. T. D. & KELLEY, P. H. (1975) Effect of minor tranquilizers on hippocampal theta rhythm mimicked by depletion of forebrain noradrenaline. *Nature*, **258**, 424–425.

GREEN, A. R. (1984) 5HT mediated behaviour. *Animal Studies Neuropharmacology*, **23**, 1521–1528.

HALL, M. E. (1976) The effects of norepinephrine biosynthesis inhibition on the consolidation of two discriminated escape responses. *Behavioural Biology*, **16**, 145–153.

HOBBS, A., PATERSON, I. A. & ROBERTS, M. H. T. (1984) The effects on social interaction of microinjections of RO15-1788 into the nucleus raphe dorsalis of the rat. *British Journal of Pharmacology*, **82**, 241P.

HOKFELT, T., FUXE, K., GOLDSTEIN, M. & JOHANSSON, O. (1974) Immunohistochemical evidence for the existence of adrenaline neurones in the rat brain. *Brain Research*, **66**, 235–257.

—— JOHANSSON, O., LJUNGDAHL, A., LUNDBERG, J. M. & SCHULTZBERG, M. (1980) Peptidergic neurones. *Nature*, **284**, 515–521.

HOLE, K., JOHNSON, G. E. & BERGE, O-G. (1977) 5, 7-dihydroxytryptamine lesions of the ascending 5-hydroxytryptaminergic pathways: habituation, motor activity and agonistic behaviour. *Pharmacology, Biochemistry and Behaviour*, **3**, 95–102.

JOHNSTONE, E. C., OWENS, D. G. C., FRITH, C. D., McPHERSON, K., DOWIE, C., RILEY, G. & GOLD, A. (1980) Neurotic illness and its response to anxiolytic and antidepressant treatment. *Psychological Medicine*, **10**, 321–328.

JORDAN, M. L., KENSHALO, D. R., MARTIN, R. F., HABER, L. H. & WILLIS, W. D. (1978) Depression of rat spinothalamic tract neurones by iontophoretic application of 5-hydroxytryptamine. *Pain*, **5**, 135–142.

KASAMATSU, T. & PETTIGREW, J. D. (1976) Depletion of brain catecholamines: failure of ocular dominance shift after monocular occlusion in kittens. *Science*, **194**, 206–208.

KELLEY, P. H., SEVIOUR, P. W. & IVERSEN, S. D. (1975) Amphetamine and apomorphine responses in the rat following 6-OHDA lesions of the nucleus acumbens septi and corpus striatum. *Brain Research*, **94**, 507–522.

LANGER, S. Z., (1978) Presynaptic receptors and neurotransmission. *Medicine and Biology*, **56**, 288–291.

—— ZARIFIAN, E., BRILEY, M., RAISMAN, R. & SECHLER, P. (1981) High-affinity binding of 3H-Imipramine in brain and platelets and its relevance to the biochemistry of affective disorders. *Life Sciences*, **29**, 211–220.

LEYSEN, J. E., VAN GROMPEL, P., VERWIMP, M. & NIEMEGEERS, C. J. E. (1983) Role and localization of serotonin 2 (S2)—receptor-binding sites: Effects of neuronal lesions. In *CNS Receptors—from Molecular Pharmacology to Behaviour* (eds. Mandel, P. and De Feudis, F. V.) New York, Raven Press.

LINDVALL, O. & BJORKLUND, A. (1974) The organization of ascending catecholamine neurone systems in the rat brain. *Acta Physiologica Scandinavica*, **92**, Suppl. 412.

LINGJAERDE, O. (1963) Tetrabenazine (Nitoman) in the treatment of the psychosis. *Acta Psychiatrica Scandinavica* Suppl. 170, 1–109.

LORDEN, J. P., RICKERT, E. J., DAWSON, R., & PELLEYMOUNTER, M. A. (1980) Forebrain norepinephrine and the selective processing of information. *Brain Research*, **190**, 569–573.

LYNESS, W. H. & MOORE, K. E. (1981) Destruction of 5-hydroxytryptaminergic neurons and the dynamics of dopamine in the nucleus accumbens and other forebrain regions of the rat. *Neuropharmacology*, **20**, 327–334.

MABRY, P. D. & CAMPBELL, B. A. (1973) Serotonergic inhibition of catecholamine-induced behavioural arousal. *Brain Research*, **49**, 381–391.

MACKINTOSH, N. J. (1974) *The Psychology of Animal Learning*. London, Academic Press

MARSHALL, J. F. & TEITELBAUM, P. (1974) Further analysis of sensory inattention following lateral hypothalamic damage in rats. *Journal of Comparative Physiology and Psychology*, **86**, 375–390.

MARTIN, L. L. & SANDERS-BUSH, E. (1982) Comparison of the pharmacological characteristics of $5HT_1$ and $5HT_2$ binding sites with those serotonin autoreceptors which modulate serotonin release. *Archives of Pharmacology*, **321**, 165–170.

MASON, S. T. (1981) Noradrenaline and selective attention: a review of the model and the evidence. *Life Sciences*, **27**, 617–631.

MILLER, N. E. (1948) Studies of fear as an acquirable drive. *Journal of Experimental Psychology*, **38**, 89–101.

MULLER, J. C., PRYOR, W. W., GIBBONS, J. E., ORGAIN, E. S. & DURHAM, N. C. (1955) Depression and anxiety occurring during Rauwolfia therapy. *Journal of the American Medical Association*, **159**, No. 9, 836–840.

NAGAYAMA, H., HINGTEN, J. N. & APRISON, M. H. (1981) Postsynaptic action by four antidepressive drugs in an animal model of depression. *Pharmacology, Biochemistry and Behaviour*, **15**, 215–230.

OLDS, J., KILLAM, K. P. & BACH-Y-RITA, P. (1956) Self-stimulation of the brain used as a screening method for tranquillizing drugs. *Science*, **124**, 265–266.

—— MILNER, P. (1954) Positive reinforcement produced by electrical stimulation of the septal area and other regions of the rat brain. *Journal of Comparative Physiology and Psychiatry*, **47**, 419–427.

PEROUTKA, S. J., LEBOVITZ, R. M. & SNYDER, S. H. (1981) Two distinct central serotonin receptors with different physiological functions. *Science*, **212**, 827–829.

—— SNYDER, S. H. (1980) Long-term antidepressant treatment decreases spiroperidol-labelled serotonin receptor binding. *Science*, **210**, 88–90.

PISA, M. & FIBIGER, H. C. (1983) Intact selective attention in rats with lesions of the dorsal noradrenergic bundle. *Behavioural Neuroscience*, **97**, 519–529.

RECH, R. H., BORYS, H. K. & MOORE, K. E. (1966) Alterations in behaviour and brain catecholamine levels in rats treated with alpha-methyltryrosine. *Journal of Pharmacology and Experimental Therapeutics*, **153**, 412–419.

REDMOND, R. C. & HUANG, Y. H. (1979) New evidence of a locus coeruleus-norepinephrine connection with anxiety in animals and humans. *Life Sciences*, **25**, 2149–2162.

ROBBINS, T. W. (1978) The acquisition of responding with conditioned reinforcement: effects of pipradrol, methylphenidate, d-amphetamine, and nomifensine. *Psychopharmacology*, **58**, 79–87.

—— EVERITT, B. J. (1982) Functional studies of central catecholamines. *International Review of Neurobiology*, **23**, 303–364.

SEEMAN, P. (1980) Brain dopamine receptors. *Pharmacology Review*, **32**, 229–313.

SCHILDKRAUT, J. J. (1965) The catecholamine hypothesis of affective disorders; a review of supporting evidence. *American Journal of Psychiatry*, **112**, 509–522.

SJOSTROM, R. & ROOS, B. E. (1972) 5-Hydroxy indoleacetic acid and homovanillic acid in cerebrospinal fluid in manic-depressive psychosis. *European Journal of Clinical Pharmacology*, **4**, 170–176.

SLATER, P. & PATEL, S. (1983) Autoradiographic distribution of serotonin$_2$ receptors in rat brain. *European Journal of Pharmacology*, **92**, 297–298.

SOLOMON, P. R., NICHOLS, G. L. & KAPLAN, L. J. (1980) Differential effects of lesions in medial and dorsal raphe of the rat: latent inhibition and septohippocampal serotonin levels. *Journal of Comparative Physiology and Psychology*, **94**, 145–154.

STANDAL, J. E. (1977) Pizotifen as an antidepressant. *Acta Psychiatrica Scandinavica*, **56**, 276–279.

STEIN, L. (1962) Effects and interactions of imipramine, chlorpromazine, reserpine and amphetamine on self-stimulation: possible neurophysiological basis of depression. In: *Recent Advances in Biological Psychiatry, IV* (ed. J. Wortis), pp. 288–308, New York, Plenum.

—— BELLUZI, J. D. & WISE, C. D. (1975) Memory enhancement by central administration of norepinephrine. *Brain Research*, **84**, 329–335.

SULSER, F., JANOWSKY, A. J., OKADA, F., MANIER, P. H. & MOBLEY, P. L. (1983) Regulation of recognition and action function of the norepinephrine (NE) receptor-coupled adenylate cyclase system in brain: implications for the therapy of depression. *Neuropharmacology*, **22**, 425–432.

SUTHERLAND, K. J., KOLB, B., WHISHAW, I. Q. & BECKER, J. (1982) Cortical noradrenaline depletion eliminates sparing of spatial learning after neonatal frontal cortex damage in the rat. *Neuroscience Letters*, **32**, 125–130.

THIEBOT, M. H., JOBERT, A., & SOUBRIE, P. (1980) Conditioned suppression of behaviour; its reversal by intra-raphe microinjection of chlordiazepoxide and GABA. *Neuroscience Letters*, **16**, 213–217.

THORNDIKE, E. L. (1981) *Animal Intelligence*. New York, Macmillan.

THORNTON, E. W. & GOUDIE, A. J. (1978) Evidence for the role of serotonin in the inhibition of specific motor responses. *Psychopharmacology*, **60**, 73–79.

TWAROG, B. M. & PAGE, I. H. (1953) Serotonin content of some mammalian tissues and urine and a method for its determination. *American Journal of Physiology*, **175**, 157–161.

TYE, N. C., EVERITT, B. J. & IVERSEN, S. D. (1977) 5-hydroxytryptamine and punishment. *Nature*, **268**, 741–743.

UNGERSTEDT, U. (1971) Adipsia and aphagia after 6-hydroxydopamine induced degeneration of the nigro-striatal dopamine system. *Acta Physiologica Scandinavica* Suppl. **467**, 69–93.

U'PRICHARD, D. C., REISINE, T. D., YAMAMURA, S., MASON, S. T., FIBIGER, H. C., EBHERT, F. & YAMAMURA, H. I. (1980) Differential supersensitivity of β-receptor subtypes in rat cortex and cerebellum after central noradrenergic denervation. *Life Sciences*, **26**, 355–364.

—— SNYDER, S. H. (1979) Distinct α-noradrenergic receptors differentiated by binding and physiological relationships. *Life Sciences*, **242**, 79–88.

VAN DER KOOY, D. & PHILLIPS, A. G. (1977) Trigeminal substrates of intracranial self-stimulation in the brain stem. *Science*, **196**, 447–449.

VAN PRAAG, H. M. & KORF, J. (1971) Retarded depression and dopamine metabolism. *Psychopharmacologia*, **19**, 199–203.

—— (1983) In search of the mode of action of antidepressants. 5HTP/tyrosine mixtures in depressions. *Neuropharmacology*, **22**, 433–440.

—— KORF, J. & SCHUT, D. (1973) Cerebral monoamines and depression; an investigation with the probenecid technique. *Archives of General Psychiatry*, **28**, 827–831.

VOGT, M. (1954) The concentration of sympathin in different parts of the central nervous system under normal conditions and after the administration of drugs. *Journal of Physiology (London)*, **123**, 451–481.

WATERHOUSE, R. D. & WOODWARD, D. J. (1980) Interaction of norepinephrine with cerebrocortical activity evoked by stimulation of somatosensory afferent pathways in the rat. *Experimental Neurology*, **67**, 11–34.

WATKINS, L. R., COBELLI, D. A. & MAYER, D. S. (1981) Footshock induced analgesia (FSIA) and classically conditioned analgesia (CCA): differential activation of opiate and non-opiate systems. *Pain*, (Suppl. 1), S263.

WEISSMAN, A. & HARBERT, C. A. (1972) Recent developments relating serotonin and behaviour. *Annual Reports in Medicine and Chemistry*, 7, 47–58.

WISE, R. A., SPINDLER, J., DE WIT, M. & GERBER, G. J. (1978) Neuroleptic induced 'anhedonia' in rats: pimozide blocks reward quality of food. *Science*, 201, 262–264.

—— (1982) Neuroleptics and operant behaviour: the anhedonia hypothesis. *Behavioural Brain Science*, 5, 39–87.

—— BERGER, B. D. & STEIN, L. (1970) Serotonin: a possible mediator of behavioural suppression induced by anxiety. *Diseases of the Nervous System*, GWAN suppl. 31, 34–37.

WOLFE, B. B., HARDEN, F. K., SPORN, R. J. & MOLINOFF, P. B. (1978) Presynaptic modulation of beta adrenergic receptors in rat cerebral cortex after treatment with antidepressants. *Journal of Pharmacology and Experimental Therapeutics*, 207, 446–457.

WONG, D. T., BYMASTER, F. P., REID, L. R. & THRELKELD, P. G. (1983) Fluoxetine and two other serotonin uptake inhibitors without affinity for neuronal receptors. *Biochemical Pharmacology*, 32, 1287–1293.

YAMAZOE, M., SHIOSAKA, S., ERNSON, P. C. & TOHYAMA, M. (1985) Distribution of neuropeptides in the lower brainstem: an immunohistochemical analysis. *Brain Research*, 355, 109–120.

2 Nature, nurture and affective disorder

PETER McGUFFIN; RANDY KATZ

Goals and strategies

Perhaps the most consistent clue to the puzzling aetiology of depression is its tendency to run in families. Here, as in other conditions, the task of psychiatric genetics is twofold. The first is to decide whether familiality can be attributed to genetic causes, shared environmental influences, or an interaction of the two. Second, if genetic factors have been shown to be involved, we must ask how? Therefore we must strive to determine the mode or modes of transmission, identify mechanisms of gene expression, and unravel important gene-environment interactions. We will begin by briefly considering the first of these tasks and the traditional methods, family, twin, and adoption studies, by which it can be accomplished.

Kraepelin (1922) maintained that about 80% of his cases of manic depressive insanity were predisposed to the disorder by an 'hereditary taint'. Simply counting how many patients with a certain disorder do or do not have close relatives with the same condition is of some value, but may be misleading. Thus, if we are dealing with a trait such as 'ever treated for psychiatric disorder', which has a high frequency in the general population (let us suppose it is about 10%), then in the absence of any familial aggregation an individual chosen at random will have a 37% chance of being 'family history positive' if we can examine four of his relatives. This rises to 41% if we can examine five, and 47% if we can examine six relatives. Therefore, statements about what proportion of patients with a certain disorder have family histories of mental illness need to be interpreted with caution and with due attention to population base rates.

A more satisfactory approach is to determine the proportion of relatives of a particular class (e.g. parents, siblings, offspring) who are affected by the condition and compare this with the frequency in the general population or that in a control sample of relatives. In the case of affective disorder this poses considerable problems since there is variable age of onset and characteristically a relapsing and remitting course. The focus of interest is thus whether the relative in question has ever had the disorder (lifetime prevalence) or what is their expectancy of developing the disorder if they live through the period of risk (lifetime incidence or morbid risk). There are a number of ways by which morbid risk can be calculated (Thompson & Weissman, 1980), but the simplest and most straightforward is the shorter method of Weinberg (Slater & Cowie, 1971) where individuals below the age of risk are ignored, unaffected relatives within the period of risk are assumed on average to be halfway through it and are weighted appropriately. To this is added the total number of relatives beyond the age of risk and the number of affected relatives giving a corrected denominator or Bezuggsiffer (BZ). The morbid risk is then simply the number of relatives affected divided by the BZ. A further problem which is sometimes overlooked is the method of selection or ascertainment of probands (or index cases). This needs to be systematic (e.g. a consecutive and unselected series of referrals) with each proband included independently (i.e. uninfluenced by the inclusion of any other cases in the sample) and the source of probands should be well defined (e.g. in-patients, out-patients, long-term day patients), since this in itself may influence the proportion and distribution of secondary cases.

Familial aggregation does not necessarily imply genetic mechanisms. Cultural or family environmental influences may be at work and twin and adoption studies are the classic 'natural experiments' by which the effects of nature and nurture can be delineated. Systematic ascertainment is perhaps even more important in twin than in family studies. A haphazard assembling of a twin series runs the risk of preferential selection of the most prominent or memorable pairs of twins who almost inevitably will tend to be monozygotic and concordant. Systematic ascertainment through a twin register overcomes this difficulty and it follows from this correct sampling procedure that the most informative way of reporting concordance rates is the probandwise method (Smith, 1974). The basic assumption of twin studies is of course that similarity of monozygotic twins is due to their having 100% of their genes in common, plus a common environment, whereas dizygotic twins have (on average) 50% of their genes in common, plus a common environment. Higher concordance rates in monozygotic pairs should therefore indicate the importance of genetic influences. The most frequent criticism of the twin method is that this implicit 'equal environments assumption' may be invalid since identical twins may have shared experiences which are at once more intimate and more pervasive than those of fraternal twins. Perhaps surprisingly, this intuitively plausible criticism has little empirical support. Where attempts have been made to rate environmental similarities in monozygotic twins (Loehlin & Nichols, 1976), these appear to have little effect on their similarities for behavioural attributes such as personality and IQ. Furthermore, in pairs of twins who are mistaken about their true zygosity (Scarr & Carter-Saltzman, 1979), assuming themselves to be monozygous when in fact they are dizygous or vice versa, appears to have little effect on their correlations for cognitive traits compared with pairs who were correct about their zygosity. Although there have been no studies of this type directly relating to affective disorder, indirect evidence from sources such as twins reared apart suggests that the equal environments assumption is not unreasonable for psychopathological traits. We will return to the theme of assessing common environmental versus genetic influences in some more detail later in the chapter.

At first sight adoption studies would appear to offer the cleanest separation between genetic and familial environmental contributors to mental illness. However, adoption is statistically an abnormal event and in practice it is likely that parents giving up children for adoption (at least in Western industrialised society) are selected for social adversity or deviancy. Thus, in modern adoption studies (e.g. Heston, 1966; Hutchings & Mednick, 1974) even control adoptees with ostensibly normal biological parents show rather high rates of psychopathology. Nevertheless, interpreted against a background of other sources of evidence, adoption studies have been able to provide important indications of a genetic aetiology for schizophrenia, antisocial personality, alcoholism and, to a lesser extent, affective disorder.

One of the major problems in studying affective disorder or in collating and comparing genetic studies from a variety of sources is that the term is used to embrace a broad spectrum of diagnostic categories ranging from a full-blown acute psychosis at one extreme to understandable adversity-related distress at the other. Terminology is confusing and unsatisfactory (Kendell, 1976). However, most genetic studies have for obvious reasons focused on 'typical' or 'endogenous' forms of affective illness. All are agreed that this includes mania, but when it comes to depression, Anglo-European psychiatrists have tended to emphasize biological or psychotic features while currently their American counterparts emphasize severity and disability for inclusion in the broad category of 'major affective disorder' (American Psychiatric Association, 1980). For a moment we will sidestep diagnostic nuances and consider the genetic evidence in typical affective disorder under the neo-Kraepelinian heading 'manic depressive illness', and for neurotic and reactive categories under the heading 'other forms'.

Manic depressive illness

It is convenient to date modern family studies from the publication 20 years ago of independent reports by Angst (1966) and Perris (1966). Both acted upon the earlier suggestion of Leonhard (1959) that manic depressive

TABLE I

Affective illness in first degree relatives of unipolar (UP) and bipolar (BP) probands

Study	Proband Type	N at risk (BZ)	Relatives Morbid Risk (%) BP	UP
Perris (1968)		627	10.2	0.5
Winokur & Clayton (1967)		167	10.2	20.4
Goetzl *et al* (1974)		212	2.8	13.7
Helzer & Winokur (1974)		151	4.6	10.6
Mendelwicz *et al* (1974)		605	17.7	
	BP	544		22.4
James *et al* (1975)		265	6.4	13.2
Gershon *et al* (1975)		341	3.8	6.8
Smeraldi *et al* (1977)		173	5.7	9.8
Angst (1980)		400.5	2.5	7.0
Winokur *et al* (1982)		196	1.5	12.4
Gershon *et al* (1982)		572.3	6.4	14.9
Perris (1966)		684	0.3	6.4
Gershon *et al* (1975)		96	2.1	11.3
Smeraldi *et al* (1977)	UP	185	1.1	11.4
Angst (1980)		766.3	0.1	5.9
Winokur *et al* (1982)		305	0.9	11.2
Gershon *et al* (1982)		132.9	1.5	16.6
Weissman *et al* (1984)		287	1.2	18.4
Pooled results	BP	3710.3	7.8	
		3648.3		11.4
	UP	2319	0.6	9.1

illness could be classified into bipolar (BP) disorder consisting of episodes of both mania and depression and unipolar (UP) disorder in which there were episodes of depression only. Although Perris (1966) found virtually complete homotypia (i.e. affected relatives at the same subtype of disorder as the probands), Angst's (1966) findings showed a somewhat more complicated pattern. Table I summarises the studies which have been published since then. There are problems in combining data across studies as the range of reported morbid risks in first degree relatives is wide, suggesting considerable heterogeneity in diagnostic practices. Nevertheless the findings are generally in keeping with those of Angst (1966) showing a high morbid risk of BP illness (weighted average 7.8%) and of UP (weighted average 11.4%) in the first degree relatives of bipolar probands. However, in the first degree relatives of UP probands there is a high risk (weighted mean 9.1%) only for the unipolar form. First degree relatives of the comparatively uncommon probands with unipolar mania, show the same pattern of illness as those of bipolar probands and so unipolar mania is usually classified as a BP disorder.

In the general population UP disorder is the more common with recent estimates of morbid risk of around 3% compared with 0.2–1.0% for BP disorder (Reich *et al*, 1982). In most studies UP illness is two to three times more common in women than men, whereas for BP illness the sex incidences are about equal or show only a modest female excess. In recent studies BP disorder has tended to show an earlier age of onset than UP disorder, and to show an overall much higher rate of affective illness in first degree relatives. Again referring to Table I, we see that the average risk in the first degree relatives is 19.2% for bipolar probands, compared with 9.7% for unipolar probands. There has also been a tendency in recent studies for early onset cases of affective illness irrespective of whether they are UP or BP forms to show high family loading (Gershon *et al*, 1976).

Table II summarises six twin studies in which the authors did not differentiate between BP and UP forms. Although not entirely free of methodological difficulties, all six do meet the basic requirements of systematic sampling and a comparatively narrow definition of affective disorder (Gershon *et al*, 1976). The concordance rate of 69% in MZ pairs compared with 13% in DZ pairs strongly suggests an important genetic contribution. Zerbin-Rudin (1969) has reviewed older studies carried out before the days of the now conventional BP/UP distinction and found a tendency for twin pairs concordant for affective illness to be concordant also for subtype. This has been confirmed by the single largest and most recent study (Bertelsen *et al*, 1977) which was based on the Danish National Twin Register, the main results of which are summarised in Table III. However, we must note that even in genetically identical individuals, MZ twins, homotypia was incomplete. Thus in 10 of 46 pairs concordant for affective illness, the proband showed one type of disorder while the co-twin showed the other.

TABLE II
Pairwise concordance in twin studies of affective illness (Modified after Gershon et al 1976)

Investigator	MZ Pairs		DZ Pairs	
	N	Concordance %	N	Concordance %
Luxenburger (1930)	4	75	13	0
Rosanoff *et al* (1935)	23	70	67	16
Slater (1953)	7	57	17	24
Kallman (1954)	27	93	55	24
Harvald and Hauge (1965)	15	67	40	5
Allen *et al* (1974)	15	33	34	0
Pooled Results	91	69	226	13

TABLE III
Proband-wise concordance for unipolar (UP) and bipolar(BP) affective illness in twins (Bertelsen et al 1977)

		Co-Twin				
	Proband	N	UP	BP	Affective illness (%)	
MZ	UP	35	15	4	64 ⎫	
	BP	34	6	21	79 ⎭	67
DZ	UP	17	3	1	24 ⎫	
	BP	37	4	3	19 ⎭	20

Data on twins reared apart need to be interpreted cautiously because of the inevitable sampling difficulties and small numbers involved. However, Price (1968) has culled 12 such pairs from the world literature in which at least one had affective illness. Eight of these proved to be concordant for the condition (67%), a rate which is strikingly similar to that for MZ twins reared together.

There is a surprising paucity of adoption data on affective illness, but that which is available mainly supports a genetic aetiology. Mendlewicz and Rainer (1977) found that 16 (28%) of the biological parents of 29 bipolar adoptees had affective illness compared with 7 (12%) of their adopted parents. The rate of affective illness in biological parents was thus similar to that in the parents of bipolar non-adoptees (26%), while the rate in adopting parents approximated to that in the parents who had adopted normal offspring (9%). However, we should note that the most common form of illness in the biological parents of bipolar adoptees was (at 12 of 16 affected) unipolar disorder. A smaller study (Cadoret 1978) dealing mainly with UP illness found a significantly higher rate of affective disorder in the adopted away offspring of biological parents with affective disorder than in adoptees whose natural parents had had other psychiatric conditions or who were psychiatrically well. Somewhat at variance with these data are the recent results of Von Knorring and her colleagues (1983) who found no evidence of an elevated rate of affective illness in either the biological or adoptive parents of 56 adoptees with affective disorder (51 UP, 5 BP) compared with the parents of matched control adoptees.

Other forms of depression

Some authors have suggested that presence or absence of an 'endogenous' pattern of depressive symptoms differentiates poorly those patients with or without familial affective illness (Winokur & Clayton, 1967; Woodruff & Pitts, 1964; Winokur, 1979). However, as we have pointed out, scoring

TABLE IV
The morbid risk of depression in first degree relatives of neurotic depressives

Study	Method	N	Morbid risk %	Population risk %
Stockholm (Stenstedt, 1966)	History	794	5.4	3
Umea (Perris *et al*, 1982)	Case Notes	390	9.0	3 (?)
London (McGuffin *et al* — Preliminary results)	Interview	146	24.9 (6.0)*	10 (2.6)*

* In-patient treated cases only.

presence or absence of secondary cases among relatives in this way is a somewhat crude and unsatisfactory approach. Unfortunately, there have been few systematic studies of the families of neurotically depressed probands, but available evidence points to a familial diathesis. Table IV summarises the results of two published Swedish studies and some preliminary findings from an investigation which is currently in progress in London. All three studies indicate that there is poor homotypia for neurotic/endogenous categories so that the affectively ill relatives of neurotic probands may have either pattern of illness. The Swedish studies suggest a morbid risk for affective disorder in these families which is somewhat lower than that in the relatives of endogenously ill probands. Our London study, on the other hand, finds a high frequency of hospital-treated depression in first degree relatives. Although the numbers involved here are still smaller than the earlier studies, the differences are unlikely all to be due to sampling error and probably two other effects are operating. The first is that personal interviews of all available relatives detect more psychopathology and yield higher rates of illness than family history or case notes studies (Thompson *et al*, 1982). Secondly, there are diagnostic differences. Stenstedt (1966) has viewed neurotic depression in a rather narrowly defined way as a condition which has a morbid risk in the general population of about 1.6% (Helgason, 1964), while the population morbid risk of depression as a whole he considers to be about 3%. Perris and colleagues cite no particular population estimate, but consider their diagnostic approach to be comparable with the earlier Swedish study. In our own study we have used the Present State Examination (Wing *et al*, 1974) together with a standardised past history schedule to assess relatives, but the figures reported in Table IV are based on hospital contact for depression rather than any explicit set of diagnostic criteria. The advantage of this is that the recorded statistics on the Camberwell Register allow a confident estimation of the population risk (Sturt *et al*, 1984), which for any hospital contact for depression (men and women combined) averages

TABLE V

Twin studies of neurotic or non-endogenous depression

Authors	Monozygotic		Dizygotic	
	N probands	Probandwise concordance % (narrow–broad)	N probands	Probandwise concordance % (narrow–broad)
Slater and Shields (1969)	8	0–38	16	0–25
Shapiro (1970)	18	22–55*	14	0–14*
Torgersen (1985)	17	36–53	33	33–45

* In Shapiro's study narrow concordance = co-twin hospitalised with depression, broad concordance = any form of treated depression in co-twin. In the two other studies narrow = depression in co-twin, broad = any psychiatric disorder.

at about 10%. It is only when we restrict consideration to those cases who have required in-patient treatment that our figures come closer to the Swedish findings. Clearly then our ability to draw inferences from family studies is dependent on accurate and reliable epidemiological data. Unfortunately, population surveys of depression have been fraught with inconsistencies (Eastwood & Kramer, 1981) with some North American researchers, in marked contrast to their Scandinavian counterparts, suggesting lifetime prevalences in excess of 20%.

Against this background twin studies are particularly advantageous since there is no necessary recourse to independent populations estimates of morbid risk. Table V gives the results of three such studies. The Maudsley study of Slater & Shields (1969) and the Norwegian Twin Register based study of Torgersen (1985) are broadly in agreement in finding little difference between MZ and DZ concordance, regardless of whether this is defined narrowly as only neurotic depression in the co-twin or broadly to include any form of psychiatric disorder. The study of Shapiro (1970) carried out in Denmark did, however, produce results suggestive of a genetic effect. An important methodological difference was that all of Shapiro's probands had received in-patient treatment for their depression and therefore were presumably a more severely ill group than those in the other studies, where admission to hospital was not an inclusion criterion. Interestingly, both Shapiro (1970) and Slater & Shields (1969) noted a high prevalence of personality abnormalities in probands and co-twins and were in agreement that what is likely to be transmitted in non-endogenous or neurotic depression is not the illness as such but a set of characterological attributes which confer susceptibility to the disorder in the face of adversity. Viewed overall, therefore, the twin and family data suggest that neurotic forms of depression are familial, but that the genetic contribution is small and perhaps indirect.

A novel and non-traditional approach to the typology of unipolar depression has been suggested by Winokur (1979). He has pointed to the frequent co-existence of alcohol problems, personality disorders and depression within some families and proposes a division of familial depressive illness into a 'pure' form where only affective disorder is transmitted and a 'depressive spectrum disease' which may be characterised by a marked female excess among depressed probands with high rates of alcoholism and antisocial behaviour among relatives, particularly males. Winokur's co-workers (Tanna *et al*, 1976; Schlesser *et al*, 1979) have reported biological differences between these two types of disorder, but the classification scheme has not won widespread acceptance. Statistical analysis of family and adoption studies suggests that although alcoholism, antisocial personality and depressive illness sometimes aggregate in the same families, the disorders are heterogeneous both clinically and aetiologically and cannot be considered as alternative expression of the same genotype (Cloningér *et al*, 1979).

Particularly telling in this respect are the Danish adoption studies on alcoholism (Goodwin, 1979) where rather high rates of depression were found in women adoptees whether or not they had an alcoholic parent (14 and 15% respectively). However, it was in those women who had not been adopted but had been raised by an alcoholic biological parent in whom the rate of depression (at 27%) was strikingly high. Thus, the connection between alcoholism and depression would appear to be more strongly mediated through shared environments than through shared genes.

Models of transmission

So far most of our discussion has centred on whether or not genes play a part in the transmission of affective disorder or subtypes of disorder. Before we can begin to answer questions about *how* genes play their part we need to review the theories of inheritance of conditions which clearly do not show simple Mendelian patterns of segregation. Broadly speaking the plausible theories can be subsumed under the category 'liability-threshold' models. Here it is assumed that a variable termed 'liability to develop the disorder' is continuously distributed within the population but that only those individuals whose liability exceeds a certain threshold manifest the disorder. The relatives of affected individuals will then on average have a higher liability than the general population mean and hence more will lie beyond the threshold for exhibiting the condition. Since studies of monozygotic twins have consistently shown concordance rates of less than 100%, we can be

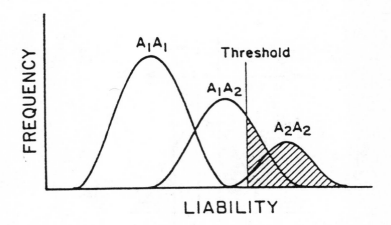

Fig. 1 — The general Single Major Locus (SML) model. The three genotypes A_1A_1, A_1A_2 and A_2A_2 differ in their mean liability to develop the disorder. Variation within each genotype is due to non-familial environmental influences. Only those individuals beyond the threshold (shaded area) exhibit the disorder.

sure that liability is in part contributed by environmental factors. The two main models concerning the genetic component of liability are single major locus (SML) and polygenic-multifactorial (MF) models. Under the SML model it is postulated that liability is due to a single gene locus at which there are two alleles (or alternative genes), A_1, A_2. Each of the three resultant genotypes, A_1A_1, A_1A_2, A_2A_2, has a different penetrance or probability of manifesting the condition, which may differ from the necessary Mendelian values of 0 or 1. Thus, the illustration in Fig. 1 shows a trait in which most of the A_2A_2 homozygotes are affected, as are a minority of A_1A_2 heterozygotes. In this example none of the A_1A_1 homozygotes are shown as affected, although it is quite possible under this general model to postulate that some will be ill, in which case they will represent 'sporadics' or non-genetic 'phenocopies'.

Under the MF model it is assumed that liability is contributed by the predominantly additive effects of genes at multiple loci which together with additive environmental effects will (as the central limit theorem predicts) result in a normally distributed liability within the population. The MF model is illustrated in Fig. 2. In many respects it must be seen as more

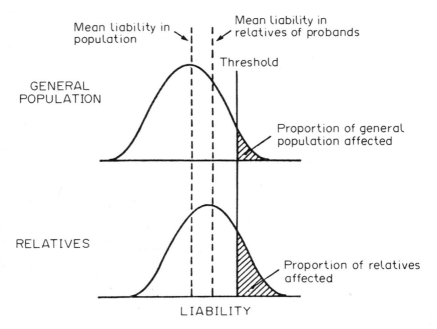

Fig. 2 — The polygenic-multifactorial/threshold model. Liability is contributed by polygenes plus environment acting in a predominantly additive fashion. Only those individuals beyond the threshold (shaded area) are affected.

plausible than the 'pure' SML model in which a major gene is the sole source of resemblance between pairs of relatives. Recent analyses support this viewing (Bucher, 1980). However, it is also possible to consider as a third alternative a 'mixed' model (Morton, 1982) in which liability is contributed by a major locus against a background of multifactorial/polygenic influences. This approach presents considerable computational difficulties, but O'Rourke *et al* (1983) have performed some preliminary analyses with interesting results suggestive of a major gene component in BP illness.

If we allow that liability is normally distributed (or that it could be transformed to normality), knowing the proportion of the general population affected and the proportion of relatives of a particular class who are affected enables us to calculate the correlation in liability (effectively a Pearsonian tetrachoric correlation) between pairs of relatives (Falconer, 1965; Reich *et al*, 1972). The correlation in liability is a useful measure of the strength of familial influences on a trait, but furthermore, knowing the correlation for twins and other categories of relative can allow us to estimate the magnitude of genetic and environmental contributions to liability.

One way of conceptualising the contributors to an observable trait or phenotype is illustrated by the path diagram in Fig. 3. The phenotype of individual P_1 is the sum of his genetic endowment or genotype (G) (half of which is received from each parent), plus the effects of that part of the environment (CE) which he shares in common with his sibling (P_2), plus those environmental effects which are special to him alone and not shared by other members of his family (SE_1). The value of the expected correlation between P_1 and any of his relatives can be worked out as the sum of the permissible connecting paths between them (Li, 1975). If P_1 and P_2 are dizygotic twins, we obtain from Fig. 3 the (intuitively obvious) result that the source of resemblance between the two is that they share half of their genes in common plus a common environment. Put algebraically, the correlation r_{DZ} is given by:

$$r_{DZ} = \tfrac{1}{4}h^2 + \tfrac{1}{4}h^2 + c^2$$
$$= \tfrac{1}{2}h^2 + c^2$$

Similarly the correlation for MZ twins who share 100% of their genes, r_{MZ} is given by:

$$r_{MZ} = h^2 + c^2$$

From these equations it is easy to obtain that

$$h^2 = 2\,(r_{MZ} - r_{DZ})$$

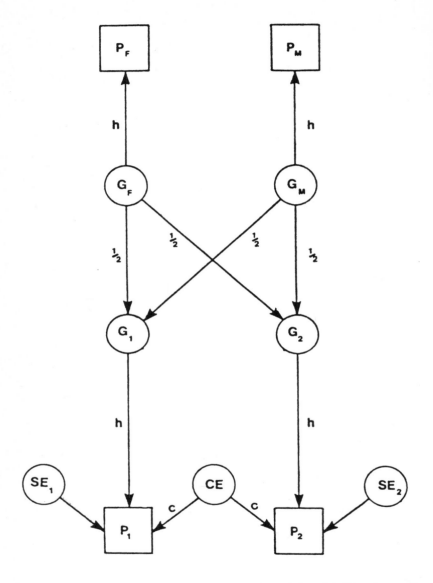

Fig. 3 — Path diagram illustrating a simple multifactorial model. The observable variables (boxes) are the phenotypes of father and mother P_f, P_m) and those of the offspring P_1, P_2 . . . P_i). The underlying (latent) variables (circles) are G the genotype, SE, specific environment (with appropriate subscripts), and CE, common environment. The path coefficients are denoted by the lower case letters h and c or in the case of G (parent) — G (off-spring), ½.

Where the commodity h^2 is the heritability or the proportion of total phenotypic variance contributed by genes.

Rearranging, we obtain

$$c^2 = 2\ r_{DZ} - r_{MZ}$$

Where c^2 is the proportion of the variance contributed by common family environment.

We can therefore begin to quantify the effects of nature and nurture. For example, if we assume a population frequency for manic depressive illness of 3% the twin study of Bertelsen *et al* (1977) gives an MZ correlation of 0.93, a DZ correlation of 0.5, giving an h^2 of 0.86 and a c^2 of only 0.07. although the standard errors of these estimates are large (in each case about ± 0.2), the calculations nevertheless suggest a very substantial genetic contribution but only a very small family environmental effect which would be in keeping with reared apart twin findings (Price, 1968) and Mendelwicz & Rainer's (1977) adoption data. By contrast, taking a population frequency for depressive neurosis of 6%, Torgersen's twin data yields an MZ correlation of 0.64, a DZ correlation of 0.59, therefore indicating a large common environment effect with a c^2 of 0.54, and a small genetic contribution to the variance with an h^2 of 0.08. Again, the standard errors of these estimates are very large (about ± 0.3 and ± 0.4 respectively) but it seems likely that the main component in the familiality of depressive neurosis is shared family environment. More complex path analytic models (Rao *et al*, 1979; Rice *et al*, 1981) permit the incorporation of other influences such as assortative mating and vertical cultural transmission. However, partitioning the variance in this way should be seen only as a starting point. Calculation of heritability is in itself an empty exercise if it does not lead to a more specific consideration of the ways in which genes and environment co-act and interact to produce the phenotype.

Hazard, heredity and depressive 'reaction types'

Some psychiatrists have used the terms *reactive* and *neurotic* depression as if they were equivalent and interchangeable. Similarly the descriptor *endogenous* is usually applied to a specific pattern of symptoms but carries obvious aetiological implications. Stenstedt (1966) noted that there were psychogenic factors in 90% of his neurotically depressed probands and other exogenous factors in the remainder. In his earlier study of manic depressive psychosis he found that those patients in whom there were obvious precipitants for illness tended to have less family loading than those who did not (Stenstedt,

1952). The implication then is one which would have an intuitive appeal to most clinicians. Some depressed patients with a marked biological/genetic diathesis develop their illness 'out of the blue', while other cases in whom there is a smaller or non-specific constitutional predisposition develop their illness as a result of obvious stress. Unfortunately, most studies have so far considered potential stressors and genetic diathesis quite separately. One exception was the investigation of Pollitt (1972) who found a morbid risk of depression among relatives which was particularly high, at around 21%, when precipitants for the probands illness were absent or doubtful. The morbid risk in relatives fell to between 6% and 12% when the probands illness was 'justifiable', in the sense that it followed severe physical stress, infection or psychological trauma.

In collaboration with colleagues at the MRC Social Psychiatry Unit, we have recently been investigating the relationship between adversity, in the form of chronic difficulties and life events (Brown & Harris, 1978), and familial aggregation of depression in a consecutive series of depressed probands and their families. However, our preliminary results have run counter to expectations and do not show the simple and intuitively appealing pattern found by Pollitt (1972). So far we have found no significant difference in the morbid risk of depression in first degree relatives of probands whose illness was associated with adversity, compared with the relatives of probands whose illness was associated with little or no adversity. Furthermore, within families there is little tendency for life event related depression to 'breed true' and in general life events in preceding months appear poor predictors of whether relatives will or will not fulfil the criteria for current 'caseness' as defined by the PSE (Wing & Sturt, 1978). However, we do find that when we compare first degree relatives of depressives with a community sample (Bebbington *et al*, 1982) not only are there significantly more relatives who are currently 'cases' of depression (19% of relatives compared with 9% of the community sample), but also significantly more relatives have experienced recent threatening life events (21% of relatives compared with 7% of community sample). This finding holds even when proband-associated events are discounted, and it therefore appears that both liability to depression and propensity to experience life events are familial. This raises the possibility that event-associated depression is something which occurs in hazard-prone rather than just stress-susceptible individuals. Furthermore, it seems possible that part of the association between life events and depression which has been consistently shown in previous studies (Paykel, 1978; Brown & Harris, 1978; Bebbington *et al*, 1982) is due to the fact that both show familial aggregation.

We must emphasise that we are putting forward speculations rather than definitive conclusions and that at this stage our family study findings, though provocative, are but preliminary. Furthermore, as we have pointed out, the inferences which can be drawn from family data alone are limited and a proper elucidation of the co-action and interaction of environmental adversity and genetic liability will require twin studies.

Heterogeneity

We have already discussed in some detail the familial patterns of transmission of BP compared with UP illness and note that the BP/UP dichotomy is probably the most widely accepted distinction in the whole contentious area of classification of affective illness. But do the phenotypic differences here reflect aetiological or genotypic differences? We have seen that the relatives of bipolar probands may present either with BP or UP illness even where the relative concerned is a monozygotic co-twin sharing 100% of their genes with the proband. Relatives of unipolar probands tend to fall ill only with UP disorder and overall have a lower morbid risk of affective illness. The most elegant and parsimonious way of explaining these findings is by recourse to a multiple threshold-liability model (Reich *et al*, 1972; 1979). Here it is assumed that the two conditions occupy the same continuum of liability and differ quantitatively rather than qualitatively such that those individuals whose liability exceeds a certain threshold, manifest the common or 'broad' form of illness, while those whose liability exceeeds a second more extreme

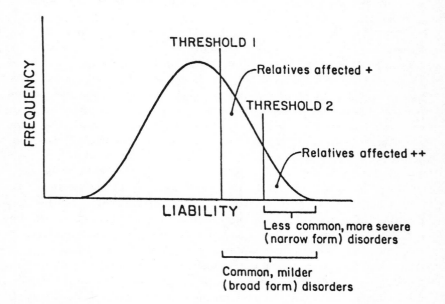

Fig. 4 — 2-Threshold multifactorial (MF) model.

threshold exhibit a less common, more severe, 'narrow' form of disorder. As in the single threshold MF model, relatives of affective probands will have an augmented mean liability compared with the general population. However, the mean liability for the relatives of narrow form probands will be greater than that for the relatives of broad form probands. Hence (Fig. 4), more relatives of narrow form probands than broad form probands will be affected. Also the affected relative of narrow form probands will comprise a mixture of narrow and broad form cases, while the relatives of broad form disorder probands will predominantly have the broad form. Both Gershon and colleagues (1982) and Tsuang and colleagues (1985) have applied a model of this type to family data on BP and UP disorder and find a satisfactory statistical fit. The study of Tsuang *et al* was restricted to BP and UP disorder whereas, more controversially, that of Gershon *et al* postulated a third and most extreme threshold beyond which schizoaffective syndromes are found. However, the number of probands involved here was small and although the morbid risk of affective disorder was impressively high at 37%, there was also a small and almost significant (exact test $p = 0.057$) excess of schizophrenics among these relatives (3.6%) compared with control relatives (0%). Thus the evidence does suggest that BP and UP disorder are on the same continuum of multifactorial liability, but the position of schizoaffective illness is more dubious since in Gershon's and in other recent studies (e.g. Angst, *et al* 1980) there are high rates of both schizophrenia and affective disorders in the families of schizoaffective probands.

Turning to UP disorder, we must ask whether genetic studies suggest qualitative differences between neurotic and endogenous conditions as postulated by Carney *et al* (1965), or do we have a neurotic-psychotic continuum of disorders as put forward by Kendell & Gourlay (1970). As we have seen, there is some evidence that relatives of typical endogenous pattern depressed probands are more commonly affected than the relatives of neurotic cases (Stenstedt, 1952; 1967; Perris *et al*, 1982). Our own preliminary findings are in agreement when we take a comparatively severe cut-off for classing relatives as affected. Thus the morbid risk of in-patient treated depression in the first degree relatives of endogenous probands is 12% compared with 6% in the relatives of neurotic probands. However, if we take any form of hospital contact for depression as our criterion, the rates in both groups of relatives are similar at around 25%. The evidence for homotypia in our family data, as in the previous literature, is unimpressive and again there are reports of identical twins concordant for depression but discordant for neurotic/endogenous subtype (Torgersen, 1985). We must conclude that the genetic evidence is against any qualitative distinction between neurotic and endogenous illness, but instead favours the continuum theory. It is also tempting to conceptualise this in terms of the type of multifactorial threshold model which has been applied to the UP/BP subtypes but with endogenous disorder as the narrow and neurotic the broad form. By and large the data would appear consistent with such a model, although this awaits formal statistical testing.

Sex differences

Most family studies of depression have been in keeping with epidemiological findings in showing more affected women than men (Gershon *et al*, 1976). Although the effect is less pronounced for BP illness, if both UP and BP ill relatives of BP probands are considered as having different manifestations of the same illness, then again a female excess is found in most family studies. The most provocative hypothesis to explain such differences is that manic depressive disorder is transmitted as an incompletely penetrant X linked dominant gene. Winokur *et al* (1969) published details on 69 families ascertained through BP probands in which the pattern of segregation was compatible with such a hypothesis. Subsequently, two large pedigrees (Reich *et al*, 1969) were reported where manic depressive illness assorted with colour blindness, a trait known to be X linked. Subsequent reports confirmed linkage between deutan and protan colour blindness and BP disorder (Mendlewicz *et al*, 1972; Baron, 1977) as well as with another X chromosome marker, the Xg blood group (Mendlewicz *et al*, 1975; Winokur & Tanna, 1969). However, it is now known that the Xg and colour blindness loci are far apart on the X chromosome so that it is implausible to postulate a third locus linked to both. More important evidence against there being an X linked mechanism for all BP disorder is that there are numerous reported instances of father-son transmission (Gershon *et al*, 1975). A recent multi-centre collaborative study (Gershon *et al*, 1980) of families informative for X linked markers and complex segregation analyses (Bucher *et al*, 1981) of published pedigrees found that X linked inheritance was improbable in BP disorder. Thus, although X linkage may still be present in a minority of families it will certainly be the exception rather than the rule and cannot explain general population sex differences.

Most recent research has therefore been concerned with liability threshold models of sex differences (Rice *et al*, 1981; 1984). Analysis of data from a multi-centre collaborative study of depression in the United States (Rice *et al*, 1984) adopted this approach. The data were compatible with a higher mean liability towards depression for women than men, which may be due to systematic biological/cultural differences, with parental transmission contributing to variation about the means. The data were not compatible with the hypothesis that women simply have a lower threshold for reporting depressive symptoms. There was also an interesting 'cohort effect' in that the sex ratio was close to one among younger age groups. Other American family studies carried out within the past few years (Gershon *et al*, 1982; Weissman *et al*, 1984) concur in finding only a modest sex difference in affected relatives, as do preliminary results from our own study in London. The morbid risk of depression in the general population as reflected in the Camberwell Register also gives some evidence of a secular trend, with male/female differences lower in recent than in previous years (Sturt *et al*, 1984). These changes over time, together with the fact that epidemiological studies of depression in non-industrialised societies (e.g. Orley & Wing, 1979) find no sex differences, suggest to us that socio-cultural factors are the main contributors to the frequently reported higher rates of depression in women. However, the cultural-genetic interaction within families is complex. For example, Rice *et al* (1984) found evidence of a maternal effect in the transmission of depression whereby mothers have a differentially greater impact on the liability of their offspring (both sons and daughters) than do fathers. This runs counter to a simple threshold model which would predict that the less commonly affected sex (equivalent to narrow form disorder under a two-threshold model) would have the higher proportion of relatives affected. The finding points to the need for further investigation of putative risk factors within families rather than in series of unrelated individuals.

Biological approaches

Our discussion has mainly concerned syndromes defined by clinical signs and symptoms. One of the problems of psychiatric genetics is that it must rely heavily on such 'exophenotypes' (Gottesman & Shields, 1972) which are difficult characters to manage in a genetic analysis (Penrose, 1971). The fact that we are able to demonstrate genetic effects in depressive disorder leads to the inference that there are connecting pathways between abnormal genes and abnormal mood states (McGuffin, 1984). Currently such paths are mysterious and obscure, but the search for biological markers can be seen as an attempt to establish useful signposts. An ability to move a step nearer to primary gene products, to discover 'endophenotypes' would enhance our abilities to dissect out the genetics of depression more effectively. As described elsewhere in this volume, we are currently at a stage where biological findings in depression are beginning to emerge in a consistent and reliable way. Unfortunately, however, we do not yet have a biological marker for depression which has all the desirable properties suggested by Reider & Gershon (1978). These are: (i) that a useful marker should be associated with an increased risk of the disorder (but the character need not always be more common among a group of patients with the clinical syndrome since there may be biological heterogeneity); (ii) the character should be heritable and not therefore a secondary effect of the illness or treatment of it; and (iii) the character should be a 'trait marker' rather than a 'state dependent' effect which is no longer present after the illness recovers (thus ruling out endocrine abnormalities, such as failure of dexamethazone suppression of cortisol).

Some of the problems concerning stability of findings and the confounding effects of treatment when studying patients *in vivo* can be overcome by recent techniques which allow *in vitro* study of culture material. An interesting finding of this type was provided by Wright *et al* (1984) who were able to show a decrease in beta-adrenoreceptors on lymphoblastoid cells in the ill members of families affected by manic depressive illness, but not among healthy relatives. The abnormalities were detected in cultured cells which had been serially passaged over many generations so that the defect could be presumed to be genetically coded. The abnormality was present in the ill members of only three out of five families studied, suggesting biological heterogeneity which would not have been readily detectable had the investigation been carried out on a group of unrelated patients. Abnormalities in catecholamines has of course long been implicated in affective disorder and it is interesting to speculate that such receptor abnormalities might also be found in the central nervous system.

Genetic markers

Complex segregation analysis (Bucher *et al*, 1981) suggests that a 'pure' SML model is unlikely to account for the transmission of affective illness. However, a major gene against a multifactorial background remains a possibility in bipolar disorder (O'Rourke *et al*, 1983). If major autosomal genes do exist, genetic marker studies hold future potential as a means by which they may be identified. Mapping of the human genome has progressed at a phenomenal pace over the past two decades. Genetic markers are those characters which have simple Mendelian modes of inheritance, exist in two or more common forms (i.e. which have a gene frequently of at least 1%), which can be reliably detected and have been mapped or can potentially be mapped to a specific chromosomal location. Over 300 genes have now been assigned to human chromosomes (American Journal of Human Genetics, 1983), but there are perhaps 100,000 genes in the entire genome.

The most straightforward form of genetic marker study is that of *association*. Here the frequency of a particular marker in a patient group is compared with that of healthy controls. Many common familial diseases have now been shown to be associated with the HLA system, the major transplant antigen system in man (Festenstein & Demant, 1978; Thomson, 1981). A variety of associations has been described between HLA antigens and both schizophrenia and affective disorder (McGuffin, 1980). But despite some early interesting results in bipolar disorder (Shapiro *et al*, 1977), agreement on affective illness studies from different centres has been poor and we must conclude against an association between depression and HLA or any other autosomal genetic marker (Goldin & Gershon, 1983).

Linkage studies present more practical difficulties, both in obtaining suitable samples and analysing the results (Sturt & McGuffin, 1985). Essentially the aim is to determine whether a particular genetic marker assorts with the illness within families. Where this occurs, it is possible to infer that the two loci are closely adjacent on the same chromosome. Again much interest has been centred on the HLA system, where there have been claims of linkage with affective illness (Weitkamp *et al*, 1981). Unfortunately, attempts at replication have proved unsuccessful (Goldin *et al*, 1983; Suarez & Reich, 1984) and similarly linkage studies with other markers have in the main been negative (Goldin & Gershon, 1983).

Greater optimism is encouraged by the revolutionary advances in 'the new genetics' (Weatherall, 1982). Recombinant DNA technology promises that there will be many new markers, so called restriction fragment length polymorphisms (RFLP) which depend upon the existence of normal variations in DNA sequences. Some authors, therefore, predict that it will not be long before the entire human genome is extensively mapped (Botstein *et al*, 1980). Unfortunately, only the offspring of a heterozygous parent are informative for linkage analysis, but most individuals are homozygous for most RFLPs discovered so far. However, the recent discovery of hypervariable regions in human DNA showing multi-allelic variation and high heterozygosity may allow this difficulty to be overcome (Jeffreys *et al*, 1985).

The most notable success regarding a trait of psychiatric relevance has been the mapping of a gene for Huntington's Chorea to chromosome 4 (Gusella *et al*, 1983). In many respects this finding was a remarkable stroke of luck and it should not be expected that other psychiatric conditions such as manic depressive illness which show non-Mendelian patterns of transmission will be mapped so readily. The problems are twofold; first, although the number of new polymorphisms being discovered is growing at a remarkable rate, there are still not enough to span the entire genome. In order to be reasonably sure of detecting linkage with a major locus in a 'blind' linkage study more than 200 markers more or less evenly spaced throughout the human gene map would be required (Lange & Boehnke, 1982). Second, conventional methods of linkage analysis require that the mode of inheritance of the main trait (in this case the 'disease gene') can be specified. Incomplete penetrance of the main trait, if not taken into account in the analysis, results in the systematic bias against detection of linkage (McGuffin *et al*, 1983). Furthermore, even if penetrance is correctly specified, low penetrance decreases the efficiency of likelihood methods of analysis (Sturt & McGuffin, 1985). One strategy for overcoming the marker problem may be to concentrate on DNA probes for substances of neurochemical importance and which have a putative relationship with psychiatric disorders (Gurling *et al*, 1984). The statistical problems, though formidable, should not in the long run prove insurmountable. A strategy which is less efficient than likelihood methods but which is robust to the problems of unknown mode of inheritance of the main trait, is to concentrate on affected sib pairs (Suarez, 1978; Green & Woodrow, 1977).

Conclusions

The evidence for a genetic contribution to typical manic depressive illness is consistent and compelling. It provides one of the firmest foundations for the conviction that there *is* a biological basis for depression. The analyses which we have carried out on twin data suggest that the magnitude of this contribution is very substantial, accounting for about 80% of the variance in liability to the illness. By contrast, for neurotic patterns of illness, although these are also familial, the effect of genes would appear to be small and non-specific. Our analysis suggest that the largest contributor to the variation in liability is common family environment. We consider that progress in understanding the aetiology of common forms of depression depends on the continuation of studies which will take into account both familial predisposition and psychosocial and other environmental factors.

Most of the heterogeneity which is seen in affective disorders can be accounted for by quantitative differences based on liability threshold models rather than discrete qualitative factors. Thus, BP and UP disorder can be considered as 'narrow' and 'broad' versions of essentially the same condition occupying the same continuum of liability. Although this is less certain (when judged from the familial-genetic evidence) for the endogenous-neurotic distinction, it seems plausible to consider these subforms of unipolar illness in the same way. Thus, we should probably think of more genetic and less genetic (or of more biological and less biological) forms of affective illness than of a genetic versus non-genetic typology. Similarly, genetic and epidemiological evidence suggest to us that sex differences in the prevalence of depression do not have a simple familial-genetic explanation, but that they most probably represent cultural-environmental influences on susceptibility to depressive symptoms.

All the above conclusions are based on data which depend on rather clumsy 'exophenotypes' derived from clinical signs and symptoms. It is quite possible that some of our conclusions, particularly those relating to heterogeneity, will need to be revised if reliable biological markers or 'endophenotypes', lying a step nearer to the primary gene product, can be discovered.

Acknowledgements

This work was supported by an MRC (UK) Senior Clinical Fellowship (Dr McGuffin) and an MRC Project Grant. We are grateful to our colleagues in the MRC Social Psychiatry Unit and in the Genetics Section, Institute of Psychiatry (Drs P. Bebbington, R. Brugha, E. Sturt, Ms J. Aldrich and B. McCarthy) for allowing us to quote preliminary results from our joint project on social and genetic factors in depression.

References

ALLEN, M. G., COHEN, S., POLLIN, W. & GREENSPAN, S. I. (1974). Affective illness in veteran twins: A diagnostic review. *American Journal of Psychiatry*, **131**, 1234–1239.
AMERICAN JOURNAL OF HUMAN GENETICS (1983) The human gene map. *American Journal of Human Genetics*, **35**, 134–156.
AMERICAN PSYCHIATRIC ASSOCIATION (1980) DSMIII. American Psychiatric Association, Washington DC.
ANGST, J. (1966) *Zur Atiologie und Nosologie endogener depressiver psychosen.* Monographen aus der Neurologie und Psychiatrie No. 112. Berlin, Springer-Verlag.
——— FREY, R., LOHMEYER, B. & ZERBIN-RUDIN, E. (1980) Bipolar manic depressive psychoses: Results of a genetic investigation. *Human. Genetics*, **55**, 237–254.
BARON, M. (1977) Linkage between an X chromosome marker (deutan color blindness) and bipolar affective illness. *Archives of General Psychiatry*, **34**, 721–725.
BEBBINGTON, P. E., TENNANT, C. & HURRY, J. (1982) Life events and the nature of psychiatric disorders in the community. *Journal of Affective Disorders*, **3**, 345–366.
BERTELSEN, A., HARVALD, B. & HAUGE, M. (1977) A Danish twin study of manic depressive disorders. *British Journal of Psychiatry*, **130**, 330–351.
BOTSTEIN, D., WHITE, R. L., STOLNICK, M. & DAVIS, R. W. (1980) Construction of a genetic linkage map in man using restriction fragment length polymorphisms. *American Journal of Human Genetics*, **32**, 312–331.
BUCHER, K. D. (1981) The transmission of manic depressive illness: I. Theory, description of the results. *Journal of Psychiatry Research*, **16**, 53–63, 1981.
——— ELSTON, R. C., GREEN, R., WHYBROW, P., HELZER, J., REICH, T., CLAYTON, R. & WINOKUR, G. (1981) The transmission of manic depressive illness — II segregation analysis of three sets of family data. *Journal of Psychiatric Research*, **16**, 65–78.
BROWN, G. W. & HARRIS, T. (1978) *The Social Origins of Depression.* London, Tavistock.
CADORET, R. J. (1978) Evidence for genetic inheritance of primary affective disorder in adoptees. *American Journal of Psychiatry*, **135**, 463–466.
CARNEY, M. W. P., ROTH, M. & GARSIDE, R. F. (1965) The diagnosis of depressive syndromes and the prediction of ECT response. *British Journal of Psychiatry*, **111**, 659–674.
CLONINGER, C. R., REICH, T., & WETZEL, R. (1979) Alcoholism and affective disorder. familial association and genetic models. In: *Alcoholism and Affective Disorders.* (ed. D. W. Goodwin & C. R. Erickson), pp. 57–86. New York, Spectrum Publications.
EASTWOOD, M. R. & KRAMER, P. M. (1981) Epidemiology and depression. *Psychological Medicine*, **11**, 229–234.

FALCONER, D. S. (1965) The inheritance of liability to certain disease, estimated from the incidence among relatives. *Annals of Human Genetics*, **29**, 51–76.

FESTENSTEIN, H. & DEMANT, P. (1978) *HLA and H2. Current Topics in Immunology*. Vol. 9. London, Edward Arnold.

GERSHON, E. S., MARK, A., COHEN, N., BALIZON, N., BARON, M. & KNOBE, K. E. (1975) Transmitted factors in the morbid risk of affective disorders. *Journal of Psychiatric Research*, **12**, 283–299.

—— BUNNEY, W. E., LECKMAN, J. F., VAN EERDEWEGH, M. & DEBAUGHCE, B. A. (1976) The inheritance of affective disorders: A review of data and hypotheses. *Behaviour Genetics*, **6**, 227–261.

—— MENDLEWICZ, J., GASTPAR, M., GOLDIN, L. R., KIELHOLZ, P., RAFAELSON, O. J., JARTANIAN, F., & BUNNEY, W. E. (1980) A collaborative study of genetic linkage of bipolar manic depressive illness and red/green color blindness. *Acta Psychiatrica Scandinavica*, **61**, 319–338.

—— HAMOVIT, J., GUROFF, J. J. *et al.* (1982) Family study of schizoaffective bipolar I, bipolar II, unipolar and normal control probands. *Archives of General Psychiatry*, **39**, 1157–1167.

GOETZL, U., GREEN, R., WHYLEROW, P. & JACKSON, R. (1974) X-linkage revisited. A further family study of manic-depressive illness. *Archives of General Psychiatry*, **31**, 665–672.

GOLDIN, L. R. & GERSHON, E. S. (1983) Association and linkage studies of genetic marker loci in major psychiatric disorders *Psychiatric Developments*, **4**, 387–418.

—— GERSHON, E. S., TARGUM, S. D., SPARKES, R. S. & MCGINNISS, M. (1983) Segregation and linkage analyses in families of patients with bipolar, unipolar and schizoaffective mood disorders. *American Journal of Human Genetics*, **35**, 274–288.

GOODWIN, D. W. (1979) Alcoholism and heredity. A review and hypothesis. *Archives of General Psychiatry*, **36**, 57–61.

GOTTESMAN, I. I. & SHIELDS, J. (1972) *Schizophrenia and Genetics: A Twin Study Vantage Point*. London. Academic Press.

GREEN, J. R. & WOODROW, J. C. (1977) Sibling method for detecting HLA-linked genes in disease. *Tissue Antigens*, **9**, 31–35.

GURLING, H. M. D., FEDER, J. & CAVALLI-SFORZA, L. L. (1984) Molecular genetic investigations into schizophrenia and bipolar disorder: DNA polymorphisms of the genes coding for ACTH, B-endorphin, CLIP, MSH and B LPH. *Clinical Neuropharmacology*, **7**, Suppl. 1. 196–197.

GUSELLA, J. F., WEXLER, N. S., CONNEALLY, P. M., NAYLOR, S. L., ANDERSON, M. A. *et al* (1983) A polymorphic marker gentically linked to Huntington's disease. *Nature*, **306**, 234–238.

HARVALD, B., & HAUGE, M. (1965) Hereditory factors elucidated by twin studies. In: *Genetics and Epidemiology of Chronic Diseases* (ed. D. V. Neel, M. W. Shaw, and W. J. Schure) PMS Publication, No. 1163, Washington D.C., Usphew.

HELGASON, T. (1964) Epidemiology of mental disorders in Iceland. *Acta Psychiatrica Scandinavica*, Suppl. 173.

HESTON, L. L. (1966) Psychiatric disorders in foster home reared children of schizophrenic mothers. *British Journal of Psychiatry*, **112**, 819–825.

HUTCHINGS, B. & MEDNICK, S. A. (1974) Registered criminality in the adopted and biological parents of registered male adoptees. In: *Genetics, Environment and Psychopathology*. (ed. S. A. Mednick, F. Schulsinger, J. Higgins, & B. Bell) Amsterdam, Elsevier.

JAMES, N. M. & CHAPMAN, C. J. (1975) A genetic study of bipolar affective disorder. *British Journal of Psychiatry*, **126**, 449–456.

JEFFREYS, A. J., WILSON, V. & THEIN, S. L. (1985) Hypervariable 'minisatellite' regions in human DNA. *Nature*, **314**, 67–73.

KALLMAN, F. (1954) Genetic principles in manic-depressive psychosis *In: Depression* (ed. P. M. Hoch, and I. Zulan) New York. Grune and Strattan.

KENDELL, R. E. & GOURLAY, J. (1970) The clinical distinction between psychotic and neurotic depression. *British Journal of Psychiatry*, **117**, 257–260.

—— (1976) The classification of depression: A review of contemporary confusions. *British Journal of Psychiatry*, **129**, 15–28.

KRAEPELIN, E. (1922) *Manic Depressive Insanity and Paranoia*. (Trans. R. M. Barclay). Edinburgh, E. & S. Livingstone.

LANGE, K. & BOEHNKE, M. (1982) How many polymorphic marker genes will it take to open the human genome. *American Journal of Human Genetics*, **34**, 842–845.

LEONHARD, K. (1959) *Anfteilung der Endogen Psychosen*. Berlin. Akademic Verlag.

LI, C. C. (1975) *Path Analysis — A Primer*. Pacific Grove, California, Boxwood Press.

LEOHLIN, J. C. & NICHOLS, R. C. (1976) *Heredity, Environment and Personality: A Study of 850 Sets of Twins*. Austin, Texas, University of Texas Press.

LUXENBURGER, M. (1930) Psychiatrisch-neuroloche. Zwillings-Pathologie. Zeitblatt Fur die gesante. *Neurologie and Psychiatrie*, **56**, 145–180.

McGUFFIN, P. (1980) What have transplant antigens got to do with psychosis? *British Journal of Psychiatry*, **136**, 510–511.

—— (1984) Biological markers and psychosis. *Psychological Medicine*, **14**, 255–258.

—— FESTENSTEIN, H. & MURRAY, R. M. (1983) A family study of HLA antigens and other genetics markers in schizophrenia. *Psychological Medicine*, **13**, 31–43.

MELZER, J. & WINOKUR, G. (1974) A family interview study of male manic-depressives. *Archives of General Psychiatry*, **31**, 73–77.

MENDLEWICZ, J., FLIESS, J. & FIEVE, R. (1972) Evidence for X linkage in the transmission of manic depressive illness. *Journal of American Medical Association*, **222**, 1624–1627.

—— FLIESS, J. & FIEVE, R., (1975) Linkage studies in affective disorders. The X_g blood group and manic depressive illness. In *Genetics and Psychopathology*, (ed. R. Fieve, D. Rosenthal, and H. Brill), Baltimore, John Hopkins Press.

—— & RAINER, J. D. (1977) Adoption study supporting genetic transmission in manic depressive illness. *Nature*, **268**, 326–329.

MORTON, N. E. (1982) *Outline of Genetic Epidemiology*. Basel: Karger.

O'ROURKE, D. H., McGUFFIN, P. & REICH, T. (1983) Genetic analysis of manic depressive illness. *American Journal of Physical Anthropology*, **62**, 51–59.

ORLEY, J. & WING, J. K. (1979) Psychiatric disorders in two African villages. *Archives of General Psychiatry*, **36**, 513–520.

PAYKEL, E. S. (1978) Contribution of life events to causation of psychiatric illness. *Psychological Medicine*, **8**, 245–253.

PENROSE, L. S. (1971) Psychiatric genetics (Editorial). *Psychological Medicine*, **1**, 265–266.

PERRIS, C. (1966) A study of bipolar, manic depressive and unipolar recurrent depressive psychoses. *Acta Psychiatrica et Neurologica Scandinavica*, Suppl. 42.

—— (1968) Genetic transmission of depressive psychoses. *Acta psychiatrica Scandinavica* Suppl. 203, 45–52.

—— PERRIS, H., ERICSSON, U. & VON KNORRING, L. (1982) The genetics of depression. A family study of unipolar and neurotic-reactive depressed patients. *Arch. Psychiatr. Nervenkr.*, **232**, 137–155.

POLLITT, J. (1972) The relationship between genetic and precipitating factors in depressive illness. *British Journal of Psychiatry*, **121**, 67–70.

PRICE, J. (1968) The genetics of depressive behaviour. In: *Recent Developments in Affective Disorders*. (ed. A. J. Coppen, & A. Walk) *British Journal of Psychiatry* Special Publication No. 2. Headley Bros. Ashford, Kent.

RAO, D. C., MORTON, N. E. & CLONINGER, C. R. (1979) Path analysis under generalised assortative mating I. Theory. *Genetic Research (Cambridge)*, **33**, 175–188.

REICH, T., CLAYTON, P. J. & WINOKUR, G. (1969) Family history studies: V. The genetics of mania. *American Journal of Psychiatry*, **125**, 1358–1369.

—— CLONINGER, C. R., WETTE, R. & JAMES, J. (1979) The use of multiple thresholds and segregation analysis in analysing the phenotypic heterogeneity of multifactorial traits. *Annals of Human Genetics*, **42**, 371.

—— JAMES, J. W. & MORRIS, C. A. (1972) The use of multiple thresholds in determining the mode of transmission of semi-conscious traits. *Annals of Human Genetics*, **36**, 163–184.

—— CLONINGER, C. R., SUAREZ, B. & RICE, J. (1982) Genetics of the affective disorders, In: *Handbook of Psychiatry, Psychoses of Unknown Aetiology*. (ed. J. K. Wing and L. Wing), pp. 147–159. Cambridge, Cambridge University Press.

REIDER, R. O. & GERSHON, E. S. (1978) Genetic strategies in biological psychiatry. *Archives of General Psychiatry*, **35**, 866–873.

RICE, J., NICHOLS, P. C. & GOTTESMAN, I. I. (1981) Assessment of sex differences for multifactorial traits using path analysis: Application to learning difficulties. *Psychiatry Research*, **4**, 301–312.
—— REICH, T., ANDREASEN, N. C., LAVORI, J. *et al* (1984) Sex related differences in depression — familial evidence. *Journal of Affective Disorders*, **7**, 199–210.
—— REICH, T., ANDREASEN, N. *et al* (1985) Sex related differences in depression, familial evidence. *Journal of Affective Disorders* (in press).
ROSANOFF, A. J., MANDY, L. M. & PLESSET, R. (1935) The etiology of manic depressive syndromes with special reference to their occurrence in twins. *American Journal of Psychiatry*, **91**, 725–762.
SCARR, S. & CARTER-SALTZMAN, (1979) Twin method: Defense of a critical assumption. *Behaviour Genetics*, **9**, 527–542.
SCHLESSER, M. A., WINOKUR, G. & SHERMAN, B. M. (1979) Genetic subtypes of unipolar primary depressive illness distinguished by hypothalamic-pituitary-adrenal axis activity. *Lancet*, **1**, 739–740.
SHAPIRO, R. W. (1970) A twin study of non-endogenous depression. *Acta Jutlandica*, **XLII** (publications of the University of Aarhus).
—— RYDER, L. P., SVEJGAARD, A. & RAFAELSON, O. J. (1977) HLA antigens and manic depressive disorder: Further evidence of an association. *Psychological Medicine*, **7**, 387–396.
SLATER, E. & SHIELDS, J. (1969) Genetic aspects of anxiety In: *Studies of Anxiety*. (ed. M. H. Lader). *British Journal of Psychiatry* Special Publication No. 3. Ashford, Headley Brothers.
—— COWIE, V. (1971) *The Genetics of Mental Disorders*, London, Oxford University Press.
—— Psychotic and Neurotic Illness in Twins, Special Reports Service, Medical Research Council, London, HMSO.
SMERALDI, F., NEGRI, F. & MELIC, A. M. (1977) A genetic study of affective disorders, *Acta Psychiatrica Scandinavica*, **56**, 382–398.
SMITH, C. (1974) Concordance in twins: Methods and interpretation. *American Journal of Human Genetics*, **26**, 454–466.
STENSTEDT, A. (1952) A study in manic depressive psychosis: Clinical social and genetic investigations. *Acta Psychiatrica*, Suppl. 79.
—— (1966) Genetics of neurotic depression. *Acta Psychiatrica Scandinavica*, **42**, 392–409.
STURT, E., KAMAKURA, N. & DER, G. (1984) How depressing life is. Life-long morbidity risk for depressive disorder in the general population, 7, 2, 109–122.
—— McGUFFIN, P. (1985) Can linkage and marker association resolve the genetic aetiology of psychiatric disorder: Review and argument. *Psychological Medicine* (in press).
SUAREZ, B. K. (1978) The affected sib pair IBD distribution for HLA-linked disease susceptibility genes. *Tissue Antigens*, **12**, 87–93.
—— REICH, T. (1984) HLA and major affective disorder. *Archives of General Psychiatry*, **41**, 22–27.
TANNA, V., WINOKUR, G., ELSTON, R. & GO, R. (1976) A linkage study of pure depressive disease. The use of the sib-pair method. *Biological Psychiatry*, **11**, 767–771.
THOMPSON, D. W. & WEISSMAN, M. M. (1981) Quantifying lifetime risk of psychiatric disorder. *Journal of Psychiatric Research*, **16**, 113–126.
THOMPSON, W. D., PRUSOFF, B. A. & KIDD, K. K. (1982) Comparison of family history method to direct interview. Factors affecting the diagnosis of depression. *Journal of Affective Disorders*, **4**, 49–59.
THOMSON, G. (1981) A review of the theoretical aspects of HLA and disease associations. *Theoretical Population Biology*, **20**, 168–208.
TORGERSEN, S. (1985) Genetic factors in moderately severe and mild affective disorders. *Archives of General Psychiatry* (in press).
TSUANG, M. T., FARAONE, S. V. & FLEMING, J. A. (1985) Familial transmission of major affective disorders. Is there evidence supporting the distinction between unipolar and bipolar disorders. *British Journal of Psychiatry*, **146**, 268–274.
VON KNORRING, A., CLONINGER, C. R., BOHMAN, M. & SIGVARDSSON, S. (1983) an adoption study of depressive disorders and substance abuse. *Archives of General Psychiatry*, **40**, 943–950.

WEATHERALL, D. J. (1982) *The New Genetics and Clinical Practice.* Nuffield Provincial Hospitals Trust.

WEISSMAN, M. M., GERSHON, E., KIDD, K. K., PRUSOFF, B. A. *et al* (1984) Psychiatric disorders in the relatives of probands with affective disorders. *Archives of General Psychiatry*, **41**, 13–21.

WEITKAMP, L. R., STANCER, H. C., PERSAD, E., FLOOD, C. & GUTTORMSEN, S. (1981) Depressive disorders and HLA: A gene on chromosome 6 that can affect behaviour. *New England Journal of Medicine*, **305**, 1301–1341.

WING, J. K., COOPER, J. E. & SARTORIUS, N. (1974) *The Measurement and Classification of Psychiatric Symptoms.* Cambridge, Cambridge University Press.

—— STURT, E. (1978) *The PSE-10-CATEGO System Supplementary Manual.* Medical Research Council. April 1978.

WINOKUR, G. & CLAYTON, P. (1967) Family history studies I. Two types of affective disorders separated according to genetic and clinical factors. *Recent Advances in Biological Psychiatry*, **9**, 35–50.

—— CLAYTON, P. J. & REICH, T. (1969) *Manic Depressive Illness*, St. Louis, C. V. Mosby.

—— (1979) Familial (genetic) subtypes of pure depressive disease. *American Journal of Psychiatry*, **136**, 911–913.

—— TANNA, V. L. (1969) Possible role of X-linked dominant factor in manic depressive illness. *Diseases of the Nervous System*, **30**, 89–94.

WOODRUFF, R. & PITTS, F. N. (1964) Monozygotic twins with obsessional illness. *American Journal of Psychiatry*, **120**, 1075–80.

WRIGHT, A. F., CRICHTON, D. N., LOUDON, J. B., MORTEN, J. E. N. & STEEL, C. M. (1984) β-adrenoceptor binding defects in cell lines from families with manic depressive disorder. *Annals of Human Genetics*, **48**, 201–214.

ZERBIN-RUDIN, E. (1969) Zur Genetik der depressiven Erkrankungen. In: *Das Depressive Syndrom.* (ed. H. Hippius, & H. Selbach) Berlin, Urban & Schwarzenberg.

3 Post-mortem neurochemical findings in suicide and depression: a study of the serotonergic system and imipramine binding in suicide victims

S. J. COOPER; F. OWEN; D. R. CHAMBERS;
T. J. CROW; J. JOHNSON; M. POULTER

'That medicinal substances do display their elective affinities is a proof, at any rate, that there are important though delicate differences in the constitution or composition of the different nervous centres, notwithstanding that we are unable to detect the nature of them. It may be also that there is shadowed out in these different effects of poison on the nervous system a means which may ultimately be of use in the investigation of the constitution of the latter.'

SIR HENRY MAUDSLEY (1872)

In the Fifty-Second Maudsley Lecture to the Royal College of Psychiatrists, Seymour Kety (1980) pointed out that Sir Henry Maudsley had anticipated the development of biochemical research into psychiatric illness and in particular how the use of pharmacological agents might be involved. Such ideas were also expressed by Kraepelin in 1892, but his efforts to test this were limited by the lack of knowledge concerning brain chemistry and the lack of suitable pharmacological agents.

The neurohumoural hypothesis was formulated by Elliott (1905), who suggested that adrenaline released from sympathetic nerve endings might mediate the effects of activity in this system. Adrenaline and acetylcholine were the final chemical transmitters to be identified. Following the recognition of monoamine neurotransmitters in the brain and the discovery 30 years ago of psychotropic drugs for the treatment of schizophrenia and depression, research into biochemical and pharmacological aspects of the psychoses developed rapidly. The observation that a proportion of patients treated with the drug reserpine (which depletes the brain of serotonin, Pletscher *et al*, 1956; noradrenaline, Holzbauer & Vogt, 1956; and dopamine Bertler, 1961) develop symptoms resembling those of depression (Freis, 1954; Muller *et al*, 1955) led to monoamine hypotheses of affective disorder. The demonstration that neuroleptic and antidepressant drugs had effects on neurotransmitters in the brain (Carlsson & Lindqvist, 1963; Spector *et al*, 1963) further encouraged monoamine hypotheses of both depression and schizophrenia. Of further importance was the demonstration by Hornykiewicz (1963) of a dopamine deficit in caudate nuclei obtained at post-mortem from patients who had suffered from Parkinson's disease.

Biochemical research into the functional psychoses has followed three main avenues: the search for 'biochemical markers' of illness; investigation of the mode of action of psychotropic drugs; and, more recently, the chemical examination of brain tissue removed post-mortem from patients. A fourth avenue, at present in its infancy, is the use of suitable positron or gamma emitting ligands for neurotransmitter receptors, the density of which can then be assessed from pictures obtained by Positron Emission Tomography or with a gamma camera (Crawley *et al*, 1983). Earlier chapters in this volume have considered aspects of the first two types of study referred to above. This chapter deals with the study of post-mortem brain tissue.

Post-mortem studies and brain disorders

Neurochemical examination of brain tissue obtained at post-mortem from patients has proved valuable in the investigation of brain disorders that are clearly 'organic' in nature, and in which structural changes of the brain are evident, e.g. in Parkinson's disease. Neurochemical studies in Alzheimer-type dementia (those types of senile and presenile dementia characterised by the presence of neurofibrillary tangles and amyloid plaques) have demonstrated losses of cholinergic neurones by deficits of the marker enzyme, choline acetyltransferase (Bowen *et al*, 1976; Perry *et al*, 1977). In addition, losses of noradrenergic neurones are suggested by the findings of reduced concentrations of noradrenaline in brain tissue (Adolfsson *et al*, 1979) and decreased activity of the marker enzyme, dopamine-beta-hydroxylase (Cross *et al*, 1981b). In Huntington's chorea, decreases in the concentration of gamma-amino-butyric acid have been demonstrated in basal ganglia (Bird & Iversen, 1974).

This approach has been applied to schizophrenia. Studies of post-mortem brain tissue from schizophrenic patients, whether previously neuroleptic treated or drug-free, have provided fairly consistent evidence of an increase in dopamine receptor density (Lee *et al*, 1978; Owen *et al*, 1978; Reisine *et al*, 1980; Cross *et al*, 1981a), though one group find no alteration in a small number of previously neuroleptic drug-free patients (MacKay *et al*, 1980). More recently, post-mortem studies have also suggested the possibility of changes within some peptidergic transmitter systems, such as that involving cholecystokinin in the hippocampus (Farmery *et al*, 1985).

However, the first neurochemical study of brain tissue in relation to a 'functional' disorder was carried out on tissue from patients who had committed suicide (Shaw *et al*, 1967).

Post-mortem studies of monoamines and their metabolites in suicide and depression

Indoleamines

Most of the cases examined by Shaw *et al* (1967) in this study of suicide had previously suffered from depression. A statistically significant decrease in 5-hydroxytryptamine (5HT) concentrations was found in the hind-brain region of the 11 previously depressed cases, compared to a control group of 17 cases who had died from natural causes. Smaller groups of previously schizophrenic and alcoholic cases demonstrated decreases in 5HT concentrations that were not statistically significant. There was no correlation between the 5HT concentrations and age. This observation provided support for the indoleamine hypothesis (Coppen *et al*, 1965) in which a deficit in serotonergic function was suggested as being of aetiological importance in depression. Further studies in which the concentrations of monoamine neurotransmitters and their metabolites have been estimated in post-mortem brain tissue are summarised in Table I. Bourne *et al* (1968) studied the hind-brain region from 23 cases of suicide, 16 of whom were thought to have been previously depressed. They did not find any difference in the concentrations of 5HT compared to their 28 control cases. Their suicide cases were significantly younger at time of death, but there was no relation between 5HT concentrations and age. Pare and colleagues (1969), in a study of 26 suicide victims, replicated the observation of a decrease in 5HT concentrations in the hind-brain, but also found 5HT concentrations to be positively correlated with age. As their control group was older than their suicide victims, this might account for the decrease observed. The development of improved biochemical techniques, requiring smaller amounts of tissue, allowed more precise dissection methods to be used and therefore more brain regions to be studied. Lloyd *et al* (1974) examined 14 brain regions from five suicide cases and five control cases; Beskow *et al* (1976) examined 13 brain regions from 23 suicide cases, only seven of whom had a previous history of depressive illness, and 62 control cases; and Cochran *et al* (1976) examined 33 brain areas from 19 cases of suicide, 10 of whom had a previous history of depression, and 12 control cases. No statistically significant differences were found between suicide cases and control cases in any of these studies. Nor did any relationships emerge between 5HT concentrations and age, post-mortem delay or storage time of frozen tissue prior to assay.

TABLE I

Monoamines and their metabolites in post-mortem brain tissue in suicide and depression

	5HT	5-HIAA	DA	HVA	NA	MHPG
Shaw *et al*, 1967	↑					
Bourne *et al*, 1968	→	↓			→	
Pare *et al*, 1969	↓	→	→		→	
Lloyd *et al*, 1974	→	→				
Moses & Robins, 1975			→		→	
Beskow *et al*, 1976	→	→	→	→	→	
Cochran *et al*, 1976	→					
Riederer *et al*, 1980					→	→

Key: → Unchanged ⎫
      ↑ Increased   ⎬ Compared to control cases
      ↓ Decreased   ⎭

Where the information was available, previous psychotropic drug treatment did not seem to influence the results.

In some studies the concentration of 5-hydroxyindoleacetic acid (5-HIAA) has also been measured. As 5-HIAA is the principle metabolite of 5HT its concentration is thought to reflect turnover of 5HT and perhaps activity within serotonergic neurones. A decrease in the concentration of 5-HIAA was found in hind-brain samples by Bourne and colleagues (1968) and in six out of eight brain areas (including hind-brain structures) by Beskow *et al* (1976). However, in the latter study there was a strong negative correlation between concentrations of 5-HIAA and the time between death and post-mortem. When this was taken into account, the difference between controls and suicide victims was no longer statistically significant. Pare *et al* (1969) and Lloyd *et al* (1974) failed to find any alteration in concentrations of 5-HIAA.

Catecholamines

Studies of catecholamines and their metabolites have also failed to reveal consistent abnormalities. Three groups have found no alteration in the concentrations of dopamine (DA) in various brain regions (Pare *et al*, 1969; Moses & Robins, 1975; Beskow *et al*, 1976). The DA metabolite homovanillic acid (HVA) was also found to be unchanged (Beskow *et al*, 1976). Concentrations of noradrenaline (NA) were found to be similar between control subjects and suicide victims in three studies (Bourne *et al*, 1968; Pare *et al*, 1969; Beskow *et al*, 1976). Moses & Robins (1975) found an increase in NA concentrations in only 3 of 30 brain regions examined. Riederer and colleagues (1980) studied brain tissue from 10 patients who had suffered from endogenous depression and died from bronchopneumonia rather than suicide. They found NA concentrations to be comparable with those from their 16 control subjects in all areas except red nucleus where there was a significant decrease. They also examined the concentration of 3-methoxy-4-hydroxyphenylethylenegylcol (MHPG) the principal metabolite of NA in the central nervous system (Wilk & Watson, 1973). This substance was reduced in 6 of 14 brain areas but not in the red nucleus.

Thus, the results of these studies do not provide any weight of evidence to support either the indolamine (Coppen *et al*, 1965) or catecholamine (Schildkraut, 1965) hypotheses of depressive illness as originally proposed. In other words no simple deficit in the brain concentration of 5HT or its turnover, as estimated by 5-HIAA, nor any unequivocal deficit in NA or its turnover, as estimated by MHPG, is evident.

Post-mortem studies of neurotransmitter receptors in suicide and depression

Receptor theories for depression

Developments of the original hypotheses for the aetiology of depressive disorders and the mode of action of antidepressant treatments have suggested that events at the neurotransmitter receptor level are important. Ashcroft *et al* (Medical Research Council Brain Metabolism Unit, 1972) were among the first to suggest such an hypothesis. Sulser *et al* (1978) demonstrated that when given to laboratory animals antidepressant treatments could produce a decrease in the sensitivity of beta-adrenoceptors in the brain. Crews & Smith (1978) demonstrated a similar effect for $alpha_2$-adrenoceptors. These decreases have been confirmed and shown to be due to a decrease in receptor density (Bergström & Kellar, 1979; Sellinger-Barnette *et al*, 1980; Deakin *et al*, 1981; Stanford & Nutt, 1982). Such results have encouraged hypotheses invoking alterations in adrenoceptor densities as the aetiology of depressive illness (Leonard, 1980). Other investigations of the effects of antidepressant treatment on the brains of laboratory animals have demonstrated changes in the density of both types of 5HT receptor. Fuxe *et al* (1981) reported a decrease in the density of $5HT_1$ receptors with long term treatment and Peroutka & Snyder (1980) demonstrated a decrease in the density of $5HT_2$ receptors. This latter finding has been confirmed by most (Kellar *et al*, 1981; Blackshear & Sanders-Bush, 1982; Goodwin *et al*, 1984) though not all (Green *et al*, 1983) other studies. Interpretation of this finding is complicated by the fact that electroconvulsive shock appears to produce an increase in $5HT_2$ receptor density (Kellar *et al*, 1981; Vetulani *et al*, 1983; Goodwin *et al*, 1984) in animal studies. Again, however, such observations allow us to suggest hypotheses involving alterations in serotenergic receptor densities

(Curzon, 1982). As with the hypotheses that suggested alterations in the concentrations of amine neurotransmitters and/or their metabolites, these newer ideas can also be tested by neurochemical examination of post-mortem brain tissues. The results of five previous studies have been reported and are summarised in' Table II.

Adrenoceptors and muscarinic receptors

Beta-adrenoceptor density has been assessed in only two studies. Myerson *et al* (1982) examined tissue from eight suicide victims compared to 10 control subjects. The density of the receptors was assessed using the ligand dihydroalprenolol (DHA) labelled with the radioactive marker tritium (^{3}H). This ligand binds to beta$_2$-adrenoceptors. No difference from control values was found. Crow *et al* (1984) also found no alteration.

The density of muscarinic cholinergic receptors has been assessed in two studies using the ligand tritiated 3-quinuclidinyl benzilate (^{3}H-QNB). Myerson *et al* (1982), in a study of brain tissue from eight suicide victims, found an increase in density of these receptors but Stanley (1984), in a study of 22 suicides, found no alteration compared to 22 control cases. In the latter study, this was also the case for a group of seven victims with no previous history of receiving psychotropic drugs, although these individuals also had no previous psychiatric history. Previous treatment with drugs such as antidepressants or neuroleptics, which have anticholinergic effects, might induce a compensatory increase in muscarinic receptor density. This could explain the result found by Myerson *et al* (1982) though such an effect is not evident in the study of Stanley (1984). Theories of a cholinergic excess, such as the cholinergic-adrenergic imbalance hypothesis of Janowsky *et al* (1972) therefore remain open.

TABLE II
Receptor changes in post-mortem brain tissue in suicide and depression

	Adrenoceptors (beta-2)	Muscarinic	5HT$_2$	Imipramine
Myerson *et al*, 1982	→	↑		↑
Stanley *et al*, 1982				↓
Perry *et al*, 1983				↓
Stanley & Mann, 1983			↑	
Stanley, 1984	→			

Key: → Unchanged
      ↑ Increased   } Compared to control cases
      ↓ Decreased

5HT receptors

Stanley and Mann (1983) have reported a 45% increase in the density of $5HT_2$ receptors, as assessed by ^3H-spiroperidol binding in frontal cortex tissue from 11 suicide victims compared to 11 control subjects. The two groups were well matched for age and time from death to post-mortem (mean value less than 24 h). However, no information was given regarding possible diagnosis or previous drug treatment of the suicide victims. Clinical data from previous neurochemical studies of suicide and from the results described later in this paper suggest that only a proportion of the suicide victims will have suffered from a depressive illness. Data from studies of the effects of antidepressant drugs in animals (reviewed above) suggests that prior treatment might decrease $5HT_2$ receptor density. However, the same studies suggest that prior treatment with electroconvulsive therapy might increase $5HT_2$ receptor density. The relevance of these observations remains uncertain in the absence of appropriate clinical data. The $5HT_2$ receptor is post-synaptic so in theory a decrease in 5HT turnover might result in a compensatory increase in $5HT_2$ receptor density. However, as reviewed above, post-mortem studies have not demonstrated an alteration in 5HT turnover.

Imipramine binding sites

Coppen *et al* (1978) and Meltzer *et al* (1981) have both found the uptake of 5HT into blood platelets from depressed patients to be reduced and have suggested that this defect may also be present in the brain. Recently, sites to which imipramine binds have been identified on both platelets and neurones (Langer *et al*, 1981) and these seem to be closely related to the uptake sites for 5HT (Sette *et al*, 1981; Raisman *et al*, 1982). A reduction in the number of these sites has been found on platelets from depressed patients (Briley *et al*, 1980; Paul *et al*, 1981). Investigation in post-mortem brain tissue from suicide victims, using ^3H-imipramine as the ligand, has suggested both an increase (Meyerson *et al*, 1982) and a decrease (Stanley *et al*, 1982) in the number of these binding sites. Again, clinical information on these cases was limited. Perry *et al* (1983) examined ^3H-imipramine binding in samples of hippocampus ($n = 7$) and occipital cortex ($n = 9$) from a group of depressed patients who had died from natural causes. Some patients had not received any antidepressant medication for some time prior to death. This group were well matched for age and delay from death to post-mortem with a group of normal cases and a group of cases who had suffered from senile dementia of the Alzheimer type (SDAT). There was a trend for binding to increase with post-mortem delay but this did not reach statistical significance. A marked decrease in the number of imipramine binding sites was found in both brain regions in the depressed group compared to the control and the demented groups. Treatment of laboratory animals with antidepressant drugs has been reported to reduce imipramine binding (Kinnier *et al*, 1980; Arbilla *et al*, 1981). However, Perry *et al* (1983) failed to find such an effect of chronic antidepressant treatment in laboratory rats and when the previously drug-free depressed cases were examined separately they demonstrated the same reduction in imipramine binding as in the treated cases. Interestingly, using learned helplessness, an animal model of depression, Sherman & Petty (1984) were able to demonstrate a reduction in imipramine binding in frontal cortical areas, but not septal or hippocampal areas, from rats made 'helpless'.

The results of a new study of post-mortem brain neurochemistry in suicide are described below. In this study a full examination is being made in a number of brain regions of many aspects of serotonergic, noradrenergic and dopaminergic function. At the present time, however, only the results for serotonergic function are available.

Cases studied

The brains of a group of 28 persons who were suspected to have committed suicide were collected from a public mortuary with the co-operation of the coroner (medical examiner, DRC). Following each inquest the coroner's notes and the pathologist's report were examined. As full a search as possible was made for hospital notes and where notes were obtained, details of the person's illness were recorded and an attempt made to apply the DSM III criteria (American Psychiatric Association, 1980). In eight cases, the death was judged to have been accidental or from natural causes. This was decided not on the basis of the final verdict at the inquest (as legalistic recording of suicide may differ from clinical recording, Clarke-Finnegan and Fahy, 1983) but from the available information and following discussion of each case between psychiatrist (SJC) and coroner (DRC). Of the eight non-suicides, three had no evidence of previous psychiatric disturbance, three had suffered from schizophrenia, one from depressive illness and one from drug addiction.

Data regarding diagnosis, age, sex and cause of death for the 20 cases of suicide remaining are described in Table III. Three cases met DSM III criteria for Major Depression and are described as 'Definite Depression'. The seven cases described as having had 'Probable Depression' were labelled as such because available evidence strongly suggested they had suffered from depression but the evidence was insufficient to fully satisfy research diagnostic criteria. In four cases, labelled 'No Diagnosis Possible', the information was too scant to allow any assessment of possible psychiatric illness present ante-mortem. The proportion of cases with good evidence of previous psychiatric disturbance accords fairly well with that found in larger surveys of suicide (Barraclough *et al*, 1974).

The brains used as control cases were collected from routine post-mortem examinations in a District General Hospital and from cases of sudden accidental death examined at a public mortuary.

Brain dissection and storage

For the suicide cases both hemispheres of the brain were stored, apart from a few cases where one hemisphere was removed for future neuropathological examination. For the control cases usually only one hemisphere was stored, the other half being removed for future neuropathological examination. These brain samples were stored at $-40°C$ until dissection, which was carried out at $-4°C$ according to a standardised method used in previous studies (Owen *et al*, 1978; Cross *et al*, 1981a). The dissection procedure involved removal of cortical tissue corresponding to Brodmann areas 10 (frontal), 7 (parietal), 21 and 22 (temporal) and 19 (occipital). Serial coronal sections were cut and tissue samples of structures, including the hippocampus, amygdala, hypothalamus, substantia nigra, red nucleus and

TABLE III
Clinical data of cases who died by suicide

Case No.	Diagnosis	Sex	Age	Mode of death
5	Definite Depression	M	61	Fall from height
2	,, ,,	F	68	Fall from height
22	,, ,,	F	51	Drug overdose
7	Probable Depression	M	36	Hanging
12	,, ,,	M	71	Drug overdose
14	,, ,,	M	73	Drug overdose
15	,, ,,	M	48	Drug overdose
9	,, ,,	F	26	Struck by train
10	,, ,,	F	41	Drug overdose
19	,, ,,	F	50	Drug overdose
3	Schizophrenia	M	36	Burns
6	,,	M	24	Fall from height
13	,,	M	24	Drug overdose
23	,,	F	58	Drug overdose
8	Personality Disorder	M	33	Drug overdose
20	,, ,,	F	21	Drug overdose
17	No diagnosis possible	M	22	Hanging
1	,, ,,	F	21	Drug overdose
18	,, ,,	F	70	Drowning
16	,, ,,	F	63	Drug overdose

TABLE IV
Details of brain tissue samples used

	Sex	Age (years)	Post-mortem delay (hours)	Storage time frozen (weeks)
		means ± s.e.m.		
Control cases	M = 11 F = 9	55 ± 3	43 ± 4	159 ± 9
Suicide cases	M = 10 F = 10	45 ± 4	47 ± 5	265 ± 15***

*** significantly different from control cases, $p < 0.001$

the parts of the basal ganglia were dissected out. The dissected brain tissue was then stored over liquid nitrogen.

Details of the delay from death to post-mortem and storage times for the suicide and control cases are given in Table IV. The groups were well matched for sex and there was no significant difference between them for age or delay from death to post-mortem. Though the mean post-mortem delay is longer than in some previous studies, previous work suggests that receptor binding site density remains fairly stable for some time after death. The time for which tissue samples were stored frozen was significantly different between the two groups but there is no evidence that significant changes occur in the parameters measured during such storage.

Neurochemical techniques

Details of the neurochemical techniques used are described in more detail elsewhere (Crow *et al*, 1984; Owen *et al*, submitted for publication). Concentrations of 5-HIAA were measured by high-pressure liquid chromatography. Ligand binding studies were carried out according to standard methods using ^{3}H-imipramine to label imipramine binding sites, ^{3}H-5HT to label the $5HT_1$ receptors and ^{3}H-ketanserin to label the $5HT_2$ receptors. Protein was estimated by a phenol reagent technique. Results for all of the neurochemical measures are expressed per milligram (mg) of protein.

Results

The neurochemical findings for the complete group of suicide cases compared to the control cases are presented in Table V(a) and (b). The results have also been separately examined in relation to the 10 cases who were strongly suspected of having suffered from depression prior to their death. In addition the data was examined for any differences between the right and left sides of the brain. Samples from the right side were examined in 14 control cases and 14 suicide cases. Samples from the left side were examined in six control cases and six suicide cases. No differences were evident between the two sides either when the control group or the suicide group were analysed separately or when the groups were combined.

5-HIAA

5-HIAA was measured only in occipital cortex and hippocampus. A moderate, but statistically significant increase was found in the hippocampal region in the suicide cases. There was no significant correlation between 5-HIAA concentrations and age, delay to post-mortem or storage time. The 'depressed' cases ('Definite' and 'Probable' depression) showed a similar increase in concentration in the hippocampal region.

Imipramine binding sites

There were no significant differences in any of the brain areas between suicide cases and controls. There was no correlation with delay to post-mortem as had been found by Perry *et al* (1983). In fact the binding was slightly reduced in the suicide cases compared to the control cases despite a longer mean interval from death to post-mortem.

5HT receptors

There were no significant differences between the suicide cases and controls for the density of either $5HT_1$ or $5HT_2$ receptors. It was not possible to

TABLE Va
Neurochemical findings in post-mortem brain tissue from 20 cases of suicide

Brain area		5-HIAA (ng/mg protein)	Imipramine sites (fmol ^{3}H-imip bound /mg protein)
Frontal cortex	Control	—	205.1 ± 9.7(12)
	Suicide	—	195.1 ± 14.2(14)
Occipital cortex	Control	4.7 ± 0.3(20)	126.8 ± 11.6(16)
	Suicide	4.9 ± 0.7(17)	118.0 ± 13.2(15)
Hippocampus	Control	18.3 ± 1.1(16)	189.4 ± 9.9(19)
	Suicide	23.2 ± 2.2*(16)	186.7 ± 11.2(14)

Results are given as mean ± s.e.m.
Figures in parentheses indicate number of samples used
* significantly different from control group, $p < 0.05$

TABLE Vb
Neurochemical findings in post-mortem brain tissue from 20 cases of suicide

Brain area		5HT$_1$ receptors (fmol ^{3}H-5HT bound /mg protein)	5HT$_2$receptors (fmol ^{3}H-ket bound /mg protein)
Frontal	Control	90.7 ± 5.3(11)	88.5 ± 7.1(12)
cortex	Suicide	72.4 ± 8.0(11)	86.2 ± 9.3(13)
Occipital	Control	37.2 ± 2.9(16)	38.0 ± 3.3(17)
cortex	Suicide	42.3 ± 5.5(12)	35.9 ± 4.7(15)
Hippocampus	Control	58.0 ± 5.7(19)	—
	Suicide	53.4 ± 5.4(15)	—

Results are given as mean ± s.e.m.
Figures in parentheses indicate number of samples used

assess the density of 5HT$_2$ receptors in the hippocampus because binding of ^{3}H-ketanserin was very low. Previous study of post-mortem brain tissue has failed to show any difference between schizophrenic and control cases in 5HT receptor density (Whitaker *et al*, 1981, using ^{3}H-LSD as ligand). It was important, therefore, to exclude the schizophrenic cases and examine the results for the 'depression' group alone. However, they did not show any significant difference from control group values.

Discussion

Approaches to the neurochemistry of affective disorder via the study of cerebrospinal fluid amine metabolite concentrations or hormone responses are indirect. The study of post-mortem brain tissue also has problems. It is more difficult to obtain tissue post-mortem than in the case of schizophrenia, sufferers from which more often die in hospital. Furthermore, patients with affective disorders may be euthymic when they die so that no more than predisposing biochemical abnormalities may be revealed. Individuals who have died by suicide are almost certainly ill at the time of death. However, it can be difficult to document the previous history of supposed victims of suicide. With regard to the cases examined in our study, fully adequate hospital notes could be traced for only eight and for four no hospital records could be found, in one case because they had been lost. Thus diagnostic accuracy cannot be achieved for all cases. Furthermore, not all suicide victims have previously suffered from an affective disorder (Table III). Also difficult to determine is the question of previous drug treatment. In this study all three cases of 'Definite Depression' and four of the cases of 'Probable Depression' had had previous treatment with antidepressant drugs but in only a few of these cases was it clear whether or not these drugs were being prescribed at the time of death. All four cases of schizophrenia were being prescribed neuroleptic drugs at the time of death.

No changes of major significance were identified in the present study. The results obtained for those cases in whom there was a previous history suggestive of depressive illness were the same as for the entire group of suicide cases. The only statistically significant finding was of an increase in the concentration of 5-HIAA in the hippocampal region in the suicide cases. Previously 5-HIAA concentrations have been reported to be decreased or unchanged in brain tissue from suicide victims (Table I). Cerebrospinal fluid concentrations of 5-HIAA are also generally (Ashcroft & Sharman, 1960; Ashcroft *et al*, 1973; Åsberg *et al*, 1984) but not always (Vestergaard *et al*, 1978) found to be reduced in depression. This applies particularly to patients with suicidal intent (Åsberg *et al*, 1976; Träskman *et al*, 1981; Brown *et al*, 1983; Banki & Arató, 1983). Treatment with antidepressant drugs seems to induce a further reduction in cerebrospinal fluid concentrations of 5-HIAA (Post & Goodwin, 1974; Träskman *et al*, 1979; Dahl *et al*, 1982) so previous drug treatment is unlikely to be responsible for the increased brain concentrations found. Beskow *et al* (1976) found a negative correlation between 5-HIAA concentrations and post-mortem delay, but in our study post-mortem delay was longer for the suicide cases. Concentrations of 5-HIAA in brain tissue tend to rise with age, as they do in cerebrospinal fluid (Young *et al*, 1980), but the suicide cases were younger on average than the control cases.

A small increase in brain tissue concentrations of 5-HIAA has, however, been noted in two previous reports. Though Lloyd *et al* (1974) found no overall difference from control cases there was a trend in some brain areas, including the hippocampus, for 5-HIAA to be elevated. Similarly, a review of results from a series of post-mortem brain studies on depression and dementia (Crow *et al*, 1984) also noted increased 5-HIAA concentrations in hippocampal tissue from depressed cases. This result might be interpreted as indicating an increase in the turnover of 5HT, perhaps to compensate for an alteration in receptor density. However, review of previous studies (Table II) and the present results do not suggest any alteration in receptor density.

The lack of evidence for a general alteration of $5HT_2$ receptor function is consistent with the results of a study in which the functional activity of $5HT_2$ receptors was assessed through the platelet aggregation response to 5HT. No significant differences were found in depressed patients compared to control subjects (Wood *et al*, 1984). Healy *et al* (1983), however did find a reduced response in depressed patients which they claimed returned toward normal if treatment was successful. This suggests that antidepressant treatment may increase $5HT_2$ receptor function, but this is in contrast to previous studies in laboratory animals. These found a decrease (Peroutka & Snyder, 1980; Kellar *et al*, 1981; Blackshear & Sanders-Bush, 1982; Goodwin *et al*, 1984) or no change (Green *et al*, 1983) unless the treatment employed was electroconvulsive shock, when an increase in density was observed (Kellar *et al*, 1981; Vetulani *et al*, 1983; Goodwin *et al*, 1984).

Previous work on post-mortem brains in suicide and depression has suggested both an increase in imipramine binding sites (Myerson *et al*, 1982) and a decrease (Stanley *et al*, 1982; Perry *et al*, 1983). Our conclusion that there is no alteration falls conveniently between these results. It is unclear whether or not antidepressant drug treatment affects imipramine binding sites in brain tissue from laboratory animals (Kinnier *et al*, 1980; Perry *et al*, 1983). There is .also disagreement as to whether treatment may normalise 5HT uptake in depressed patients (Coppen *et al*, 1978; Healy *et al*, 1983).

Conclusions

The results of the present study of serotonergic function in brain tissue from suicide victims gives no support to the hypothesis of an abnormality in this system in affective disorder or to claims that imipramine binding sites are significantly changed. Previous studies have produced conflicting results. The difficulties involved in this kind of study have been illustrated.

References

ADOLFSSON, R., GOTTFRIES, G. C., ROOS, B. E. & WINBLAD, B. (1979) Changes in brain catecholamines in patients with dementia of Alzheimer-type. *British Journal of Psychiatry*, **135**, 216–223.

AMERICAN PSYCHIATRIC ASSOCIATION (1980) *DSM III: Diagnostic and Statistical Manual of Mental Disorders (3rd edition)*. Washington, D.C.: APA.

ARBILLA, S., BRILEY, M., CATHALA, F., LANGER, S. Z., PORNIN, D. & RAISEMAN, R. (1981) Parallel changes in (^{3}H)-imipramine binding sites in cat brain and platelets following chronic treatment with imipramine. *British Journal of Pharmacology*, **72**, 154–155.

ÅSBERG, M., BERTILSSON, L. MÅRTENSON, B., SCALIA-TOMBA, G.-P., THOREN, P. & TRASKMAN-BENDZ, L. (1984) CSF monoamine metabolites in melancholia. *Acta Psychiatrica Scandinavica*, **69**, 201–219.

—— TRÄSKMAN, L. & THORÉN, P. (1976) 5-HIAA in the cerebrospinal fluid: a biochemical suicide predictor? *Archives of General Psychiatry*, **33**, 1193–1197.

ASHCROFT, G. W., BLACKBURN, I. M., ECCLESTON, D., GLEN, A. I. M., HARTLEY, W., KINLOCH, N. E., LONERGAN, M., MURRAY, L. G. & PULLAR, I. A. (1973) Changes on recovery in the concentrations of tryptophan and the biogenic amine metabolites in the cerebrospinal fluid of patients with affective illness. *Psychological Medicine*, **3**, 319–325.

—— SHARMAN, D. F. (1960) 5-hydroxyindoles in human cerebrospinal fluids. *Nature*, **186**, 1050–1051.

BANKI, C. M. & ARATÓ, M. (1983) Amine metabolites and neuroendocrine responses related to depression and suicide. *Journal of Affective Disorders*, **5**, 223–232.

BARRACLOUGH, B., BUNCH, J., NELSON, B. & SAINSBURY, P. (1974) A hundred cases of suicide: clinical aspects. *British Journal of Psychiatry*, **125**, 355–373.

BERGSTROM, D. A. & KELLAR, K. J. (1979) Effect of electroconvulsive shock on monoaminergic receptor binding sites in rat brain. *Nature*, **278**, 464–466.

BERTLER, A. (1961) Effect of reserpine on the storage of catecholamines in brain and other tissues. *Acta Physiologica Scandinavica*, **51**, 75–83.

BESKOW, J., GOTTFRIES, C. G., ROOS, B. E. & WINBLAD, B. (1976) Determination of monoamine and monoamine metabolites in the human brain: post mortem studies in a group of suicides and in a control group. *Acta Psychiatrica Scandinavica*, **53**, 7–20.

BIRD, E. D. & IVERSEN, L. L. (1974) Huntington's chorea: post-mortem measurement of glutamic acid decarboxylase, choline acetyltransferase and dopamine in basal ganglia. *Brain*, **97**, 457–472.

BLACKSHEAR, M. A. & SANDERS-BUSH, E. (1982) Serotonin receptor sensitivity after acute and chronic treatment with mianserin. *Journal of Pharmacology and Experimental Therapeutics*, **221**, 303–308.

BOURNE, H. R., BUNNEY, W. E. COLBURN, R. W., DAVIS, J. M., DAVIS, J. N., SHAW, D. M. & COPPEN, A. (1968) Noradrenaline, 5-hydroxytryptamine and 5-hydroxyindoleacetic acid in hindbrains of suicidal patients. *Lancet*, **2**, 805–808.

BOWEN, D. M., SMITH, C. B., WHITE, P. & DAVISON, A. N. (1976) Neurotransmitter-related enzymes and indices of hypoxia in senile dementia and other abiotrophies. *Brain*, **99**, 457–496.

BRILEY, M. S., LANGER, S. Z., RAISMAN, R., SECHTER, D. & ZARIFIAN, E. (1980) ^{3}H-imipramine binding sites are decreased in platelets of untreated depressed patients. *Science*, **209**, 303–305.

BROWN, G. L., EBERT, M., H., GOYER, P. F., JIMERSON, D. C., KLEIN, W. J., BUNNEY, W. E. & GOODWIN, F. K. (1982) Aggression, suicide and serotinin: relationships to CSF amine metabolites. *American Journal of Psychiatry*, **139**, 741–746.

CARLSSON, A. & LINDQVIST, M. (1963) Effect of chlorpromazine and haloperidol on formation of 3-methoxy-tyramine and normetanephrine in mouse brain. *Acta Pharmacologica et Toxicologica*, **30**, 140–144.

CLARKE-FINNEGAN, M. & FAHY, T. J. (1983) Suicide rates in Ireland. *Psychological Medicine*, **13**, 385–391.

COCHRAN, E., ROBINS, E. & GROTE, S. (1976) Regional serotonin levels in brain: a comparison of depressive suicides and alcoholic suicides with controls. *Biological Psychiatry*, **3**, 283–294.

COPPEN, A., SHAW, D. M., MALLERSON, A., ECCLESTON, E. & GUNDY, G. (1965) Tryptamine metabolism in depression. *British Journal of Psychiatry*, **111**, 993–998.

—— SWADE, C. & WOOD, K. (1978) Platelet 5-hydroxytryptamine accumulation in depressive illness. *Clinical Chimica Acta*, **87**, 165–168.

CRAWLEY, J. C. W., SMITH, T., VEALL, N., ZANELLI, G. D., CROW, T. J. & OWEN, F. (1983) Dopamine receptors displayed in living human brain with [77]Br-p-bromospiperone. *Lancet*, **2**, 975.

CREWS, F. T. & SMITH, C. B. (1978) Presynaptic alpha-receptor subsensitivity after long-term antidepressant treatment. *Science*, **202**, 322–324.

CROSS, A. J., CROW, T. J. & OWEN, F. (1981a) ^{3}H-flupenthixol binding in post-mortem brains of schizophrenics: evidence for a selective increase in dopamine D2 receptors. *Psychopharmacology*, **74**, 122–124.

—— CROW, T. J., PERRY, E. K., PERRY, R. H., BLESSED, G. & TOMLINSON, B. E. (1981b) Reduced dopamine-beta-hydroxylase activity in Alzheimer's disease. *British Medical Journal*, **282**, 93–94.

CROW, T. J., CROSS, A. J., COOPER, S. J., DEAKIN, J. F. W., FERRIER, I. N., JOHNSON, J. A., JOSEPH, M. H., OWEN, F., POULTER, M., LOFTHOUSE, R., CORSELLIS, J. A. N., CHAMBERS, D. R., BLESSED, G., PERRY, E. K., PERRY, R. H. & TOMLINSON, B. E. (1984) Neurotransmitter receptors and monoamine metabolites in the brains of patients with Alzheimer-type dementia and depressioin, and suicides. *Neuropharmacology*, **23**, 1561–1569.

CURZON, G. (1982) Transmitter amines in depression. *Psychological Medicine*, **12**, 465–470.

DAHL, L.-E., LUNDIN, L., LE FÈVRE HONORÉ, P. & DENCKER, S. J. (1982) Antidepressant effect of femoxetine and desipramine and relationship to the concentration of amine metabolites in cerebrospinal fluid. *Acta Psychiatrica Scandinavica*, **66**, 9–17.

DEAKIN, J. F. W., OWEN, F., CROSS, A. J., & DASHWOOD, M. J. (1981) studies on possible mechanisms of action of electroconvulsive therapy: effects of repeated electrically induced seizures on rat brain receptors for monoamines and other neurotransmitters. *Psychopharmacology*, **73**, 345–349.

ELLIOTT, T. R. (1905) The action of adrenaline. *Journal of Physiology*, **32**, 401–467.

FARMERY, S. M., OWEN, F., POULTER, M. & CROW, T. J. (1985) Reduced high affinity cholecystokinin binding in hippocampus and frontal cortex of schizophrenic patients. *Life Sciences*, **36**, 473–477.

FREIS, E. (1954) Mental depression in hypertensive patients treated for long periods with large doses of reserpine. *New England Journal of Medicine*, **251**, 1006–1008.

FUXE, K., OGREN, S.-O., AGNATI, L. F., ENEROTH, P., HOLM, A.C. & ANDERSSON, K. (1981) Long-term treatment with zimelidine leads to a reduction in 5-hydroxytryptamine transmission within the central nervous system of the mouse and rat. *Neuroscience Letters*, **21**, 57–62.

GOODWIN, G. M., GREEN, A. R. & JOHNSON, P. (1984) 5-HT$_2$ receptor characteristics in frontal cortex and 5-HT$_2$ receptor-mediated head-twitch behaviour following antidepressant treatment to mice. *British Journal of Pharmacology*, **83**, 235–242.

GREEN, A. R., HEAL, D. J., JOHNSON, P., LAURENCE, B. E., & NIMGAONKAR, V. L. (1983) Antidepressant treatments: effects in rodents on dose-response curves of 5-hydroxytryptamine and dopamine-mediated behaviours and 5-HT$_2$ receptor number in frontal cortex. *British Journal of Pharmacology*, **80**, 377–385.

HEALY, D., CARNEY, P. A., & LEONARD, B. E. (1983) Monoamine-related markers of depression: changes following treatment. *Journal of Psychiatric Research*, **17**, 251–260.

HOLZBAUER, M. & VOGT, M. (1956) Depression by reserpine of the noradrenaline concentration in the hypothalamus of the cat. *Journal of Neurochemistry*, **1**, 8–11.

HORNYKIEWICZ, O. (1963) Die topische lokalisation und das verhalten von noradrenalin und depamin in der substantia nigra des normalen und parkinsonkranken menschen. *Wiener Kliniche Wochenschrift*, **75**, 309–312.

JANOWSKY, D. S., EL-YOUSEF, N. K., DAVIS, J. M. & SEKERKE, H. J. (1972) A cholinergic-adrenergic hypothesis of mania and depression. *Lancet*, **2**, 632–635.

KELLAR, K. J., CASCIO, C. S., BUTLER, J. A. & KURTZKE, R. N. (1981) Differential effects of electroconvulsive shock and anti-depressant drugs on serotonin – 2 receptors in rat brain. *European Journal of Pharmacology*, **69**, 515–518.

KETY, S. S. (1980) The syndrome of schizophrenia: unresolved questions and opportunities for research. *British Journal of Psychiatry*, **136**, 421–436.

KINNIER, W. J., CHUANG, D. M. & COSTA, E. (1980) Down regulation of dihydroalprenolol and imipramine binding sites in brain of rats repeatedly treated with imipramine. *European Journal of Pharmacology*, **67**, 289–294.

KRAEPELIN, E. (1892) *Über die Beeinflussung einfacher psychischer Vorgänge durch einige Arzneimittel*. Jena, Gustav Ficher.

LANGER, S. Z., ZARIFIAN, E., BRILEY, M., RAISMAN, R. & SECHTER, D. (1981) High-affinity binding of ^{3}H-imipramine in brain and platelets and its relevance to the biochemistry of affective disorders. *Life Sciences*, **29**, 211–220.

LEE, T., SEEMAN, P., TOURTELLOTTE, W. W., FARLEY, I. J. & HORNYKIEWICZ, O. (1978) Binding of ^{3}H-apomorphine in schizophrenic brains. *Nature*, **274**, 897–900.

LEONARD, B. E. (1980) Pharmacological properties of some 'second generation' antidepressant drugs. *Neuropharmacology*, **19**, 1175–1183.

LLOYD, K. G., FARLEY, I. J., DECK, J. H. N. & HORNYKIEWICZ, O. (1974). Serotonin and 5-hydroxyindole acetic acid in discrete areas of the brainstem of suicide victims and control patients. *Advances in Biochemical Psychopharmacology*. **11**, 387–397.

MACKAY, A. V. P., BIRD, E. D., SPOKES, E. G., ROSSER, M., IVERSEN, L. L., CREESE, I. & SNYDER, S. H. (1980) Dopamine receptors and schizophrenia: drug effect or illness? *Lancet*, **2**, 915–916.

MAUDSLEY, H. (1872) *The Physiology and Pathology of Mind*. New York, Appleton and Co.

MEDICAL RESEARCH COUNCIL BRAIN METABOLISM UNIT. (1972) Modified amine hypothesis for the aetiology of affective illness. *Lancet*, **2**, 573–577.

MELTZER, H. Y., ARORA, R. C., BABER, R. & TRICOU, B. J. (1981) Serotonin uptake in blood platelets of psychiatric patients. *Archives of General Psychiatry*, **38**, 1322–1326.

MEYERSON, L. R., WENNOGLE, L. P., ABEL, M. S., COUPET, J., LIPPA, A. S., RAUH, C. E. & BEER, B. (1982) Human brain receptor alterations in suicide victims. *Pharmacology, Biochemistry and Behaviour*, **17**, 159–163.

MOSES, S. G. & ROBINS, E. (1975) Regional distribution of norepinephrine and dopamine in brains of depressive suicides and alcoholic suicides. *Psychopharmacology Communications*, **1**, 327–337.

MULLER, J. C., PRYER, W. W., GIBBONS, J. E. & ORGAIN, E. S. (1955) Depression and anxiety occurring during rauwolfia therapy. *Journal of the American Medical Association*, **159**, 836–839.

OWEN, F., CHAMBERS, D. R., COOPER, S. J., CROW, T. J. & POULTER, M. (1984) Central serotonergic mechanisms in suicide. *Brain Research*, submitted for publication.

—— CROSS, A. J., CROW, T. J., LONGDEN, A., POULTER, M. & RILEY, G. J. (1978) Increased dopamine receptor sensitivity in schizophrenia. *Lancet*, **2**, 223–226.

PARE, C. M. B., YEUNG, D. P. H., PRICE, K. & STACEY, R. S. (1969) 5-hydroxytryptamine, noradrenaline and dopamine in brainstem, hypothalamus and caudate nucleus of controls and of patients committing suicide by coal-gas poisoning. *Lancet*, **2**, 133–135.

PAUL, S. M., REHAVI, M., SKOLNICK, P., BALLENGER, J. C. & GOODWIN, F. K. (1981) Depressed patients have decreased binding of tritiated imipramine to platelet serotonin 'transporter'. *Archives of General Psychiatry*, **38**, 1315–1317.

PEROUTKA, S. J. & SNYDER, S. H. (1980) Long-term antidepressant treatment decreased spiroperidol-labelled serotonin receptor binding. *Science*, **210**, 88–90.

PERRY, E. K., MARSHALL, E. F., BLESSED, G., TOMLINSON, B. E. & PERRY, R. H. (1983) Decreased imipramine binding in the brains of patients with depressive illness. *British Journal of Psychiatry*, **142**, 188–192.

—— PERRY, R. H., BLESSED, G. & TOMLINSON, B. E. (1977) Necropsy evidence of central cholinergic deficits in senile dementia. *Lancet*, **1**, 189.

PLETSCHER, A., SHORE, P. A. & BRODIE, B. B. (1956) Serotonin as a mediator of reserpine action in the brain. *Journal of Pharmacology*, **116**, 84–89.

POST, R. M. & GOODWIN, F. K. (1974) Effect of amitriptyline and imipramine on the concentration of 5-HIAA and HVA in the cerebrospinal fluid of depressed patients. *Archives of General Psychiatry*, **30**, 234–239.

RAISMAN, R., BRILEY, M. S., BOUCHAMI, F., SECHTER, D., ZARIFIAN, E. & LANGER, S. Z. (1982) ^{3}H-imipramine binding and serotonin uptake in platelets from untreated depressed patients and control volunteers. *Psychopharmacology*, **77**, 332–335.

REISINE, T. D., ROSSOR, M., SPOKES, E., IVERSEN, L. L. & YAMAMURA, H. I. (1980) Opiate and neuroleptic receptor alterations in human schizophrenic brain tissue. In: *Receptors for Neurotransmitters and Peptide Hormones*, (ed. G. Pepue, M. J. Kuhar and S. J. Enna) pp. 443–450. New York, Raven Press.

REIDERER, P., BIRKMAYER, W., SEEMAN, D., & WINKFICH, S. (1980) 4-hydroxy-3-methoxy-phenylglycol as an index of brain noradrenaline turnover in endogenous depression. *Acta Psychiatrica Scandinavica*, **61**, 251–257.

SCHILDKRAUT, J. J. (1965) The catecholamine hypothesis of affective disorders: a review of the supporting evidence. *American Journal of Psychiatry*, **122**, 509–522.

SELLINGER-BARNETTE, M. M., MENDELS, J. & FRAZER, A. (1980) The effect of psychoactive drugs on beta-adrenergic receptor binding sites in rat brain. *Neuropharmacology*, **19**, 447–454.

SETTE, M., RAISMAN, R., BRILEY, M., & LANGER, S. Z. (1981) Localisation of tricyclic antidepressant binding sites on serotonin nerve terminals. *Journal of Neurochemistry*, **37**, 40–42.

SHAW, D. M., CAMPS, F. E. & ECCLESTON, E. G. (1967) 5-hydroxytryptamine in the hind-brain of depressive suicides. *British Journal of Psychiatry*, **113**, 1407–1411.

SHERMAN, A. D. & PETTY, F. (1984) Learned helplessness decreases (^{3}H) imipramine binding in rat cortex. *Journal of Affective Disorders*, **6**, 25–32.

SPECTOR, S., HIRSCH, C. W. & BRODIE, B. B. (1963) Association of behavioural effects of pargyline, a non-hydrazide MAO inhibitor with increase in brain norepinephrine. *International Journal of Neuropharmacology*, **2**, 81–93.

STANFORD, S. C. & NUTT, D. J. (1982) Comparison of the effects of repeated electroconvulsive shock on α_2- and β-adrenoceptors in different regions of rat brain. *Neuroscience*, **7**, 1753–1757.

STANLEY, M. (1984) Cholinergic receptor binding in the frontal cortex of suicide victims. *American Journal of Psychiatry*, **141**, 1432–1436.

—— MANN, J. J. (1983) Increased serotonin-2 binding sites in frontal cortex of suicide victims. *Lancet*, **1**, 214–216.

—— VIRGILIO, J., & GERSHON, S. (1982) Tritiated imipramine binding sites are decreased in the frontal cortex of suicides. *Science*, **216**, 1337–1339.

SULSER, F., VETULANI, J., & MOBLEY, P. L. (1978) Mode of acting of antidepressant drugs. *Biochemical Pharmacology*, **27**, 257–261.

TRÄSKMAN, L., ÅSBERG, M., BERTILSSON, L., CRONHOLM, B., MELLSTRÖM, B., NECKERS, L. M., SJOQVIST, F., THORÉN, P. & TYBRING, G. (1979) Plasma levels of chlorimipramine and its demethyl metabolite during treatment of depression. *Clinical Pharmacology and Therapeutics*, **26**, 600–610.

—— ÅSBERG, M., BERTILSSON, L., & SJÖSTRAND, L. (1981) Monoamine metabolites in CSF and suicidal behaviour. *Archives of General Psychiatry*, **38**, 631–636.

VESTERGAARD, P., SØRENSEN, T., HOPPE, E., RAFAELSEN, O. J. YATES, C. M. & NICOLAOU, N. (1978) Biogenic amine metabolites in cerebrospinal fluid of patients with affective disorders. *Acta Psychiatrica Scandinavica*, **58**, 88–96.

VETULANI, J., SZPAK, J. & PILC, A. (1983) Spaced electroconvulsive treatment: effects on responses associated with α_2- and 5-HT$_2$-receptors. *Journal of Pharmacy and Pharmacology*, **35**, 326–328.

WHITAKER, P. M., CROW, T. J. & FERRIER, I. N. (1981) Tritiated LSD binding in frontal cortex in schizophrenia. *Archives of General Psychiatry*, **38**, 278–280.

WILK, S. & WATSON, E. (1973) VMA in spinal fluid: evaluation of the pathways of cerebral catecholamine metabolism in man. In: *Frontiers in Catecholamine Research*, (ed. E. Usdin and S. Snyder) pp. 1067–1069. London, Pergamon Press.

WOOD, K., SWADE, C., ABOU-SALEH, M. & COPPEN, A. (1984) Peripheral serotonergic receptor sensitivity in depressive illness. *Journal of Affective Disorders*, **7**, 59–65.

YOUNG, S. N., GAUTHIER, S., ANDERSON, G. M. & PURDY, W. C. (1980) Tryptophan, 5-hydroxyindoleacetic acid and indoleacetic acid in human cerebrospinal fluid: interrelationships and the influence of age, sex, epilepsy and anticonvulsant drugs. *Journal of Neurology, Neurosurgery and Psychiatry*, **43**, 438–445.

4 5HT Neuroendocrinology: changes during depressive illness and antidepressant drug treatment

P. J. COWEN; I. M. ANDERSON

The role of brain 5-hydroxytryptamine (5HT, serotonin) pathways in the aetiology of depressive illness has proved difficult to determine. However, certain biochemical investigations, particularly of 5HT metabolite concentration in cerebrospinal fluid (Åsberg et al, 1976; Träskman et al, 1981) and 5HT transport in blood platelets (1979; Coppen et al; Tuomisto et al, 1978) have suggested that abnormalities of 5HT function may be present in depressive disorders (Goodwin & Post, 1983). There is a need for a further means of assessing brain 5HT function and neuroendocrine challenge tests offer a possible approach.

The development of neuroendocrine challenge tests rests on the demonstration that the release of certain anterior pituitary hormones is controlled by brain monoamine pathways. Thus, monoamine function can be assessed by measurement of the hormonal response in plasma which follows stimulation of a particular brain monoamine pathway by a specific drug (Checkley, 1980). The size of the hormonal response is taken as an index of the functional activity of the monoamine synapses with which the drug interacts.

It will be apparent that for a neuroendocrine challenge test to provide a valid measure of brain 5HT function it must be demonstrated that the hormone measured is indeed under the control (though not necessarily the exclusive control) of brain 5HT pathways and that the drug employed to produce the hormonal response is acting specifically through 5HT synapses.

5HT Pathways and anterior pituitary hormones

The interaction between brain monoamine pathways and pituitary hormone release has been investigated extensively in animals (Muller et al, 1977). While these data provide valuable clues into possible mechanisms in man, species differences make direct comparison unreliable and in this discussion only human data will be considered in detail.

TABLE I

Drugs increasing brain 5HT function and 5HT receptor antagonists used in neuroendocrine studies

Mechanism of Action	Drugs
5HT precursors:	L-tryptophan (LTP); 5-hydroxytryptophan (5HTP)
5HT receptor agonists:	quipazine; N, N-dimethyltryptamine (NNDMT)
5HT releasing agent:	fenfluramine (also blocks 5HT uptake)
5HT uptake blockers:	chlorimipramine; zimelidine; fluoxetine
5HT receptor antagonists:	methysergide; metergoline; cyproheptadine; ketanserin

In man, investigation of the role of 5HT in pituitary hormone release is necessarily limited to measuring the effects of drugs which either increase brain 5HT function in various ways or decrease it, usually by 5HT receptor antagonism (Table I). Despite this it is common for studies to contradict each other in a confusing way. The differing results probably reflect the tendency of investigators to test small numbers of subjects with varying protocols of drug administration. In addition, available 5HT antagonists have mixed pharmacological properties which complicate interpretation of results obtained from their use. Finally, increasing brain 5HT function in man not infrequently causes both gastrointestinal upset, especially nausea, and psychological symptoms, such as dysphoria, stresses which can themselves stimulate anterior pituitary hormone release.

Prolactin (PRL)

In animals there is good evidence that 5HT can increase prolactin (PRL) release. This action probably takes place at hypothalamic level (Meites & Sonntag, 1981) via the stimulation of a Prolactin Releasing Factor (Clemens *et al*, 1978) by 5HT neurones originating in the medial and dorsal raphé nuclei (Fessler *et al*, 1984).

In man, oral administration of drugs which increase 5HT function fails to elevate plasma PRL levels consistently. Thus oral administration of L-tryptophan (LTP) (Woolfe & Lee, 1977; Fraser *et al*, 1979), 5-hydroxytryptophan (5HTP) (Handwerger *et al*, 1975; Meltzer *et al*, 1982; Westenberg *et al*, 1982), quipazine (Parati *et al*, 1980), zimelidine (Syvälahti *et al*, 1979) and chlorimipramine (Francis *et al*, 1976; Jones & Luscombe, 1976) do not reliably stimulate PRL release. A notable exception is fenfluramine which in single oral doses of 60 mg and above does appear to produce a consistent increase in plasma PRL (Quattrone *et al*, 1983).

A robust increase in plasma PRL is usually found following intravenous (i.v.) administration of LTP (Macindoe & Turkington, 1973; Charney *et al*, 1982) and also 5HTP (Lancranjan *et al*, 1977; Maschat *et al*, 1983) and chlorimipramine (Laakmann *et al*, 1984) though the latter drugs cause a high incidence of gastrointestinal side effects. The 5HT antagonists, methysergide and metergoline, decrease basal plasma PRL (Ferrari *et al*, 1978; Crosignani *et al*, 1979), which is consistent with a facilitatory effect of 5HT on PRL release. However, both these drugs have dopamine agonist properties and could therefore reduce plasma PRL levels by a direct action on the pituitary (Krulich *et al*, 1981). The 5HT antagonist, cyproheptadine, also has antihistamine and anticholinergic properties (Leysen *et al*, 1981). It has been reported to attenuate the PRL increase which follows 5HTP administration (Kato *et al*, 1974).

Taken together the findings indicate that 5HT pathways can stimulate PRL release in man. Whether 5HT plays a role in PRL secretion under basal conditions is unclear.

Growth hormone (GH)

In animal studies there are conflicting claims concerning the role of 5HT in growth hormone (GH) release, which may be a reflection of species differences (Muller *et al*, 1977). In man oral administration of LTP and 5HTP does not result in a consistent elevation in plasma GH (Wolf & Lee, 1977; Fraser *et al*, 1979; Handwerger *et al*, 1975; Meltzer *et al*, 1982; Westenberg *et al*, 1982) whereas i.v. LTP and 5HTP usually produce a reliable GH increase (Charney *et al*, 1982; Cowen *et al*, 1985; Lancranjan, 1977; Maschat *et al*, 1983), though one study using i.v. LTP did not find this (Macindoe & Turkington, 1973). While the 5HT agonist, N, N-dimethyltryptamine (NNDMT) given i.v. increases plasma GH (Meltzer *et al*, 1982), i.v. administration of fenfluramine has produced inconsistent effects on both basal and stimulated GH levels in plasma (Turtle & Burgess, 1973; Sulaiman & Johnson, 1973). Chlorimipramine given i.v. increased plasma GH in half the subjects studied (Laakman *et al*, 1984) but the noradrenaline (NA) uptake blocking properties of this drug complicates interpretation of the findings.

5HT antagonists given alone have been reported to have little consistent effect on GH secretion. Cyproheptadine may reduce sleep-induced GH secretion (Chihara *et al*, 1976) but in the same situation methysergide stimulated GH release, possibly through DA agonist action (Mendelson *et al*, 1975). Oral cyproheptadine is reported to reduce the GH response to oral LTP (Fraser *et al*, 1979) but in our own study did not attenuate the plasma GH increase following i.v. LTP (Cowen *et al*, 1985). Cyproheptadine given i.v. reduced the GH response to 5HTP (Nakai *et al*, 1974).

From the foregoing account, it will be apparent that the role of 5HT in GH secretion in man is far from clear, although a stimulatory effect is possible. Matters are further complicated by the fact that although i.v. LTP and 5HTP stimulate GH secretion, mechanisms other than increased 5HT function may be responsible (see below).

ACTH

In animals 5HT appears to be involved in the regulation of the circadian rhythm of ACTH secretion but its role in acute stress-related increases in ACTH is unclear (Muller *et al*, 1977; Joseph & Kennett, 1983). A number of investigations have indicated that increasing brain 5HT function increases cortisol levels in rats (Naumenko, 1969; Fuller, 1981). In man studies tend to equate cortisol responses with those of ACTH, which may not be justified since peripheral factors could play a part in determining cortisol levels, which will then not reflect solely the activity of the hypothalamic-pituitary axis.

Oral and intravenous 5HTP appears to stimulate ACTH and cortisol secretion in most, but not all studies (Imura *et al*, 1973; Meltzer *et al*, 1982; Westenberg *et al*, 1982; Petraglia *et al*, 1984), whereas LTP orally and intravenously has not increased and occasionally has decreased cortisol levels (Macindoe & Turkington, 1973; Woolfe & Lee, 1977; Modlinger *et al*, 1979). Oral administration of quipazine (Parati *et al*, 1980) and NNDMT (Meltzer *et al*, 1982) seems to elevate cortisol levels as does fluoxetine, the selective 5HT uptake blocker (Petraglia *et al*, 1984). Similarly, fenfluramine has been reported to increase plasma ACTH and cortisol (Lewis & Sherman, 1984). Methysergide alone does not alter basal cortisol levels but may inhibit the cortisol response to 5HTP (Petraglia *et al*, 1984). Cyproheptadine, however, had variable effects in inhibiting the cortisol response to NNDMT (Meltzer *et al*, 1982).

The evidence of 5HT involvement in the secretion of ACTH and cortisol is suggestive but many findings are contradictory. It seems unlikely that 5HT is a major influence in the acute release of these hormones in man.

Other hormones

There is preliminary evidence that 5HT pathways in man may stimulate the release of melanocyte stimulating hormone, beta-lipotropin and beta-endorphin (Muller *et al*, 1977; Petraglia *et al*, 1984). There are also suggestions that 5HT neurones inhibit the secretion of thyroid stimulating hormone, luteinising hormone and follicle stimulating hormone (Macindoe & Turkington, 1974; Muller *et al*, 1977). None of these endocrine effects is sufficiently well established to be considered at present for study in neuroendocrine challenge tests of brain 5HT function.

Conclusions

The evidence linking 5HT pathways to PRL secretion in man is strong and convincing. 5HT may also be implicated in the release of GH and cortisol but the evidence is less compelling and confirmation awaits the development of more selective agonist and antagonist drugs.

5HT Neuroendocrine challenge tests

A suitable neuroendocrine challenge test should produce a reliable increase in plasma levels of a given hormone by means of a well-tolerated drug with a clearly defined mechanism of action. It should be possible to administer the drug parenterally and the hormonal response should be dose-related and consistent (see Checkley, 1980). For certain monoamine challenge tests, for example, the elevation of plasma GH by the dopamine agonist, apomorphine (Checkley, 1980), these criteria are fulfilled. However, none of the available 5HT neuroendocrine challenges can yet be considered fully satisfactory.

We will consider three 5HT neuroendocrine challenge tests which have been employed in current studies.

Fenfluramine

Fenfluramine is a 5HT releasing agent and uptake blocker (Garattini *et al*, 1975). At higher concentrations in animals it affects DA transmission but in man at clinical doses probably acts only on 5HT pathways (Garattini *et al*, 1975; Shoulson & Chase, 1975).

Fenfluramine is usually given orally and produces a dose-related increase in plasma PRL which peaks approximately 4 h after administration (Quattrone *et al*, 1983). Pretreatment with the 5HT antagonist, metergoline, blocks this response (Quattrone *et al*, 1983), suggesting it is probably mediated by 5HT receptors. The use of fenfluramine has drawbacks: it produces dysphoric effects in some subjects and also requires a total 5 h sampling procedure which is stressful and not always well-tolerated. Finally, possible differences in gastrointestinal absorption of fenfluramine may lead to spurious abnormalities in endocrine response.

L-tryptophan (LTP)

Since oral LTP is inconsistent in producing endocrine changes (see above), it is usual to administer LTP in the form of an i.v. infusion usually in a dose of 5.0–7.5 g. Given in this way LTP reliably elevates plasma PRL and GH (see above). It is assumed that in brain 5HT neurones the LTP is converted by the enzyme tryptophan hydroxylase to 5HTP, which is in turn decarboxylated to 5HT. A further assumption is that some of the newly synthesised 5HT 'spills over' into the synapse and thus becomes functionally active (Grahame-Smith, 1971).

In man LTP infusion has been shown to cause a large increase in brain tryptophan and an increase in 5HT turnover in the CSF without any effect on DA turnover (Gillman *et al*, 1981). Animal studies indicate that tryptophan hydroxylase is the rate limiting enzyme in 5HT synthesis and is normally unsaturated with its substrate (Fernstrom & Wurtman, 1971). Since the enzyme is found exclusively in 5HT neurones (Moir & Eccleston, 1968) it has been concluded that the endocrine effects of LTP, particularly the increase in PRL, are specifically mediated by 5HT pathways (Macindoe & Turkington, 1974; Charney *et al*, 1982).

Attempts to confirm this view by blocking the LTP-induced increase in plasma PRL with 5HT receptor antagonists have, however, proved inconclusive. While methysergide may have reduced the PRL response to

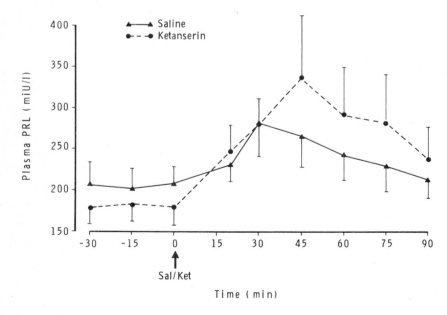

Fig. 1 — Mean (± S.E.M.) plasma PRL response to LTP (5.0 g) in 6 normal male subjects. Subjects were tested on two occasions receiving either i.v. ketanserin (10 mg) or saline at time 0, followed by LTP infused over 15 min. No significant difference between the PRL response in the two tests (analysis of variance).

LTP in two subjects (Macindoe & Turkington, 1974), we found no effect of oral cyproheptadine (Cowen *et al*, 1985). Further, in a recent study we have found that i.v. administration of the 5HT receptor antagonist ketanserin, does not attenuate the increase in plasma PRL following LTP (Fig. 1) (Anderson, unpublished observations). However, the poor brain penetration of ketanserin may be responsible for its inability to antagonise the effect of LTP (see Meltzer *et al*, 1983).

It is also unclear whether the elevation in plasma GH following LTP is mediated by increases in brain 5HT function or rather is produced by the same mechanism by which infusions of other amino acids increase plasma GH (see Scanlon *et al*, 1979). We have found that patients on chronic neuroleptic treatment have a decreased GH response to LTP (Cowen *et al*, 1985), which could implicate either 5HT or DA pathways in the GH response.

LTP infusion is generally well-tolerated and peak hormone responses occur within 30–45 min of the end of the infusion (Charney *et al*, 1982). The response is dose-related (Cowen *et al*, 1985). While intravenous administration of LTP overcomes problems associated with gastrointestinal absorption, LTP is actively transported across the blood brain barrier (Joanny *et al*, 1968), and alterations in this process could complicate interpretation of endocrine responses.

5-Hydroxytryptophan (5HTP)

The 5HT precursor, 5HTP, is decarboxylated to 5HT in a single step. However, this metabolic conversion is not limited to 5HT neurones and can also occur in catecholamine pathways. The 5HT formed in these latter sites may release dopamine and noradrenaline by displacement (Ng *et al*, 1972) and thus the endocrine effects of 5HTP may not be specifically mediated by 5HT pathways.

Given parenterally 5HTP elevates plasma cortisol, GH and PRL (see above). However, this route of administration may cause unacceptable side effects (Macindoe & Turkington, 1974) or otherwise requires pretreatment with a peripheral decarboxylase inhibitor. Decarboxylase inhibition, however, may itself increase plasma PRL (Lancranjan *et al*, 1977) probably by inhibition of dopamine synthesis in the pituitary gland and median eminence.

Oral 5HTP in doses of 150–200 mg is usually reasonably tolerated but apart from the general problems associated with oral administration is unreliable in increasing plasma levels of PRL, GH and cortisol (Kato *et al*, 1974; Handwerger *et al*, 1975; Westenberg *et al*, 1982; Meltzer *et al*, 1982; Petraglia *et al*, 1984).

Conclusions

It would appear that the PRL response to fenfluramine is at present the most pharmacologically specific test of 5HT function in man. LTP has the advantage of good subject tolerance and i.v. administration but further work is required to elucidate the pharmacological mechanisms of the hormonal responses. In addition, changes in amino acid transport into the brain may pose complications in interpretation of results. On the present data oral 5HTP would seem the least satisfactory drug for a 5HT neuroendocrine challenge because of the inconsistent endocrine responses.

5HT Neuroendocrine studies in depressive illness

In the previous section we discussed the pharmacological problems associated with current 5HT neuroendocrine challenge tests. A further drug-related difficulty in neuroendocrine tests is the effect of previous and current psychotropic medication. It has been demonstrated, for example, that the tricyclic antidepressant (TCA), desmethylimipramine (DMI), treatment attenuates the GH response to clonidine; moreover, the decreased response is still apparent three weeks following DMI discontinuation (Corn *et al*, 1984). Clearly, if a depressed patient is tested with clonidine after a three-week tricyclic 'washout' period it would be easy to attribute mistakenly the reduced GH response to the effects of depressive illness rather than the preceding drug treatment. A further problem is that many patients are tested while taking benzodiazepine drugs, which, in animal studies at any rate, are known to alter noradrenaline and 5HT turnover (Haefely, 1983).

The diagnosis of depression in most neuroendocrine studies is made using the Research Diagnostic Criteria or DSM-III. While such operational criteria may improve diagnostic reliability, it seems likely that this is at the expense of specificity, and patients with an 'endogenous' symptom profile, who are more likely to exhibit biochemical abnormalities, may be present in a minority (see Carroll, 1983). This could account for inconsistent findings between different neuroendocrine studies. A further important source of subject error is failure to control adequately for factors such as age, weight

TABLE II
Problems encountered in neuroendocrine testing of depressed patients

1) Selectivity of drug challenge
2) Current and previous psychotropic medication
3) Diagnosis of depressive disorder
4) Control for effects of age, sex and hormonal status
5) Interpretation of abnormal findings

TABLE III
5HT neuroendocrine testing in depression

Study	Drug Challenge	Findings in Depressed Subjects
Takahashi et al (1974)	5HTP (200 mg p.o.)	Decreased GH response
Meltzer et al (1984)	5HTP (200 mg p.o.)	Increased cortisol response
Heninger et al (1984)	LTP (7.0 g i.v.)	Decreased PRL response
Siever et al (1984)	Fenfluramine (60 mg p.o.)	Decreased PRL response

and hormonal status (Checkley, 1980). The GH response to clonidine, for example, may differ according to the stage of the menstrual cycle (Matussek et al, 1984).

In the following sections the findings from some 5HT neuroendocrine challenge tests in depressed patients will be reviewed (Table III).

Fenfluramine challenge

In a study by Siever et al (1984) the effect of fenfluramine (60 mg orally) on plasma PRL levels was compared in 18 depressed patients and 10 normal controls. Fenfluramine produced a slow elevation in plasma PRL, which was significantly less in the depressed patients 4 and 5h after fenfluramine ingestion. One problem in interpreting this study is that when the patients were age and sex matched the basal PRL concentration was almost twice as high in the depressed patients as in the normal controls, though the authors argued that basal PRL concentration was not related to subsequent hormonal response. A further point was that the drug-free period of some of the patients was only two weeks, but again the authors maintained that the length of drug-free 'washout' did not correlate with the subsequent PRL response to fenfluramine.

Although factors such as poor absorption of fenfluramine in the depressed group cannot be ruled out, this study suggests that there is a decreased responsiveness of the 5HT pathways involved in PRL release in depressed patients. Since fenfluramine acts on presynaptic 5HT terminals to increase 5HT transmission, the deficit might be pre- or post-synaptic.

L-tryptophan challenge

Heninger et al (1984) studied the effects of an intravenous infusion of L-tryptophan (7.0 g) on the plasma PRL response in 24 depressed patients compared to 19 age, weight and sex matched controls. A minimum three-week drug-free period was required. The mean basal PRL concentration of depressed patients was not different to the controls but the peak increase following L-tryptophan was markedly reduced. This study therefore also suggests a decreased PRL response to 5HT stimulation in depression. However, as the authors point out, the neuroendocrine tests of the female subjects were not controlled for the stage of the menstrual cycle and it may be significant that when the post-menopausal female patients were compared with the post-menopausal controls no decrease in the PRL response was apparent. Further, while all 24 patients met DSM-III criteria for major depressive disorder, only three of them received an additional diagnosis of psychotic depression, while a further four were diagnosed as major depression with melancholia, suggesting that most of the patients did not have 'endogenous' features of depression.

While the use of i.v. LTP overcomes problems of gastrointestinal absorption, it has been suggested that depressed patients may transport tryptophan into body tissue differently from normal subjects (Coppen *et al*, 1974). Clearly an abnormality in this process could be a confounding factor in interpreting the differences in endocrine responses. However, if the fenfluramine study of Siever *et al* (1984) is accepted, any deficit in PRL response to LTP is presumably at least at the level of the presynaptic 5HT neurone.

5HTP challenge

An early study by Takahashi *et al* (1973) measured the GH response to 5HTP in 14 depressed patients. They found that the response was reduced compared to that of a previous control series. However, it must be questioned whether this method of comparing controls from another study with depressed patients is acceptable.

Hormonal responses to 5HTP were studied by Westenberg *et al* (1982). The administration of 5HTP (200 mg orally), together with a peripheral decarboxylase inhibitor, produced inconsistent cortisol, GH and PRL responses in both normal subjects and depressed patients. The authors concluded that 5HTP had limitations as a test of 5HT endocrine function in man.

In a subsequent investigation Meltzer *et al* (1984a) measured the cortisol response to 5HTP (200 mg orally) in 44 depressed patients and 24 normal controls of a similar age. It was found that whereas the controls had an inconsistent and overall a non-significant increase in plasma cortisol following 5HTP, the depressed patients showed a robust and markedly enhanced response. The basal cortisol levels were higher in the depressed subjects than the controls, but the authors argued that baseline cortisol did not correlate with subsequent response to 5HTP.

A further and remarkable finding was that the peak cortisol response to 5HTP correlated positively and significantly with the subjects' depression rating scores on the Schedule for Affective Disorders and the presence of a suicide attempt during the current episode (Meltzer *et al*, 1984b). While the authors found an enhanced cortisol response to 5HTP, they concluded that the primary 5HT abnormality in depressed patients was decreased 5HT transmission which in turn led to supersensitive post-synaptic 5HT receptors. Thus administration of 5HTP caused an enhanced cortisol response due to post-synaptic 5HT receptor supersensitivity. While this argument could be correct, it shows that abnormalities in neuroendocrine tests will often bear a number of interpretations.

Conclusions

The studies outlined above suggest that PRL response to drugs which increase brain 5HT function is impaired in depressed patients. However, it has also been reported that the PRL response to morphine may be blunted in depressed subjects (Extein *et al*, 1980). Thus it remains to be established that the reduced PRL responses to fenfluramine and L-tryptophan represent specific deficits in 5HT pathways rather than a primary abnormality in the control of PRL release at hypothalamic or pituitary level (Siever *et al*, 1984).

The increased cortisol response to 5HTP in depressed patients is more difficult to interpret but could represent the 5HT receptor supersensitivity suggested by the authors. However, as noted previously, the 5HTP challenge test is associated with inconsistent endocrine responses. Clearly, a neuro-endocrine challenge test employing a well-tolerated 5HT receptor agonist would have great value in clarifying both changes in depressed patients and whether any 5HT deficit is pre- or post-synaptic.

5HT Neuroendocrine studies during antidepressant drug treatment

Many different antidepressant treatments produce changes in brain 5HT pathways in animals (see Charney *et al*, 1981). However, the dosage regimes employed are often inappropriate and species differences in biochemical adaptation limit the applicability of findings to man. A further use of 5HT neuroendocrine tests is to assess the effect of a clinical course of antidepressant treatment on 5HT-mediated responses in man.

Tricyclic antidepressants (TCAs)

The effect of TCAs on 5HT pathways in experimental animals is complex with both increased and decreased 5HT function being reported (see Charney

TABLE IV
*Tricyclic antidepressants and 5HT function: Effects of
repeated administration in rats*

1. Blockade 5HT uptake ⎫
                          ⎬ acute effects
2. Blockade $5HT_2$ receptors ⎭

3. Down-regulation $5HT_2$ receptors

4. Reduced 5HT-mediated behaviours

5. Increased electrophysiological
    responses to 5HT

et al, 1981). The reason for the controversy probably rests with the different experimental models employed (Table III).

When TCAs are administered acutely to animals they inhibit the uptake of 5HT (see Iversen & MacKay, 1979) and also block $5HT_2$ receptors, a 5HT receptor subtype located post-synaptically which mediates certain 5HT-induced behaviours (Peroutka *et al*, 1981; Green *et al*, 1983). Longer-term treatment for the periods of time usually required to obtain a clinical response in depressed patients, results in the development of adaptive changes at 5HT synapses (Table IV). Most studies have found that repeated administration of TCAs reduces brain $5HT_2$ receptor binding (Peroutka & Snyder, 1980) and decreases 5HT-induced behavioural responses (Stoltz *et al*, 1983; Goodwin *et al*, 1984). Some workers have reported enhanced behavioural responses a few days following cessation of TCA treatment (Friedman *et al*, 1983) but it seems probable that these represent a withdrawal phenomenon (Stoltz *et al*, 1983; Goodwin *et al*, 1984). However, electrophysiological responses to iontophoretically applied 5HT are enhanced after chronic TCA administration (De Montigny & Aghajanian, 1978). Thus it is clearly of interest to ascertain the effect of TCA treatment on 5HT function in man.

In a study in depressed patients Charney *et al* (1984) showed that the PRL response to LTP was increased following treatment with amitriptyline or desmethylimipramine (DMI). This suggests that TCAs enhance 5HT-mediated reponses in man but the situation is complicated by the fact that the depressed patients had decreased PRL responses to LTP prior to antidepressant therapy (see above) and it is possible that the enhanced responses therefore represent a return to normal PRL release following clinical recovery.

In order to resolve this question we investigated the effects of DMI treatment in 9 normal volunteers. Following 16 days' treatment we found that the PRL response to LTP was enhanced (Fig. 2), which supports the suggestion that in man TCAs enhance certain 5HT-mediated responses.

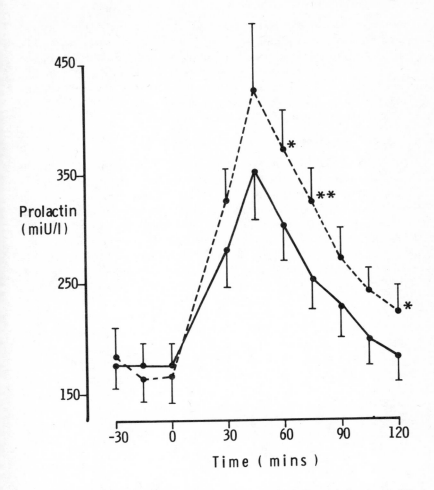

Fig. 2 — Mean (± S.E.M.) plasma PRL response to LTP (7.5 g) infused over 25 min from time 0 in nine normal male subjects. Subjects were tested on two occasions a) prior to treatment (solid line) and b) on the 16th day of DMI treatment (150 mg daily) (broken line). The PRL response during DMI treatment is significantly greater ($p < 0.05$, analysis of variance). (Reproduced from Cowen *et al*, 1986).

We also found that DMI reduced platelet 5HT uptake and increased platelet 5HT receptor binding. Similar changes occurring in the brain could account for the increase in 5HT-mediated neuroendocrine responses which we observed with LTP (Cowen *et al*, 1986).

Meltzer *et al* (1984c) investigated the effect of a variety of antidepressant drugs, including some TCAs on the cortisol response to 5HTP. Overall a tendency for a decreased cortisol response was noted following antidepressant therapy, but the lower basal cortisol following treatment complicates interpretation of this finding, as does the variety of drugs used. The explanation given for the decreased response following TCA treatment was that the TCAs had increased 5HT transmission, thus down-regulating the previously 'supersensitive' post-synaptic 5HT receptors (see above) and hence reducing their functional responsiveness.

Other antidepressants

The enhanced electrophysiological responses to 5HT in experimental animals are seen after a variety of antidepressant treatments, including monoamine oxidase inhibitors and electroconvulsive shock. It has been suggested that an important common effect of antidepressant treatments is to enhance brain 5HT receptor sensitivity (see Charney *et al*, 1984).

To test this hypothesis we are investigating the effects of the antidepressant drug, mianserin, on PRL responses to LTP in depressed subjects before and during treatment. Mianserin does not inhibit 5HT uptake but antagonises the $5HT_2$ receptor with a high affinity (see Hall & Ogren, 1981). In a

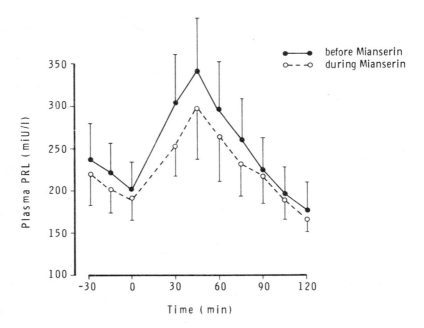

Fig. 3 — Mean ($\pm$ S.E.M.) plasma PRL response to LTP (100 mg/kg) infused over 25 min from time 0 in seven depressed patients. Subjects were tested on two occasions a) prior to treatment and b) during 4 weeks' mianserin administration (60 mg nocte). No significant difference between the PRL response in the tests (analysis of variance).

preliminary study of seven patients, who received 60 mg of mianserin daily for four weeks, we have not found any evidence of increased PRL responses to LTP (Fig. 3).

Conclusions

There is good evidence that a clinical course of DMI administration results in an increase in the PRL response to LTP, suggesting that certain 5HT-mediated responses are enhanced by this treatment. However, the antidepressant drug, mianserin, does not appear to increase the PRL response to LTP, suggesting that in man antidepressant drugs have dissimilar effects on brain 5HT function.

Acknowledgements

We thank Professor M. G. Gelder, Professor D. G. Grahame-Smith and Dr. A. R. Green for advice and encouragement. I.A. was supported by the Wellcome Trust. The studies of the authors described in this paper were supported by grants from the Wellcome Trust and Medical Research Council, to whom grateful acknowledgement is made. We also thank Janssen Pharmaceutical Ltd. and E. Merck Ltd. for supplies of ketanserin and L-tryptophan respectively, and for additional financial assistance.

References

ÅSBERG, M., TRÄSKMAN, L. & THUREN, P. (1976) 5-HIAA in the cerebrospinal fluid. A biochemical suicide predictor? *Archives of General Psychiatry*, **33**, 1193–1197.

CARROLL, B. J. (1983) Problems of paradigm, definition and method in depression. In *The Origin of Depression: Current Concepts and Approaches* (ed. J. Angst). Berlin: Springer-Verlag.

CHARNEY, D. S., HENINGER, G. R., RENHARD, J. F., STERNBERG, D. E. & HAFSTEAD, K. M. (1982) Effect of intravenous L-tryptophan on prolactin and growth hormone and mood in healthy subjects. *Psychopharmacology*, **77**, 217–222.

—— HENINGER, G. R. & STERNBERG, D. E. (1984) Serotonin function and mechanism of action of antidepressant treatment: effect of amitriptyline and desipramine. *Archives of General Psychiatry*, **41**, 359–365.

—— MENKES, D. & HENINGER, G. R. (1981) Receptor sensitivity and the mechanism of action of antidepressant treatment. *Archives of General Psychiatry*, **38**, 1160–1180.

CHECKLEY, S. A. (1980) Neuroendocrine tests of monoamine function in man: a review of basic theory and its application to the study of depressive illness. *Psychological Medicine*, **10**, 35–53.

CHIHARA, K., KATO, Y., MAEDA, K., MATSAKURA, S. & IMURA, H. (1976) Suppression by cyproheptadine of human growth hormone and cortisol secretion during sleep. *Journal of Clinical Investigation*, **57**, 1393–1402.

CLEMENS, J. A., ROUSH, M. E. & FULLER, R. W. (1978) Evidence that serotonin neurones stimulate secretion of prolactin releasing factor. *Life Sciences*, **22**, 2209–2214.

COPPEN, A., BROOKSBANK, B. W. L., ECCLESTON, E., PEET, M. & WHITE, S. G. (1974) Tryptophan metabolism in depressive illness. *Psychological Medicine*, 4, 164–173.

—— SWADE, C. & WOOD, K. (1978) Platelet 5-hydroxytryptamine accumulation in depressive illness. *Clinica Chimica Acta*, 87, 165–168.

CORN, T. H., THOMPSON, C. & CHECKLEY, S. A. (1984) Effects of desimipramine treatment upon central adrenoceptor function in normal subjects. *British Journal of Psychiatry*, 145, 139–145.

COWEN, P. J., GADHUI, H., GOSDEN, B. & KOLAKOWSKA, T. (1985) Responses of prolactin and growth hormone to L-tryptophan infusion: effects in normal subjects and schizophrenic patients receiving neuroleptics. *Psychopharmacology*, 86, 164–169.

—— GEANEY, D. P., SCHÄCHTER, M., GREEN, A. R. & ELLIOTT, J. M. (1986) Desmethylimipramine treatment in normal subjects: effects on neuroendocrine responses to L-tryptophan and platelet 5-HT-related receptors. *Archives of General Psychiatry*, 43, 61–67.

CROSIGNANI, P. G., LOMBROSO, G. C., MATTEI, A., CACCAMO, A. & TROJSI, L. (1979) Effect of three serotin antagonists on plasma prolactin response to suckling in puerperal women. *Journal of Clinical Endocrinology and Metabolism*, 48, 335–337.

DE MONTIGNY, C. & AGHAJANIAN, G. K. (1978) Tricyclic antidepressants: long-term treatment increases responsivity of rat forebrain neurons to serotonin. *Science*, 202, 1303–1306.

EXTEIN, I., POTTASH, A. L. C., GOLD, M. S., SWEENEY, D. R., MARTIN, D. M. & GOODWIN, F. K. (1980). Deficient prolactin response to morphine in depressed patients. *American Journal of Psychiatry*, 137, 845–846.

FERNSTROM, J. D. & WURTMAN R. J. (1971) Brain serotonin content: physiological dependence on plasma tryptophan levels. *Science*, 173, 149–152.

FERRARI, C., CALDARA, R., ROMUSSI, M., RAMPINI, P., TELLOZI, P., ZAATAR, S. & CURTARELLI, G. (1978) Prolactin suppression to serotonin antagonists in man: further evidence for serotoninergic control of prolactin secretion. *Neuroendocrinology*, 25, 319–328.

FESSLER, R. G., DEYO, S. N., MELTZER, H. Y. & MILLER, R. J. (1984) Evidence that the medial and dorsal raphé nuclei mediate serotonergically-induced increases in prolactin release from the pituitary. *Brain Research*, 229, 231–237.

FRANCIS, A. T., WILLIAMS, P., WILLIAMS, R., LINK, J., COLE, E. N. & HUGHES, D. (1976) The effect of clomipramine on prolactin levels — pilot studies. *Postgraduate Medical Journal*, 52, Suppl. 3, 87–91.

FRASER, W. M., TUCKER, H. T., GRUBB, S. R., WIGAND, U. P. & BLACKARD, W. G. (1979) Effect of L-tryptophan on growth hormone and prolactin release in normal volunteers and patients with secretory pituitary tumours. *Hormone and Metabolic Research*, 11, 149–155.

FRIEDMAN, E., COOPER, T. B. & DALLOB, A. (1983) Effects of chronic antidepressant treatment on serotonin receptor sensitivity in mice. *European Journal of Pharmacology*, 89, 69–76.

FULLER, R. W. (1981) Serotonergic stimulation of pituitary-adrenocortical function in rats. *Neuroendocrinology*, 32, 118–127.

GARATTINI, S., BUCZKO, N., SORI, A. & SAMININ, R. (1975) The mechanism of action of fenfluramine. *Postgraduate Medical Journal*, 51, Suppl. 1, 27–35.

GILLMAN, P. K., BARTLETT, J. R., BRIDGES, P. K., HUNT, A., PATEL, A. J., KANTAMENENI, B. D. & CURZON, G. (1981) Indolic substances in plasma CSF and frontal cortex of human subjects infused with saline or L-tryptophan. *Journal of Neurochemistry*, 37, 410–417.

GOODWIN, F. K. & POST, R. N. (1983) 5-Hydroxytryptamine and depression: a model for the interaction of normal variance and pathology. *British Journal of Clinical Pharmacology*, 15, 393S–405S.

GOODWIN, G., GREEN, A. R. & JOHNSON, P. (1984) $5-HT_2$ receptor-mediated head-twitch behaviour following antidepressant treatment to mice. *British Journal of Pharmacology*, 83, 235–242.

GRAHAME-SMITH, D. G. (1971) Studies *in vivo* on the relationship between brain tryptophan, brain 5-HT synthesis and hyperactivity in rats treated with a monoamine oxidase inhibitor and L-tryptophan. *Journal of Neurochemistry*, 18, 1053–1066.

GREEN, A. R., O'SHAUGHNESSY, K., HAMMOND, M., SCHÄCHTER, M. & GRAHAME-SMITH, D. G. (1983) Inhibition of 5-hydroxytryptamine-mediated behaviours by the putative $5-HT_2$ antagonist pirenperone. *Neuropharmacology*, 22, 573–578.

HAEFELY, W. (1984) Tranquillizers. In *Psychopharmacology, Vol. 1* (eds. D. G. Grahame-Smith & P. J. Cowen). Amsterdam, Oxford, Princeton: Excerpta Medica.

HALL, H. & OGREN, S.-O. (1981) Effect of antidepressant drugs on different receptors in the brain. *European Journal of Pharmacology*, **70**, 393–407.

HANDWERGER, S., PLONK, J. W., LEBOVITZ, H. E., BIVENS, C. H. & FELDMAN, J. M. (1975) Failure of 5-HTP to stimulate prolactin and growth hormone secretion in man. *Hormone and Metabolic Research*, **7**, 214–216.

HENINGER, G. R., CHARNEY, D. S. & STERNBERG, D. E. (1984) Serotonergic function in depression: prolactin response to intravenous tryptophan in depressed patients and healthy subjects. *Archives of General Psychiatry*, **41**, 398–402.

IMURA, H., NAKAI, Y. & YUSHIMI, T. (1973) Effect of 5-hydroxytryptophan (5HTP) on growth hormone and ACTH release in man. *Journal of Clinical Endocrinology and Metabolism*, **36**, 204–206.

IVERSEN, L. L. & MACKAY, A. V. P. (1979) Pharmacodynamics of antidepressant drugs. In *Psychopharmacology of Affective Disorders* (eds, E. S. Paykel & A. Coppen). Oxford: Oxford University Press.

JOANNY, P., BARBARA, E. & CORRIOL, J. (1968) Accumulation active de quelques acides aminés dans les coupes de cerveau du rat. *Journal of Physiology (Paris)*, Suppl. 60, 265.

JONES, R. B. & LUSCOMBE, D. K. (1976) Plasma prolactin in normal subjects and depressive patients following oral clomipramine. *Postgraduate Medical Journal*, **52**, Suppl. 3, 62–67.

JOSEPH, N. H. & KENNETT, G. (1983) Corticosteroid response to stress depends on increased tryptophan availability. *Psychopharmacology*, **79**, 79–81.

KATO, Y., NAKAI, Y., IMURA, H., KAZYO, C. & OHGO, S. (1974) Effect of 5-hydroxytryptophan on plasma prolactin levels in man. *Journal of Clinical Endocrinology and Metabolism*, **38**, 695–697.

KRULICH, L., MCANN, S. M. & MAYFIELD, M. A. (1981) On the mode of the prolactin release inhibiting action of the serotonin receptor blockers metergoline, methysergide and cyproheptadine. *Endocrinology*, **108**, 1115.

LAAKMANN, G., GUGATH, M., KUSS, H.-J. & ZYGAN, K. (1984) Comparison of growth hormone and prolactin stimulation induced by chlorimipramine and desimipramine in man in connection with chlorimipramine metabolism. *Psychopharmacology*, **82**, 62–67.

LANCRANJAN, I., WIRZ-JUSTICE, A. & PUHRINGER, DEL POZO, E. (1977) Effect of 1-5 hydroxytryptophan infusion on growth hormone and prolactin secretion in man. *Journal of Clinical Endocrinology and Metabolism*, **45**, 588–593.

LEWIS, D. A. & SHERMAN, B. M. (1984) Serotonergic stimulation of adrenocorticotropin secretion in man. *Journal of Clinical Endocrinology and Metabolism*, **58**, 458–462.

LEYSON, J. E., AWOUTERS, F., KENNIS, L., LADURON, P. M., VANDENBERK, J. & JANSSEN, P. A. J. (1981) Receptor binding profile of R41468, a novel antagonist at 5-HT_2 receptors. *Life Sciences*, **28**, 1115–1122.

MACINDOE, J. H. & TURKINGTON, R. W. (1973) Stimulation of human prolactin secretion by intravenous infusion of L-tryptophan. *Journal of Clinical Investigation*, **52**, 1972–1978.

MASCHAT, A. C., KLETZKY, A., SPENCER, C. & ARTAL, R. (1983) Transient effect of L-5-hydroxytryptophan on pituitary function in men and women. *Journal of Clinical Endocrinology and Metabolism*, **56**, 170–176.

MATUSSEK, N., ACKENHEIL, M. & HERZ, M. (1984) The dependence of the clonidine growth hormone test on alcohol drinking habits and the menstrual cycle. *Psychoneuroendocrinology*, **9**, 173–177.

MEITES, J. & SONNTAG, W. E. (1981) Hypothalamic, hypophysiotropic hormones and neurotransmitter regulation: current views. *Annual Review of Pharmacology and Toxicology*, **21**, 295–322.

MELTZER, H. Y., WIITA, B., TRICOU, B. J., SIMONOVIC, M., FANG, V. & MANOV, G. (1982) Effect of serotonin precursors and serotonin agonists on plasma hormone levels. In: *Serotonin in Biological Psychiatry* (ed. B. J. Ho *et al*). New York: Raven Press.

—— SIMONOVIC, M. & GUDELSKY, G. A. (1983) Effects of pirenperone and ketanserin on rat prolactin secretion *in vivo* and *in vitro*. *European Journal of Pharmacology*, **92**, 83–89.

—— PERLINE, R., TRICOU, B. J., LOWY, M. & ROBERTSON, A. (1984a) Effect of 5-hydroxytryptophan on serum cortisol levels in major affective disorders: I. Enhanced response in depression and mania. *Archives of General Psychiatry*, **41**, 366–374.

—— PERLINE, R., TRICOU, B. J., LOWY, M. & ROBERTSON, A. (1984b) Effect of 5-hydroxytryptophan on serum cortisol levels in major affective disorders: II. Relation to suicide, psychosis and depressive symptoms. *Archives of General Psychiatry*, **41**, 379–387.

—— LOWY, M., ROBERTSON, A., GOODNICK, P. & PERLINE, R. (1984c) Effect of 5-hydroxytryptophan on serum cortisol levels in patients with major affective disorders: III. Effect of antidepressant and lithium carbonate. *Archives of General Psychiatry*, **41**, 391–397.

MENDELSON, W. B., JACOBS, L. S., REICHMANN, J. D., OTHMER, E., CRYER, P. E., TRIVEDI, B. & DAUGHADAY, W. H. (1975) Methysergide suppression of sleep-related prolactin secretion and enhancement of sleep-related growth hormone secretion. *Journal of Clinical Investigation*, **56**, 690–697.

MODLINGER, R. S., SCHONMULLER, J. M. & ARORA, S. P. (1979) Stimulation of aldosterone, renin, and cortisol by tryptophan. *Journal of Clinical Endocrinology and Metabolism*, **48**, 599–605.

MOIR, A. T. B. & ECCLESTON, D. (1968) The effects of precursor loading in the cerebral metabolism of 5-hydroxyindoles. *Journal of Neurochemistry*, **15**, 1093–1108.

MULLER, E. E., NISTICO, G. & SCAPAGNINI, U. (1977) *Neurotransmitters and Anterior Pituitary Function*. New York: Academic Press.

NAKAI, Y., IMURA, H., SAKURAI, H., KURAHACHI, H. & YOSHIMI, T. (1974) Effect of cyproheptadine on human growth hormone secretion. *Journal of Clinical Endocrinology and Metabolism*, **38**, 446–449.

NAUMENKO, E. V. (1969) Effect of local injection of 5-hydroxytryptamine into rhinencephalic and menencephalic structures on pituitary-adrenal function in guinea-pigs. *Neuroendocrinology*, **5**, 81–88.

NG, L. K. Y., CHASE, T. N., COLBURN, R. W. & KOPIN, I. J. (1972) Release of [³H] dopamine by L-5-hydroxytryptophan. *Brain Research*, **45**, 499–505.

PARATI, E. A., ZANARDI, P., COCCHI, D., CARANCENI, T. & MULLER, E. E. (1980) Neuroendocrine effects of quipazine in man in health state or with neurological disorders. *Journal of Neural Transmission*, **47**, 273–297.

PEROUTKA, S. J., LEBOVITZ, R. M., SNYDER, S. H. (1981) Two distinct serotonin receptors with different physiological functions. *Science*, **212**, 827–829.

—— SNYDER, S. H. (1980) Long-term antidepressant treatment decreases spiroperidol-labelled serotonin binding. *Science*, **210**, 88–90.

PETRAGLIA, F., FACCHINETTI, F., MARTIGNONI, E., NAPPI, G., VOLPE, A., GENAZZANI, A. R. (1984) Serotonergic agonists increase plasma levels of β-lipotropin in humans. *Journal of Clinical Endocrinology and Metabolism*, **59**, 1138–1142.

QUATTRONE, A., TEDESCHI, A., AGUGLIA, U., SCOPACASA, F., DIRENZO, G. F. & ANNUNZIATO, L. (1983) Prolactin secretion in man: a useful tool to evaluate the activity of drugs on central 5-hydroxytryptaminergic neurones: studies with fenfluramine. *British Journal of Clinical Pharmacology*, **16**, 471–475.

SCANLON, N. F., POURMOND, M., McGREGOR, A. M., RODRIGUEZ-ARNAO, M. D., HALL, K., GOMEZ-PAN, A. & HALL, R. (1979) Some current aspects of clinical and experimental neuroendocrinology with particular reference to growth hormone, thyrotropin and prolactin. *Journal of Endocrinological Investigation*, **2**, 307–331.

SHOULSON, I. & CHASE, T. N. (1975) Fenfluramine in man: hypophagia associated with diminished serotonin turnover. *Clinical Pharmacology and Therapeutics*, **17**, 616–621.

SIEVER, L. J., MURPHY, D. L., SLATER, S., DE LA VEGA, E. & LIPPEN, S. (1984) Plasma prolactin following fenfluramine in depressed patients compared to controls: an evaluation of central serotonergic responsivity in depression. *Life Sciences*, **34**, 1029–1039.

STOLTZ, J. F., MARSDEN, C. A. & MIDDLEMISS, D. N. (1983) Effect of chronic antidepressant treatment and subsequent withdrawal on [³H]-5-hydroxytryptamine and [³H]-spiperone binding in rat frontal cortex and serotonin receptor mediated behaviour. *Psychopharmacology*, **80**, 150–155.

SULAIMAN, W. R. & JOHNSON, R. H. (1973) Effect of fenfluramine on human growth hormone release. *British Medical Journal*, **2**, 329–332.

SYVÄLAHTI, E., NAGY, A. & VAN PRAAG, H. M. (1979) Effects of zimelidine, a selective 5-HT uptake inhibitor, on serum prolactin levels in man. *Psychopharmacology*, 64, 251–253.

TAKAHASHI, S., KONDO, H., YOSHIMURA, M., OCHI, Y. & YOSHIMI, T. (1973) Growth hormone responses to administration of L-5-hydroxytryptophan (L-5-HTP) in manic depressive psychoses. *Folia Psychiatrica Neurologica Japonica*, 27, 197–206.

TRÄSKMAN, L., ÅSBERG, M., BERTILSSON, L. & SJÖSTRAND, L. (1981) Monoamine metabolites in CSF and suicidal behaviour. *Archives of General Psychiatry*, 38, 631–636.

TUOMISTO, J., TUKIAINEN, E. & AHLFORS, U. G. (1979) Decreased uptake of 5-hydroxytryptamine in blood platelets from patients with endogenous depression. *Psychopharmacology*, 65, 141–147.

TURTLE, J. R. & BURGESS, J. A. (1973) Hypoglycaemic action of fenfluramine in diabetes mellitus. *Diabetes*, 22, 858–867.

WESTENBERG, H. G. M., VAN PRAAG, H. M., DE JONG, T. U. M. & THIJSSEN, J. H. H. (1982) Post-synaptic serotonergic activity in depressive patients: evaluation of neuroendocrine strategy. *Psychiatry Research*, 7, 361–371.

WOOLFE, P. D. & LEE, L. (1977). Effect of the serotonin precursor tryptophan on pituitary hormone secretion. *Journal of Clinical Endocrinology and Metabolism*, 45, 123–133.

5 5HT Transport and the mediation of action of antidepressants. Do antidepressant treatments facilitate 5HT transport?

KEITH WOOD

The hypothesis that monoamines such as noradrenaline (NA) and 5-hydroxytryptamine (5HT) are involved in the pathology of depression is still largely based on pharmacological evidence. The most important components of this evidence are the depression-mimicking action of a monoamine depletor (reserpine) and the antidepressant action of inhibitors of monoamine inactivation (monoamine oxidase inhibitors and tricyclic antidepressants).

Unfortunately, there is no direct evidence nor is there any single direct experimental procedure to ascertain whether there are decreased amounts of these monoamines in the synapse or for that matter in the central nervous system (CNS) of depressive patients. Therefore, the elucidation of 5HT's role in the pathogenesis of depressive episodes must rely on a variety of approaches. One such approach has been the study of various aspects of platelet function. Human platelet plasma membrane-mediated 5HT uptake is a sodium dependent co-transport process (Sneddon 1973). The easy isolation of blood platelets coupled with the similarities in properties of the platelet 5HT uptake system to the brain's pre-synaptic 5HT uptake system (Pletscher 1978) have led to these elements of the blood being used as a biochemical model system for the study of 5HT transport. This model system has, therefore, been used (a) to determine whether there is an abnormality in this uptake process during a depressive episode, (b) to determine the effect of tricyclic antidepressants on this system, and (c) to determine if there was any relationship between the degree of uptake inhibition and clinical outcome.

Platelet 5HT uptake

Blood obtained by venepuncture was centrifuged to provide plasma rich in platelets (platelet-rich-plasma; PRP). This PRP was incubated at 37°C with varying concentrations of radioactive 5HT and after 2 min the reaction was stopped by the addition of ice-cold formaldehyde which prevented further uptake. After centrifugation the platelets were digested and counted for radioactivity which was proportional to the amount of 5HT accumulated. Parallel experiments were conducted at 4°C to compensate for passive accumulation (diffusion). The overall uptake, $\overline{y}$ (the mean uptake over the concentrations of radioactive 5HT used) was calculated. The double-reciprocal plot of Lineweaver and Burk (1934) was used to calculate the values of Km (affinity constant) and Vmax (velocity of uptake).

Patients

Male and female patients who were diagnosed as suffering from a major depressive disorder (Spitzer *et al*, 1978) were studied. No patient had a history of mania. All patients remained drug-free and were treated with placebo tablets and general clinical care for 7–10 days. At the end of this drug-free period, the patients were assessed for the severity of their symptoms using the Hamilton Depression Rating Scale (HDRS: Hamilton, 1967) and only patients with a HDRS score of 16 or more were included in the study. Blood was obtained at 09.00 hrs for the estimation of platelet 5HT uptake. Blood was also collected from a group of normal controls.

Since uptake inhibition has been suggested to be the therapeutic mode of action of the tricyclic antidepressants, then one might expect there to be a clear relationship between clinical improvement of depressive symptoms and the degree of platelet 5HT uptake inhibition in patients receiving antidepressant therapy. This question formed the basis of a study in which depressed patients were randomly allocated to receive either amitriptyline or zimeldine as their antidepressant treatment (Coppen *et al*, 1979a). Fifteen patients received 75 mg amitriptyline as a single dose at 8 p.m.; the dose was increased to 150 mg (75 mg bd) after three days and was continued until the end of the active treatment period of six weeks. Fifteen patients

TABLE I
5HT uptake characteristics (K_m, V_{max} and $\overline{y}$) of platelets from depressed patients and controls

	n	K_m (μmol/1)	V_{max} (pmol/10^8 platelets/min)	$\overline{y}$
Controls	20	0.54 ± 0.04	25.8 ± 2.2	15.2 ± 1.4
Depressed Patients, Drug-free	13	0.53 ± 0.06	$18.2 \pm 1.8^*$	11.7 ± 1.1

Significantly lower than controls * $p < 0.02$
Results as means $\pm$ S.E.M. Reproduced from Coppen *et al* (1978a) by permission of Elsevier Biomedical Press B.V.

received 100 mg zimeldine as a single dose at 8 p.m.; the dose was increased to 200 mg (100 mg b.d.) after three days and was continued until the end of the active treatment period of six weeks. The HDRS assessments were made at 0, 2, 4 and 6 weeks by independent assessors. Clinical change during active treatment was expressed in two ways: (a) as the HDRS score after six weeks' treatment and (b) as the percentage improvement on the HDRS scores from the baseline of the six week score.

Results and comments

Platelet 5HT uptake in depressives and controls

The characteristics of 5HT uptake into platelets from depressed patients and controls are shown in Table I. It can be seen that while there is no difference in the value of Km between controls and depressed patients, Vmax is significantly reduced in the depressed patients.

Previously, other workers (Tuomisto & Tukiainen, 1976) reported a similar finding and they suggested that their results were consistent with the fact that there were less of the amine carriers in the cell membrane or that some of them were in an inactive state. Those carriers that did remain, however, were in a fully functional state as indicated by the unchanged Km.

It is of interest that this finding is one of the most consistent in biological psychiatry. Leonard's group (Healy *et al*, 1983) in Ireland and a group in the U.S.A. (Meltzer *et al*, 1981) have also reported such an abnormality of transport in platelets from depressed patients. However, this abnormality does not seem to be specific to depression. Malmgren *et al*. (1980) and Coppen *et al* (1979b) have found reduced 5HT uptake in patients with migraine, and other groups (Rotman *et al*, 1979; Arora and Meltzer, 1982) have found this 5HT abnormality in patients in the acute phase of schizophrenia. Hypertension (Kamal *et al*, 1984), proliferative disorders

TABLE II

Platelet 5HT uptake characteristics (K_m and $\overline{y}$) from 14 patients treated with amitriptyline and 13 patients treated with zimeldine

Uptake characteristics		Amitriptyline		Zimeldine	
Apparent K_m (μmol/1)	Baseline	0.60	$\pm$ 0.09	0.71	$\pm$ 0.09
	4 weeks	2.65*	$\pm$ 0.64	4.68**†	$\pm$ 0.74
$\overline{y}$ (pmol/10^8 platelet/min)	Baseline	13.2	$\pm$ 1.3	17.6	$\pm$ 2.1
	4 weeks	8.6***	$\pm$ 0.9	6.1**†	$\pm$ 0.7

Significantly different from baseline, $*p < 0.01$; $**p < 0.001$; $***p < 0.02$
Significantly different from amitriptyline group $\pm$ $p < 0.05$
Results as means $\pm$ S.E.M. Reproduced from Coppen *et al* (1979a) by permission of Springer-Verlag

(Caranobe *et al*, 1984) and asthma (Malmgren *et al*, 1980) are other syndromes that have been associated with reduced platelet 5HT uptake.

Drug effects on clinical state and 5HT uptake

The 5HT uptake characteristics of patients after receiving amitriptyline and zimeldine are shown in Table II. Km was significantly increased under both treatments, and $\overline{y}$, the overall uptake was significantly decreased. These changes were significantly greater with zimeldine than with amitriptyline. Vmax was not significantly changed in either group.

The relationship between changes in 5HT uptake characteristics (Km and $\overline{y}$) and therapeutic outcome with amitriptyline and zimeldine were also examined. No significant correlations were obtained between measures of 5HT uptake and measures of clinical change with amitriptyline (Table III) or zimeldine (Table IV) or the two groups combined (not shown). Thus it appears that 5HT uptake into blood platelets is reduced during a depressive illness and this abnormality is accentuated by the administration of anti-depressants such as amitriptyline and zimeldine. Furthermore, there seems to be no relationship between uptake inhibition and therapeutic outcome.

Uptake inhibition and the mechanism of antidepressant drug action

The absence of any significant linear or curvilear relationship between uptake inhibition and clinical outcome was one of the doubts expressed in the 1970s about uptake inhibition being the therapeutic mode of action of these drugs. There was also experimental evidence that suggested a similar lack of a significant relationship between the uptake inhibition of NA and therapeutic outcome (Ghose & Coppen 1977).

Moreover, it has been proposed that there is a considerable time-lag between inhibition which is seen almost immediately, and clinical improvement which is not usually apparent until after several weeks of

TABLE III

Correlation coefficients (r) between platelet 5HT uptake characteristics (K_m and $\overline{y}$) and clinical change in 13 patients after 6 weeks treatment with amitriptyline

Clinical assessment	K_m			$\overline{y}$		
	4 weeks	change	% change	4 weeks	change	% change
6 week HDRS score	0.01	0.04	– 0.48	– 0.08	0.31	– 0.48
% change in HDRS	0.07	0.10	0.05	0.07	– 0.29	0.45

Reproduced from Coppen *et al* (1979a) by permission of Springer-Verlag

TABLE IV

Correlation coefficients (r) between platelet 5HT uptake characteristics (K_m and $\overline{y}$) and clinical change in 13 patients after 6 weeks treatment with zimeldine

Clinical assessment	K_m			$\overline{y}$		
	4 weeks	change	% change	4 weeks	change	% change
6 week HDRS score	0.30	0.32	0.01	0.21	0.33	− 0.12
% change in HDRS	− 0.45	− 0.33	− 0.10	− 0.51	0.00	0.12

Reproduced from Coppen *et al* (1979a) by permission of Springer-Verlag

treatment. There is also evidence to suggest that atypical antidepressants such as mianserin and iprindole do not block the reuptake of 5HT or NA following chronic administration. A newer hypothesis of depression was proposed by Vetulani's group (Vetulani *et al*, 1976) which accounted for most of the above mentioned discrepancies. It was proposed that the therapeutic action of antidepressants could be related to postsynaptic adaptive changes in the sensitivity of the noradrenergic adenyl cyclase receptor system in the limbic forebrain. This hypothesis was attractive firstly since these adaptive changes took place on a time scale that was thought to be more relevant to their therapeutic action (2–3 weeks) and secondly because several different antidepressant treatments (typical and atypical tricyclics, monoamine oxidase inhibitors, and electroconvulsive shock) all produced these changes.

Consequently, the mid 1970s saw many investigations into the adaptive changes occurring in noradrenergic systems during antidepressant administration.

Therapeutic improvement and facilitation of 5HT uptake

During the compilation of a review of the pharmacodynamics of zimeldine (Wood *et al*, 1982), it became apparent to me that although there was no statistically significant relationship between uptake inhibition and therapeutic outcome (see Tables III and IV), there was, however, a trend for clinical improvement to occur in those patients who had a smaller, rather than a greater, degree of inhibition of platelet 5HT uptake. This apparently paradoxical finding, together with the findings listed below, reawakened my interest in the importance of 5HT transport in the pathology of depressive illness. Whilst examining the effect of various antidepressants and putative antidepressants on the uptake of 5HT into platelets from normal controls *in vitro*, it was noted that amitriptyline and desipramine, amongst others, at concentrations of 0.1–0.01 μmol/1, actually stimulated the uptake of 5HT into platelets of normal controls (see Wood & Coppen 1985). These experiments *in vitro* were then complemented by studies *ex vivo*. Eleven depressed patients were treated with 150 mg of amitriptyline for four weeks. Platelet 5HT uptake characteristics were determined at baseline i.e. the day before administration of amitriptyline and then after four weeks of treatment. Analysis of the results indicated that the eleven patients could be classified into two distinct groups i.e. those who had an inhibition of platelet 5HT uptake and those who had an apparent stimulation of uptake. Stimulation of uptake could not be accounted for by low plasma levels of amitriptyline nor of its metabolite nortriptyline. Of the seven patients who had an inhibition of uptake none improved by more than 50% on the HDRS whereas of the four patients who had stimulation of uptake, three attained at least 50% improvement based on their HDRS score. Therapeutic improvement may, therefore, be related to a facilitation of uptake rather than inhibition. Healy *et al* (1983) have also demonstrated that platelet 5HT uptake is increased (indicated by an increase in Vmax) during successful treatment with either amitriptyline or trazodone. Tuomisto and colleagues (1979) have also presented data to suggest that the Vmax of 5HT transport is increased after successful treatment with imipramine.

What other evidence is available that would substantiate my claim that therapeutic improvement is associated with a facilitation rather than an inhibition of platelet 5HT uptake? Coppen *et al* (1976) found that whole blood 5HT is significantly reduced in drug-free depressed patients and, therefore, concurs with the platelet 5HT uptake data. Upon recovery from depressive illness, the 5HT content is increased and approaches that of normal controls. However, Coppen *et al* (1978a) indicated that drug-free recovered patients still had abnormally low transport rates and, therefore, does not concur with the platelet 5HT content data.

Drugs and facilitation of 5HT uptake

Mück-Seler *et al* (1983) have shown in a series of moderately to severely depressed patients that maprotiline treatment results in an increase in platelet 5HT content (measured in platelet-rich-plasma samples) with a corresponding decrease in the severity of their depressive symptoms. This increase in platelet 5HT content is consistent with the facilitation of 5HT uptake by maprotiline.

Banki (1978) has also shown that depressed patients have reduced levels of platelet 5HT and treatment with amitriptyline or dibenzepine causes a statistically significant increase in platelet 5HT content at the end of the treatment period.

In addition to amitriptyline, (Wood and Coppen, 1985) trazodone, (Healy *et al* 1983), maprotiline (Mück-Šeler *et al* 1983) and imipramine (Tuomisto *et al* 1979), other antidepressant treatments have also been shown to be able

TABLE V
5HT uptake characteristics (K_m and V_{max}) of platelets from controls, depressed patients, recovered depressed patients and patients receiving prophylactic lithium therapy

	n	K_m (μmol/1)	V_{max} (pmol/10^8 platelets/min)
Controls	32	0.51 ± 0.03	30.6 ± 2.6 (1)
Depressed Patients, drug-free	26	0.57 ± 0.04	23.2 ± 1.8 (2)
Recovered Depressives, drug-free	25	0.58 ± 0.04 (3)	19.5 ± 1.8 (4)
Unipolar Lithium Patients	28	0.76 ± 0.06 (5)	27.8 ± 2.4 (6)
Bipolar Lithium Patients	7	0.89 ± 0.10	33.0 ± 6.2

(1) lower than controls $p < 0.05$
(2) lower than controls $p < 0.01$
(3) higher than controls $p < 0.001$, depressed and recovered patients $p < 0.02$
(4) higher than recovered depressives $p < 0.01$
(5) higher than controls $p < 0.001$, depressed and recovered depressives $p < 0.01$
(6) higher than depressed patients $p < 0.05$ and recovered depressives $p < 0.01$

Results as means $\pm$ S.E.M. Reproduced from Coppen *et al* (1980) with permission of the Royal College of Psychiatrists

to facilitate 5HT uptake into platelets. For example, Murphy *et al* (1970) have shown that lithium leads to a significant increase in 5HT uptake.

Our investigation (Coppen *et al* 1980) and others (Born *et al* 1980) indicated that prophylactic lithium treatment restored the abnormally low platelet 5HT uptake seen in depressive patients towards normal control values. The 5HT uptake characteristics are illustrated in Table V. These results have also been confirmed by Meltzer's group in the U.S.A. Coppen *et al* (1976) have shown that after clinical recovery, patients' whole blood 5HT content returned to normal during lithium treatment; a similar result has been reported by Corona *et al* (1982). It appears that there is a large body of evidence which suggests that successful antidepressant treatment increases platelet 5HT uptake and content towards normal control values.

As discussed earlier, one of the other criticisms that uptake inhibition was not the therapeutic mode of action of antidepressants was that drugs such as mianserin and iprindole did not block the uptake of monoamines following chronic administration. However, during an investigation into the effect of mianserin on the peripheral uptake mechanisms for NA and 5HT (Coppen *et al* 1978b) it was concluded that mianserin appeared to have little effect on peripheral NA uptake but mianserin did have a significant effect on platelet 5HT uptake: the abnormally low transport rate was returned towards normal control values after six weeks of treatment. These mianserin results are illustrated in Table VI. It is worth while to note in that investigation

TABLE VI

5HT uptake characteristics (K_m, V_{max} and $\overline{y}$) of platelets from controls and patients before and during treatment with mianserin

	n	K_m (μmol/1)	V_{max} (pmol/10^8 platelets/min)	$\overline{y}$
Controls	10	0.57 ± 0.04	28.0 ± 3.0	15.3 ± 1.9
Patients before therapy	7	0.47 ± 0.04	$13.0 \pm 1.4^*$	$8.7 \pm 1.0^*$
Patients during mianserin therapy	7	0.57 ± 0.04	$20.4 \pm 4.3^{**}$	$12.5 \pm 2.5^{**}$

* Significantly lower than controls, $p < 0.02$
** Significantly higher than baseline patients, $p < 0.05$
Results as means $\pm$ S.E.M.
Reproduced from Coppen *et al* (1978b) by permission of the British Journal of Clinical Pharmacology.

TABLE VII

Correlation between plasma mianserin concentration after 6 weeks treatment and 5HT uptake characteristics

	n	K_m	V_{max}	$\overline{y}$
Values at 6 weeks	7	0.22	-0.62	-0.67
Difference between baseline and 6 weeks	7	-0.14	-0.47	-0.49

Reproduced from Coppen *et al* (1978b) with permission of the British Journal of Clinical Pharmacology

that there was a trend, albeit not statistically significant, for lower plasma levels of mianserin to be associated with higher uptake values (Table VII).

Facilitation of 5HT uptake and biological theories of depression

The amine deficiency hypothesis was criticised since it did not explain the discrepancy between the onset of action of the pharmacological effect of antidepressant drugs, i.e. uptake inhibition, which occurred within minutes and their therapeutic action which did not become apparent until the second or third week of treatment.

Vetulani and his colleagues (1976) put forward a new possible common mechanism of action of antidepressant treatments which involved a delayed reduction in the sensitivity of the noradrenergic cAMP generating system in the limbic forebrain. Criticism of this newer hypothesis could be levelled at the desirability of having a common mechanism of action of antidepressant treatments. For example, would one prescribe an MAO inhibitor to a highly endogenously depressed patient or prescribe ECT for a reactive patient?

It has also been reported that the ability of antidepressant drugs to desensitise beta receptors is *inversely* correlated with their clinical potency (Willner, 1984). Uptake inhibition would not seem to be the explanation of antidepressant treatment since inhibition would occur after a relatively short interval after administration of the drug. If facilitation of 5HT uptake occurs, one could envisage a time-lag before clinical efficacy becomes apparent since the build-up of depleted stores of 5HT would occur only after a substantial period of time. It is also worth while to note that some clinical studies have indicated that prompt clinical improvement can occur within one week of zimeldine treatment (Wålinder *et al* 1981) or with a combination treatment (Riise & Holm, 1984).

In conclusion, it becomes apparent that in patients with a depressive illness who have an abnormality in their peripheral 5HT uptake mechanisms, there is ample evidence to suggest that successful treatment with a variety of antidepressant treatments actually facilitates rather than inhibits platelet 5HT uptake.

Acknowledgements

I am indebted to all my scientific and clinical colleagues for their assistance during these investigations. I am grateful to Dr A. Coppen for his hospitality during my stay at the MRC Laboratory in Epsom.

References

ARORA, R. C. & MELTZER, H. Y. (1982) Serotonin uptake blood platelets of schizophrenic patients. *Psychiatry Research*, **6**, 327–333.

BANKI, C. M. (1978) 5-Hydroxytryptamine content of the whole blood in psychiatric illness and alcoholism. *Acta Psychiatrica Scandinavica*, **57**, 232–238.

BORN, G. V. R., GRIGNANI, G. & MARTIN, K. (1980) Long-term effect of lithium on the uptake of 5-hydroxytryptamine by human platelets. *British Journal of Clinical Pharmacology*, **9**, 321–325.

CARANOBE, C., SIÉ, P., FERNANDEZ, F., PRIS, J., MOATTI, S. & BONEU, B. (1984) Abnormal platelet serotonin uptake and binding sites in myeloproliferative disorders. *Thrombosis Haemostasis (Stuttgart)*, **51**, 349–353.

COPPEN, A., TURNER, P., ROWSELL, A. R. & PADGHAM, C. (1976) 5-Hydroxytryptamine (5HT) in the whole-blood of patients with depressive illness. *Postgraduate Medical Journal*, **52**, 156–158.

—— SWADE, C. & WOOD, K. (1978a) Platelet 5-hydroxytryptamine accumulation in depressive illness. *Clinica Chimica Acta*, **87**, 165–168.

—— GHOSE, K., SWADE, C. & WOOD, K. (1978b) Effect of mianserin hydrochloride on peripheral uptake mechanisms for noradrenaline and 5-hydroxytryptamine in man. *British Journal of Clinical Pharmacology*, **5**, 13s–17s.

—— RAO, V. A. R., SWADE, C. & WOOD, K. (1979a) Inhibition of 5-hydroxytryptamine reuptake by amitriptyline and zimeldine and its relationship to their therapeutic action. *Psychopharmacology*, **63**, 125–129.

—— SWADE, C., WOOD, K. & CARROLL, J. D. (1979b) Platelet 5-hydroxytryptamine accumulation and migraine. *Lancet*, **2**, 914.

—— SWADE, C. & WOOD, K. (1980) Lithium restores abnormal platelet 5-HT transport in patients with affective disorders. *British Journal of Psychiatry*, **136**, 235–238.

CORONA, G. L., CUCCHI, M. L., SANTAGOSTINO, G., FRATTINI, P., ZERBI, F., FENOGLIO, L. & SAVOLDI, F. (1982) Blood noradrenaline and 5-HT levels in depressed women during amitriptyline or lithium treatment. *Psychopharmacology*, **77**, 236–241.

GHOSE, K. & COPPEN, A. (1977) Noradrenaline, depressive illness, and the action of amitriptyline. *Psychopharmacology*, **54**, 57–60.

HAMILTON, M. (1967) Development of a rating scale for primary depressive illness. *British Journal of Social and Clinical Psychology*, **6**, 278–296.

HEALY, D., CARNEY, P. A. & LEONARD, B. E. (1983) Monoamine-related markers of depression: changes following treatment. *Journal of Psychiatric Research*, **17**, 251–260.

KAMAL, L. A., LE QUAN-BUI, K. H. & MEYER, P. (1984) Decreased uptake of H-serotonin and endogenous content of serotonin in blood platelets in hypertensive patients. *Hypertension*, **6**, 568–573.

LINEWEAVER, M. & BURK, D. (1934) The determination of enzyme dissociation constants. *Journal of American Chemical Society*, **56**, 658–666.

MALMGREN, E., OLSSON, P., TORNLING, G. & UNGE, G. (1980) The 5-hydroxytryptamine uptake mechanism in normal platelets and platelets from migraine and asthmatic patients. *Thrombosis Research*, **18**, 733–741.

MELTZER, H. Y., ARORA, R. C., BABER, R. & TRICOU, B. J. (1981) Serotonin uptake in blood platelets of psychiatric patients. *Archives of General Psychiatry*, **38**, 1322–1326.

MÜCK-ŠELER, D., DEANOVIĆ, Ž., JAMNICKY, B., JAKUPČEVIĆ, M. & MIHOVILOVIĆ, M. (1983) Maprotiline in the treatment of endogenous depression: comparison of therapeutic effect with serotonin level in blood platelets. *Psychopharmacology*, **79**, 262–265.

MURPHY, D. L., COLBURN, R. W., DAVIS, J. M. & BUNNEY, W. E. (1970) Imipramine and lithium effects on biogenic amine transport in depressed and manic-depressed patients. *American Journal of Psychiatry*, **127**, 339–344.

PLETSCHER, A. (1978) Platelets as models for monoaminergic neurones. *Essays in Neurochemistry and Neuropharmacology* (ed. M. B. H. Youdim, W. Lovenberg, D. F. Sherman & J. R. Lagnado). Chichester: J. Wiley & Sons.

RIISE, I. S. & HOLM, P. (1984) Concomitant isocarboxazid/mianserin treatment of major depressive disorder. *Journal of Affective Disorders*, **6**, 175–179.

ROTMAN, A., MODAI, I., MUNITZ, H. & WIJSENBEEK, H. (1979) Active uptake of serotonin by blood platelets of schizophrenic patients. *FEBS Letters*, **101**, 134–136.

SNEDDON, J. M. (1973) Blood platelets as a model for monoamine-containing neurones. *Progress Neurobiology*, **1**, 151–198.

SPITZER, R. L., ENDICOTT, J. & ROBINS, E. (1978) Research diagnostic criteria. Rationale and reliability. *Archives of General Psychiatry*, **35**, 773–782.

TUOMISTO, J. & TUKIAINEN, E. (1976) Decreased uptake of 5-hydroxytryptamine in blood platelets from depressed patients. *Nature*, **262**, 596–598.

—— TUKIAINEN, E. & AHLFORS, U. G. (1979) Decreased uptake of 5-hydroxytryptamine in blood platelets from patients with endogenous depression. *Psychopharmacology*, **65**, 141–147.

VETULANI, J., STAWARZ, R. J., DINGELL, J. V. & SULSER, F. (1976) A possible common mechanism of action of antidepressant treatments. *Naunyn-Schmiedeberg's Archives of Pharmacology*, **293**, 109–114.

WÅLINDER, J., CARLSSON, A. & PERSSON, R. (1981) 5-HT reuptake inhibitors plus tryptophan in endogenous depression. *Acta Psychiatrica Scandinavica*, **63**, suppl. 290, 179–190.

WILLNER, P. (1984) The ability of antidepressant drugs to desensitize β-receptors is inversely correlated with their clinical potency. *Journal of Affective Disorders*, **7**, 53–58.

WOOD, K. M., SWADE, C. & COPPEN, A. J. (1982) Zimeldine: a pharmacokinetic and pharmacodynamic study in depressive illness. *British Journal of Clinical Practice*, Supplement **19**, 42–47.

—— COPPEN, A. (1985) Platelet transport and receptor sites in depressive illness. In: *Psychopharmacology: Recent Advances and Future prospects*. British Association for Psychopharmacology Monograph No. 6 (ed. S. Iversen) Oxford: Oxford University Press.

6 The responsiveness of central alpha$_2$ adrenoceptors in depression

S. A. CHECKLEY; T. H. CORN; I. B. GLASS; S. W. BURTON; C. A. BURKE

Depression has long been thought to be associated with altered central noradrenergic neurotransmission (Schildkraut, 1965). This view has rested upon the ability of acute antidepressant drug treatments to increase intrasynaptic noradrenaline concentrations. More recently it has been recognised that neuroceptors adapt to changes in the ambient concentrations of their neurotransmitters. Thus all antidepressant treatments which increase intrasynaptic noradrenaline concentrations reduce the number or function of beta adrenoceptors (Sulser et al, 1978). Some of these drugs also reduce the number or function of alpha$_2$ adrenoceptors and increase the functional responses to the stimulation of alpha$_1$ adrenoceptors (Charney et al, 1981). Clearly if these adaptive changes at adrenoceptors occur in patients being treated with antidepressant drugs then the changes at receptors could modify or even reverse the overall drug effect upon noradrenergic neurotransmission. If down-regulation of post-synaptic adrenoceptors is sufficiently marked then the net effect of antidepressant treatment could be to reduce rather than to increase adrenergic neurotransmission. Some have argued that this is the case (Sulser et al, 1978) and have suggested that depression may be characterised by an over-activity rather than an underactivity of central noradrenergic mechanisms.

3-methoxy-4-hydroxyphenylethyleneglycol (MHPG) in depression

For many years the only clinically available measure of central noradrenergic function was the measurement of MHPG concentrations in body fluids. Since MHPG is a major metabolite of noradrenaline its production should be reduced if there is a generalised reduction in noradrenaline release. Unfortunately studies of MHPG are beset with many problems (Leckman & Maas, 1984; Post et al, 1984) of which just three will be mentioned.

Firstly MHPG is produced by the peripheral sympathetic nervous system as well as by the central nervous system. Although in some situations the two noradrenergic systems appear to be functionally linked this cannot be assumed. Furthermore since free MHPG readily crosses the blood brain barrier it cannot be assumed that cerebrospinal fluid (CSF) MHPG is a better measure of central noradrenaline release than is plasma MHPG. A third problem is that much of the MHPG in lumbar CSF is of spinal origin.

Although three studies have reported reduced CSF concentrations of MHPG in drug free patients with endogenous depression (Post *et al*, 1973; Subrahmanyam, 1975; Subrahmanyam & Ramamurthi, 1979) many more studies have reported normal values of MHPG in CSF (Post *et al*, 1984) and also in plasma (Leckman & Maas, 1984) from patients with endogenous depression. These findings rule out the possibility that depression is accompanied by a generalised alteration in the release of noradrenaline in the central and sympathetic nervous systems. The studies do not exclude the possibility of a generalised change in central noradrenaline release and such metabolic studies could never investigate the possibility of localised changes in noradrenergic function in specific brain regions.

Compared to such metabolic approaches challenge tests offer a number of advantages as will be illustrated in this chapter by studies of the effects of clonidine upon growth hormone and blood pressure. It will be seen that these challenge studies provide measures of the responsiveness of defined receptor sub-types within specific anatomical locations within the brain. The GH response to clonidine will be described as an example of a measure of the responsiveness of forebrain alpha₂ adrenoceptors while the hypotensive effect of clonidine will be described as an example of a hind-brain alpha₂ adrenoceptor function.

Animal studies of the growth hormone (GH) response to clonidine

The GH response to clonidine depends upon the stimulation of alpha₂ rather than alpha₁ adrenoceptors since it is inhibited by alpha₂ but not by alpha₁ antagonists. Since these studies have been reported using rats (Eriksson *et al*, 1981; Kruhlich *et al*, 1982) dogs (Cella *et al*, 1983 and 1984) rhesus monkeys (Gold *et al*, 1978) and baboons (McWilliam & Meldrum, 1983), it seems reasonable to apply the findings to man.

Central alpha₂ adrenoceptors are located both pre- and post-synaptically and most though not all of the published evidence suggests that the receptors mediating this response are post-synaptic (Terry & Martin, 1981; Kruhlich *et al*, 1982; McWilliam and Meldrum, 1983; Cella *et al*, 1984).

Experiments in anaesthetised dogs provide good evidence for a forebrain location of alpha₂ adrenoceptors mediating the GH response to clonidine. The response is inhibited by the injection of phenoxybenzamine into the third but not the fourth ventricle (Lovinger *et al*, 1976). In a second series of experiments the circle of Willis was divided to separate the territories of the vertebral and cerebral arteries. Under these conditions a small dose of clonidine which had no effect upon GH when given intravenously released GH when given into the carotid but not the vertebral arteries (Rudolph *et al*, 1980). The converse findings applied to the hypotensive effect of clonidine which was seen following the injection of clonidine into the vertebral but not the carotid arteries.

Treatment of neonatal rats with monosodium glutamate causes a selective lesion in the hypothalamic arcuate nucleus. As rats so treated have abnormal GH responses to clonidine but normal GH responses to prostaglandin E_1, it is probable that the GH response to clonidine depends upon the stimulation of alpha$_2$ adrenoceptors in the arcuate nucleus (Katakami *et al*, 1984). The arcuate nucleus is of great relevance since it is the main site in the human brain of cell bodies which contain growth-hormone releasing factor (GRF) (Bloch *et al*, 1983). Further, GRF is known to be involved in the GH response to clonidine since in rats this response is inhibited by pre-treatment with anti-GRF antibodies (Miki *et al*, 1984). Pretreatment with anti-somatostatin antibodies by contrast has no effect upon the GH response to clonidine (Eden *et al*, 1981).

In summary, the GH response to clonidine depends upon stimulation of forebrain alpha$_2$ adrenoceptors. Many of these receptors are probably located in the arcuate nucleus of the hypothalamus from which GRF containing axons descend to terminate about the portal capillaries in the median eminence.

The hypotensive effect of clonidine in experimental animals

As was the case for the GH response, so too the hypotensive effect of clonidine is inhibited by a variety of alpha$_2$ antagonists (Schmitt *et al*, 1972; Schmitt *et al*, 1977; Hamilton *et al*, 1980; Timmermans *et al*, 1981; Beckett & Finch, 1982). Furthermore, the most selective of these, idazoxan, has been shown to inhibit the hypotensive effect of clonidine in man (Clifford, 1982). The fact that the alpha$_1$ antagonist prazosin also inhibits the hypotensive effect of clonidine (Van Zwieten *et al*, 1978; Timmermans *et al*, 1979) suggests that alpha$_1$ as well as alpha$_2$ adrenoceptors may be involved. However, the experiments with prazosin are complicated by its own hypotensive properties and the best way to distinguish between alpha$_1$ and alpha$_2$ adrenoceptor mediated responses is by use of the stereoisomers of yohimbine, namely rauwolscine and coryanthine. Rauwolscine is an alpha$_2$ antagonist and blocks the hypotensive effect of clonidine. Coryanthine is an alpha$_1$ antagonist and does not (Timmermans *et al*, 1981). Since they are stereoisomers of the same molecule it is unlikely that they have physicochemical or other differences. Consequently it can be assumed that the hypotensive effect of clonidine does involve the stimulation of $alpha_2$ adrenoceptors.

These $alpha_2$ adrenoceptors are almost certainly post-synaptic in location since the hypotensive effect of clonidine survives chronic depletion of presynaptic noradrenaline stores (Haeusler, 1974; Kobinger & Pichler, 1976; Warnke & Hoefke, 1977).

Evidence has already been reviewed which suggests that the receptors mediating the hypotensive effect of clonidine are within the territory of the vertebral artery. Within the territory the hypotensive effect of clonidine has been elicited following its iontophoretic application to the locus coeruleus (Zandberg *et al*, 1979), the nucleus of the tractus solitarius (Rockhold & Caldwell, 1979) and the lateral reticular formation (Wolf & Mohrland, 1984). Furthermore lesions in and around the nucleus of the tractus solitarius inhibit the hypotensive effect of clonidine in spontaneously hypotensive rats (Rockhold & Caldwell, 1979).

It has even been suggested (Sharma *et al*, 1978) that clonidine acts upon the so-called 'excitatory cardiovascular neurones' — cells whose firing rate decreases as blood pressure rises. The firing rate of these cells is reduced by clonidine while the 'inhibitory cardiovascular neurones' (whose firing increases as blood pressure rises) are unaffected. There is some evidence that clonidine may behave as a noradrenaline antagonist at hind-brain sites which is in contrast to its agonist properties elsewhere (Sharma *et al*, 1978; Tadepalli & Mills, 1978).

Although the hind-brain is involved in the hypotensive effect of clonidine the forebrain is also implicated. In rats with brains transected at midcollicular level clonidine still reduces blood pressure when injected into the third ventricle (Tadepalli & Mills, 1978). Since the third ventricle was isolated from the fourth, the hypotensive effect of clonidine must have been elicited from the stimulation of forebrain structures. Whereas clonidine acts as an antagonist to lower blood pressure in hind-brain regions, in the anterior hypothalamus clonidine probably acts as an agonist since clonidine and an alpha antagonist had opposite effects upon blood pressure following their injection into the third ventricle (Tadepalli & Mills, 1978).

Summary

A detailed presentation has been made of the evidence which differentiates between the sites of action involved in the GH and hypotensive responses to clonidine. The GH response depends upon an $alpha_2$ agonist action at forebrain structures, particularly the arcuate nucleus of the hypothalamus. The hypotensive effect of clonidine mainly involves hind-brain structures particularly the locus coeruleus: however some forebrain may be involved

TABLE I

Matched comparisons of GH responses to clonidine between patients with endogenous depression and normal volunteers

	Matussek et al, 1980	Checkley et al, 1981a	Charney et al, 1982a	Siever et al, 1982a
Number of patients with endogenous depression	10	10	11	14
Criteria for diagnosing endogenous depression	ICD	RDC + Newcastle	RDC	RDC
Weeks drug-free	4	3	2	4
Number of normal subjects compared to patients	32	10	11	14
Matching for age, sex and menopausal status	Approximate	Exact	Approximate	Exact
Dose of clonidine	0.2 µg/kgm iv	0.2 µg/kgm iv	5.0 µg/kgm oral	0.2 µg/kgm iv
Testing for significance of reduction in endogenous depression	$p < 0.05$	$p < 0.05$	$p < 0.05$	$p < 0.05$

TABLE II

Matched comparisons of GH responses to clonidine in patients with endogenous and reactive depression

	Matussek et al, 1980	Checkley et al, 1984
Number of patients with endogenous depression	10	10
Number of patients with reactive depression	12	10
Criteria for distinguishing between the two	ICD	Newcastle scale
Matching for age, sex and menopausal status	Approximate	Exact
Drug-free period	4 weeks	3 weeks
Testing for significance of reduction in endogenous as compared to reactive depression	$p < 0.05$	$p < 0.05$

also. The hypotensive response may depend upon an alpha₂ antagonist action of clonidine in the hind-brain but an alpha₂ agonist action of clonidine in the forebrain may also be involved. The importance of these differences is that in depression, the GH resonse is impaired (see below) whereas the hypotensive effect of clonidine is normal.

The growth hormone (GH) response to clonidine in patients with endogenous depression

Four groups have independently reported that the GH response to clonidine is impaired in patients with endogenous depression when compared with the response in matched, non-depressed controls (Matussek *et al*, 1980; Checkley *et al*, 1981a; Charney *et al*, 1982a; Siever *et al*, 1982a). Table I summarises the important features of these four studies. Two groups have independently reported that the GH response to clonidine is also impaired in patients with endogenous depression when their responses are compared to those of matched controls suffering from reactive depression (Matussek *et al*, 1980; Checkley *et al*, 1984). Table II summarises the important features of these two studies. These same endogenously depressed patients had normal hypotensive (Checkley *et al*, 1981a; Charney *et al*, 1982a) and sedative (Checkley *et al*, 1981a) effects of clonidine.

The purpose of this chapter is to consider whether or not the impaired GH response to clonidine is due to a defect of the forebrain alpha₂ adrenoceptors which mediate this response. An earlier review (Checkley, 1980) has indicated that the following variables influence GH secretion in man and may confound the interpretation of GH responses in depression.

(i) baseline GH
(ii) age and sex
(iii) psychotropic drugs (including alcohol and nicotine)
(iv) starvation and body weight
(v) the non-specific 'stress' of any psychiatric illness

Since that review a sixth possible cause of variation has been described. Circadian rhythms have been described for the number of alpha and beta adrenoceptors in rat brain (Kafka *et al*, 1981). Consequently it is possible that a change in the responsiveness at, for example, alpha$_2$ adrenoceptors at 09.00 hours could be due to the temporal displacement (phase advance or phase delay) of an otherwise normal rhythm of receptor number. However, this explanation is unlikely to apply to the GH response to clonidine since we have been unable to find any variation in the GH response to clonidine at various times of the day (Honer *et al*, 1984).

However, factors (i)-(v) above certainly can alter GH secretion in man and it remains to be seen whether or not these account for the reduced GH response to clonidine in endogenous depression.

(i) Baseline GH

Since GH inhibits its own secretion (Sakuma & Knobil, 1970) it is logical to study only those patients with low basal GH secretion. Different groups have excluded patients with baseline GH of 3 ng/ml (Checkley *et al*, 1981a) or 5 ng/ml (Siever *et al*, 1982a) but there has not previously been empirical evidence in favour of these or indeed any cut-off points.

(ii) Age

GH secretion is maximal in childhood and puberty and then declines throughout adult life until in old age very little is secreted at all (Shibasaki *et al*, 1984). Consequently age must be controlled for preferably by the individual matching of patient and controls for age (Checkley *et al*, 1981a; Siever *et al*, 1982a).

(iii) Sex and ovarian status

Since oestrogen enhances GH secretion women secrete more GH than men until the menopause (Frantz & Rabkin, 1965; Merimee & Fineberg, 1971). Thus patient and controls should be matched individually for sex and menopausal status (Checkley *et al*, 1981a; Siever *et al*, 1982a) as well as for age. Whether or not the GH response to clonidine varies throughout the menstrual cycle is controversial (Matussek *et al*, 1984; Eriksson personal communication, 1985) and so it may or may not be necessary to control for the time of the menstrual cycle (Siever *et al*, 1982a).

(iv) Psychotropic drugs

The GH response to clonidine is altered by desipramine (Glass *et al*, 1982; Corn *et al*, 1984c) by alcohol (Matussek *et al*, 1980 and 1984) by nicotine and quite possibly by many other psychotropic drugs. Although it is self evident that such effects must be excluded it is not clear how long should be the drug-free interval before a patient is free of drug effect. Different groups have used drug-free periods of one (Meltzer *et al*, 1984), three (Checkley *et al*, 1981a and 1984) and four weeks (Siever *et al*, 1982a). However the adequacy of any of these wash-out periods is questioned by a preliminary finding that in four normal volunteers the GH response to clonidine remained impaired at three weeks after stopping a three week course of treatment with desipramine in therapeutic doses (Corn *et al*, 1984c). The influence of length of drug-free period upon the GH response to clonidine will be investigated in this report.

(v) Starvation and body weight

Starvation is known to raise basal GH secretion and both obesity and weight loss are known to reduce GH secretion (Checkley, 1980). Hitherto no studies have reported upon the effect of body weight upon GH secretion in depression.

(vi) The non-specific 'stress' of any psychiatric illness

Since noradrenaline has been implicated in the pathogenesis of anxiety and since anxiety is a feature of many psychiatric conditions it is possible that altered noradrenergic responses in depression might be due to associated anxiety. Against this explanation are reports of normal or even increased GH responses to clonidine in patients with acute schizophrenia and reactive depression (Matussek *et al*, 1981; Checkley *et al*, 1984). A further mechanism whereby 'stress' could alter GH is by increasing cortisol secretion since in Cushing's syndrome GH secretion is reduced.

To investigate these five issues we present data from all of our drug-free depressed patients who have received clonidine (0.13 μg/kg) and for whom data on points (i)-(vi) above are available.

Factors influencing the GH response to clonidine in 55 drug-free patients with major depressive disorder

Methods

Patients with clinical diagnoses of depression were selected if they also met Research Diagnostic Criteria for Major Depressive Disorder (Spitzer *et al*,

1977). With the exception of night sedation with benzodiazepines, all were drug-free for at least three weeks. None had other medical or psychiatric diagnoses and none consumed as much alcohol as the equivalent of two litres of beer a day (Matussek *et al*, 1981). Whereas in our initial report (Checkley *et al*, 1981a) all patients received clonidine (0.2 µg/kgm) this report only included patients who had received a smaller dose (0.13 µg/kgm) which we have found is more acceptable to elderly patients. This report includes the patients mentioned in earlier reports (Glass *et al*, 1982; Corn *et al*, 1984a and b; Checkley *et al*, 1984) but also data from an additional five patients.

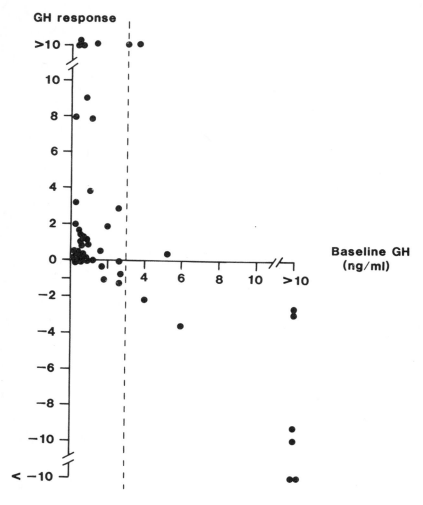

Fig. 1 — Relationship between GH response to clonidine and baseline GH level.

The clonidine tests were performed as has recently been described (Checkley *et al*, 1984).

(i) *The effect of baseline GH upon the GH response to clonidine in patients with depression*

In Fig. 1 are shown the GH responses to clonidine measured by the area under the growth hormone response curve in the 55 drug-free depressed patients plotted against baseline GH. It can be seen that whenever the plasma GH was greater than 3 ng/ml at the start of the infusion then an apparently 'negative' GH response to clonidine was obtained. However inspection of the raw data revealed that most of these 'negative responses' began before the infusion of clonidine. In other words a burst of GH secretion had occurred around the time of insertion of the cannula and from then onwards plasma GH concentrations fell throughout the sampling period; clearly it could not be meaningful to include any such data in any study of GH responses.

The selection of a cut-off point to exclude patients with raised plasma GH concentrations is inevitably an arbitary decision although the data in Fig. 1 are the most complete data available for the GH response to clonidine in drug-free depressed patients. The data are consistent with our long standing practice of excluding patients with baseline GH values of greater than 3 ng/ml and this practice will be employed throughout the remainder of this chapter. Data henceforth will only be presented when the baseline GH concentration is 3 ng/ml or less.

The remainder of the analysis is restricted to the 45 drug-free patients with baseline GH of 3 ng/ml or less. As can be seen from Fig. 1 both the baseline GH level (GHO) and the area under the GH response curve (GHA) have skew distributions, both these variables were therefore subjected to a log transformation creating the variables LGHO and LGHA. The GH responses were then correlated with the following variables:

(a) age
(b) sex
(c) baseline GH level
(d) length of drug-free period
(e) body weight at time of testing
(f) weight loss item from Hamilton Depression Rating Scale (Hamilton 1967)
(g) RDC diagnosis of endogenous or non-endogenous depression
(h) Newcastle diagnostic score for endogenous depression on the Carney Roth Garside (1965) questionnaire
(i) total score on items 10 and 11 for anxiety on the Hamilton Depression Rating Scale
(j) total Hamilton Depression Rating Scale.

TABLE III

Correlations of GH response to clonidine with age, RDC diagnosis, Newcastle diagnostic score, and baseline GH level

Statistical technique, and GH response parameter employed	RDC diagnosis	Newcastle score	Age	Baseline GH level (LGHO)
(1) Correlation with LGHA ($n = 45$)	-0.43^{**}	-0.37^{*}	-0.39^{**}	-0.08
(2) Partial correlation with LGHA age forced ($n = 45$)	-0.30^{*}	-0.25	—	-0.10
(3) Correlation with GHA-CAT ($n = 45$)	-0.35^{*}	-0.38^{*}	-0.37^{*}	-0.06
(4) Correlation with LGHA (excluding GHa > 2.5) ($n = 34$)	-0.34^{*}	-0.04	-0.11	-0.45^{**}
(5) Rank correlation with LGHA ($n = 45$)	-0.46^{**}	-0.34^{*}	-0.31^{*}	-0.15
(6) Rank correlation with GHA-CAT ($n = 45$)	-0.37^{*}	-0.33^{*}	-0.38^{*}	-0.06
(7) Rank correction with LGHA (excluding GHA > 2.5) ($n = 34$)	-0.32^{*}	-0.19	-0.05	-0.35^{*}

Significance level of correlation: * $p < 0.05$
　　　　　　　　　　　　　　　　　　 ** $p < 0.01$

Items (e) and (f) were to test for effects of weight loss upon the response and items (i) and (j) were to test for differing non-specific effects of psychiatric illness upon the GH response to clonidine. The hypothesis that endogenous depression causes blunted GH responses to clonidine predicts significant correlation between the GH response and variables (g) and (h) but not with variables (i) and (j). The hypothesis that the blunted GH response to clonidine is a non-specific effect of stress predicted that the response should be correlated with the anxiety scores on the HDRS together with the total HDRS score.

Results

The GH response to clonidine (measured by variable LGHA) was significantly correlated with age, with RDC diagnosis, and with Newcastle diagnostic score (Table III); the correlation with baseline GH level (LGHO) failed to reach significance. No other parameters of those listed above were correlated to the GH response to clonidine. Since age, RDC diagnosis and Newcastle diagnostic score were significantly correlated (Table IV) a partial correlation adjusting for age was calculated (Table III); the correlation between RDC diagnosis and GH response to clonidine remained significant. Since the distribution of GH scores was heavily skewed with a large number of very small responses (Fig. 1) further correlations were computed to test the robustness of the correlations between the GH response and the RDC diagnosis of endogenous depression. The GH responses were categorised into five categories (<2.5, $2.5-5$, $5-10$, $10-20$, and >20), thus creating the parameter GHA-CAT. This parameter proved to be significantly correlated with age, RDC diagnosis of endogenous depression and Newcastle diagnostic score (Table III). As a further test of the reliability of the findings the relatively small group of patients (11) with GH responses of greater than 2.5 were excluded; again the correlation of GH response and RDC diagnosis was statistically significant. The same correlations were performed using Spearman's rank correlation coefficient; again significant correlations with age, RDC diagnosis and diagnostic score were obtained (Table III). The correlations with RDC diagnosis though not age remained significant after excluding the 11 patients with GH responses of greater than 2.5. To ensure

TABLE IV

Correlations between age, RDC diagnosis, and Newcastle diagnostic score

	Age	RDC diagnosis	Newcastle score
Age	—		
RDC diagnosis	0.50*	—	
Newcastle score	0.40*	0.56*	—

Significance level of correlation $*p<0.01$

that the conclusions held for both sexes LGHA was correlated with all other variables for males and females separately. A similar pattern of correlation was found in each sex as in the whole sample, and specifically the correlation between LGHA and age was similar in both sexes.

It is concluded that there is a robust relationship between the GH response to clonidine and the RDC diagnosis of endogenous depression and that this is independent of the relationships between the diagnosis of endogenous depression and age. There is also a relationship between the diagnostic score for endogenous depression on the Newcastle Scale (Carney, *et al*, 1965) and the GH response to clonidine.

Discussion

Of the variables thought to influence the size of the GH response to clonidine in depression only two have been found to be significantly correlated with the response in an analysis of 45 drug-free depressed patients who had been drug-free for three weeks at the time of testing.

The dominant influence is that of the two measures of endogenous depression (Carney *et al*, 1965; Spitzer *et al*, 1977). There is also an effect of age.

It remains to discuss how adequately have the other influences upon the GH response to clonidine been excluded.

Sex and menopausal status

Surprisingly the GH response to clonidine did not differ between males and females. Although our sample is not large enough to separate out within the females the effects of age and menopausal status, our data suggested that the reported effect of menopause upon the GH response to clonidine may simply be an effect of age which is also found in males.

(ii) Delayed effects of psychotropic drugs

Within our sample of 45 depressed patients with baseline GH of 3 ng/ml or less were 12 patients who were drug-free for six months or longer. 25 were drug-free for only three weeks and the remainder had drug-free periods of between three weeks and six months. There was no significant relationship between the length of the drug-free period and of size of the GH response to clonidine. It is therefore likely that in these patients it is the diagnosis of endogenous depression rather than persisting drug action which accounts for the reduced GH responses to clonidine.

(iii) Starvation and weight loss

The acute effect of starvation was excluded by the study design in two ways.

Firstly all of the severely depressed patients (and nearly all of the sample) were studied as in-patients; no depressed patients are entered into our research studies if they are refusing to eat. Secondly acute starvation raises plasma GH and patients with raised plasma GH are excluded from the analysis of data.

Whereas the size of the GH response to clonidine was robustly correlated with the experimental measures of diagnosis of endogenous depression, no such correlations were found with body weight or with the weight loss item on the Hamilton Rating Scale. We believe that since nearly all of the sample were in-patients subjected to weekly if not daily body weighing that the information on the HDRS for weight loss is reliable. The fact that this variable did not correlate with the size of the GH response to clonidine whereas the measures for diagnosing endogenous depression did, is evidence that the reduced GH responses in these patients were related to diagnosis of endogenous depression and not to weight loss.

Several independent lines of evidence support this same conclusion. Firstly preliminary data (see below) suggest that the GH response to clonidine is impaired in recovered depressives with no weight loss. Secondly weight loss would be expected to effect GH secretion in general. Evidence to be reviewed below suggests normal GH responses to dopamine agonists in depression.

A final consideration is that Fichter *et al*, (1984) have reported that reduced GH responses to clonidine, with raised baseline GH, are seen in normal volunteers while on a zero calorie diet. Such a mechanism is unlikely to apply to our patients partly because none had stopped eating and partly because none had raised baseline GH.

(iv) Non-specific effects of 'stress'

The analysis above was planned in part to test the hypothesis that the reduced GH response to depression is an effect of stress. We predicted that in this case the response should correlate either with total HDRS score (as a measure of severity of illness) or with the HDRS items 10 and 11 (for somatic and psychic anxiety). The failure to find such correlations in an analysis which found significant correlations with the measures of endogenous depression is evidence that the GH response in depression is reduced in the presence of endogenous symptoms rather than by stress.

Further evidence that the GH response to clonidine is unrelated to stress comes from our study of the effect of ECT upon the GH response to clonidine (Slade & Checkley, 1980). Reduced GH responses were found both before ECT and also at 24 hours after the seventh ECT when most patients were clinically recovered and so presumably free from the effects of 'stress'. In a similar manner the evidence (see below) that the GH response to clonidine is impaired in recovered depressives is also evidence that it is endogenous depression rather than stress which accounts for a reduced GH response to clonidine in depression.

The GH response to clonidine in recovered depressives

Reference has already been made to the theoretical importance of measuring GH responses to clonidine in recovered depressives. Such data is included in studies of patients treated with ECT (Slade & Checkley, 1980), desipramine (Checkley *et al*, 1981b; Glass *et al*, 1982), amitriptyline (Charney *et al*, 1982b), clorgyline (Siever *et al*, 1982b) and psychosurgery (Corn *et al*, 1984a). In all of these studies reduced GH responses to clonidine were found in recovered patients. However, at least one of these treatments is known to reduce the GH response to clonidine (Corn *et al*, 1984c) and therefore it is necessary to measure GH responses in recovered patients in the drug-free state.

We have followed up all of the patients included in this study and in our earlier (Checkley *et al*, 1981a) study. Only seven were fully recovered and free of psychotropic drugs. Six of these still had absent GH responses to clonidine and one had a normal response. Both Matussek (personal communication, 1984) and Siever (personal communication, 1984) have each tested one patient both in a drug-free depressed and then in a drug-free recovered state, with normal basal GH on both occasions. Both of these patients had reduced GH responses, both depressed and recovered.

Clearly it is not easy to find recovered drug-free patients who have formally had endogenous depression. Eight out of the nine such patients who have been tested have had reduced GH responses both in the depressed and in the recovered states.

GH responses to other drugs in depression

As has been mentioned in an earlier review (Checkley, 1980) many of the stimuli which have been used in studies of GH secretion lack in pharmacological specificity and depend upon the stimulation of alpha adrenoceptors as well as other receptors. Consequently reports of impaired GH responses to hypoglycaemia (Gruen *et al*, 1975), and to 5HTP (Takahashi *et al*, 1974), are consistent with an alpha adrenoceptor defect although they are also open to other interpretations.

A more specific challenge to the adrenergic system is desipramine. This releases GH through the stimulation of $alpha_2$ adrenoceptors (Laakmann, 1980). This response also is impaired in patients with endogenous depression (Laakmann, 1980; Calil *et al*, 1984).

The GH response to apomorphine is a measure of the responsiveness of dopamine receptors since this response is inhibited following the blockade of dopamine receptors (Lal *et al*, 1977; Nair *et al*, 1979; Rotrosen *et al*, 1979). Although further studies of this response are needed it may be normal in patients with endogenous depression (Frazer, 1975; Caspar *et al*, 1977;

Meltzer *et al*, 1984) and even in those same patients who have impaired GH responses to clonidine (Corn *et al*, 1984b).

Although further work is needed at present it would seem that patients with endogenous depression can secrete GH normally after the stimulation of dopamine but not alpha receptors. This is evidence for a defect at central alpha$_2$ adrenoceptors in endogenous depression.

Finally consideration should be given to the role of acetylcholine. Atropinic drugs have shown to inhibit the GH responses to both clonidine and apomorphine in man (Delitala *et al*, 1983; Casanueva *et al*, 1984). However, it is unlikely that an underactivity of these receptors produces the reduced GH response to clonidine in depression since a reduced GH response to apomorphine would be produced by the same mechanism and this is not seen. Furthermore, the cholinergic receptors regulating GH secretion are if anything hyper-responsive in depression since the GH response to physostigmine has been reported to be increased in depression (Risch *et al*, 1984).

Other effects of clonidine in patients with endogenous depression

There is general agreement that the hypotensive effect of clonidine is normal in patients with endogenous depression (Checkley *et al*, 1981a; Charney *et al*, 1982; Siever *et al*, 1982a; Checkley *et al*, 1984; Siever *et al*, 1984b).

The other effects of clonidine have received less detailed study and no consensus has been achieved. The sedative effect of clonidine involves the stimulation of central alpha$_2$ adrenoceptors (Delini-Stula *et al*, 1979; Drew *et al*, 1979). This effect of clonidine has been reported to be normal in endogenous depression (Checkley *et al*, 1981a) although no other group has as yet reported on this response. The plasma MHPG response to clonidine is presumably a measure of the responsiveness of central and peripheral pre-synaptic alpha$_2$ adrenoceptors. It has been reported to be normal (Charney *et al*, 1982a) and reduced (Siever *et al*, 1984a) in depression.

The effect of clonidine upon cortisol and pulse may be reduced in depression (Siever *et al*, 1984b) although not at all the testing of these differences reached statistical significance.

It is clear that although the GH response to clonidine is impaired in endogenous depression, some other effects of clonidine are normal. A generalised abnormality of alpha$_2$ adrenoceptors in depression can be excluded. The hind-brain alpha$_2$ adrenoceptors which mediate the hypotensive effect of clonidine would thus appear to function normally in depression. Endogenous depression may be characterised by altered responses of forebrain alpha$_2$ adrenoceptors, particularly those in the arcuate nucleus which are crucial for the GH response to clonidine (Bloch *et al*, 1983; Katakami *et al*, 1984; Miki *et al*, 1984).

Conclusion

Four years ago we concluded that impaired GH responses to clonidine in depression 'may indicate a defect at central alpha adrenoceptors at least in neuroendocrine systems' (Checkley *et al*, 1981a). This conclusion has withstood testing both in animal as well as in clinical studies.

(i) There is now much more evidence that the GH response to clonidine depends upon the stimulation of alpha$_2$ adrenoceptors. The forebrain location of these receptors has been confirmed and possibly located to the arcuate nucleus of the hypothalamus.

(ii) The finding of impaired GH responses to clonidine in endogenous depression has been confirmed by several other groups.

(iii) The findings in the present report suggest that it is endogenous depression itself rather than weight loss, stress or drug effects which causes the impaired response.

(iv) Although further studies are needed it would seem that the GH response to dopamine agonists may be normal in depression.

References

BECKETT, P. J. & FINCH, L. (1982) The α_1 and α_2 adrenoceptor involvement in the central cardiovascular action of clonidine in the conscious renal hypertensive cat. *European Journal of Pharmacology*, **82**, 155–160.

BLOCH, B., BRAZEAU, P., LING, N., BOHLEN, P., ESCH, F., WEHRENBERG, W. B., BENOIT, R., BLOOM, F. & GUILLEMIN, R. (1983) Immunohistochemical detection of growth hormone-releasing factor in brain. *Nature*, **301**, 607–608.

CASPAR, R. C., DAVIS, J. M., PANDEY, G. N., GARVER, D. & DEKIRMENJIAN, H. (1977) Neuroendocrine and amine studies in affective illness. *Psychoneuroendocrinology*, **2**, 105–114.

CALIL, H. M., LESIEUR, P., GOLD, P. W., BROWN, G. M., ZAVADIL, P. & POTTER, W. Z. (1984) Hormonal response to zimelidine and desipramine in depressed patients. *Psychiatry Research*, **13**, 231–243.

CARNEY, M. W. P., ROTH, M. & GARSIDE, R. F. (1965) The diagnosis of depressive symptoms and the prediction of ECT response. *British Journal of Psychiatry*, **111**, 659–674.

CASANUEVA, F. F., VILLANUEVA, L., CABRANES, J. A., CABEZAS-CERRATO, J. & FERNANDES-CRUZ, A. (1984) Cholinergic mediation of growth hormone secretion elicited by arginine, clonidine and physical exercise in man. *Journal of Clinical Endocrinology and Metabolism*, **59**, 526–530.

CELLA, S. C., PICOTTI, G. B. & MULLER, E. E. (1983) α_2 adrenergic stimulation enhances growth hormone secretion in the dog. *Life Sciences*, **32**, 2785–2792.

—— PICOTTI, G. B., MORGESE, M., MANTAGAZZA, P. & MULLER, E. E. (1984) Presynaptic alpha$_2$ adrenergic stimulation leads to growth hormone release in the dog. *Life Sciences*, **34**, 447–454.

CHARNEY, D. S., MENKES, D. B. & HENINGER, G. R. (1981) Receptor sensitivity and the mechanism of action of antidepressant treatment: implications for the aetiology and therapy of depression. *Archives of General Psychiatry*, **38**, 1160–1168.

—— HENINGER, G. R., STEINBERG, D.E., REDMOND, D. E., LECKMAN, J. F., MAAS, J. W. & ROTH, R. H. (1982a) Adrenergic receptor sensitivity in depression: effects of clonidine in depressed patients and healthy patients. *Archives of General Psychiatry*, **39**, 290–294.

—— HENINGER, G. R. & STERNBERG, D. E. (1982b) Failure of chronic antidepressant treatment to alter growth hormone response to clonidine. *Psychiatry Research*, **6**, 90.

CHECKLEY, S. A. (1980) Neuroendocrine tests of monoamine function in man: a review of basic theory and its application to the study of depressive illness. *Psychological Medicine*, **10**, 35–53.

—— SLADE, A. P. & SHUR, E. (1981a) Growth hormone and other responses to clonidine in patients with endogenous depression. *British Journal of Psychiatry*, **138**, 51–55.

—— SLADE, A. P., SHUR, E. & DAWLING, S. (1981b) A pilot study of the mechanism of action of desipramine. *British Journal of Psychiatry*, **138**, 248–251.

—— GLASS, I. B., THOMPSON, C., CORN, T. & ROBINSON, P. (1984) The GH response to clonidine in endogenous as compared to reactive depression. *Psychological Medicine*, **14**, 773–777.

CLIFFORD, J. M. (1982) Reversal of some effects of clonidine by RX781094, an alpha₂ antagonist. A pilot study in normal volunteers. *British Journal of Clinical Pharmacology*, **13**, 609P.

CORN, T., HOENIG, A., THOMPSON, C., BRIDGES, P. K., BARTLETT, J. R. & CHECKLEY, S. A. (1984a) A neuroendocrine study of stereotactic subcaudate frontal tractotomy. *British Journal of Psychiatry*, **144**, 417–420.

—— HALE, A. S., THOMPSON, C., BRIDGES, P. K. & CHECKLEY, S. A. (1984b) A comparison of the GH responses to clonidine and apomorphine in the same endogenous depressed patients. *British Journal of Psychiatry*, **144**, 636–639.

—— THOMPSON, C. & CHECKLEY, S. A. (1984c) Effects of desipramine treatment upon central adrenoceptor function in normal subjects. *British Journal of Psychiatry*, **145**, 139–145.

DELINI-STULA, A., BAUMANN, P. & BUCH, O. (1979) Depression of exploratory activity by clonidine in rats as a model for the detection of relative pre- and post-synaptic central noradrenergic receptor selectivity of α-adrenolytic drugs. *Naunyn-Schmiedeberg's Archives of Pharmacology*, **307**, 115–112.

DELITALA, G., MAJOLI, M., BRIANDA, S., PALERMO, M. & MANNELLI, M. (1983) Cholinergic receptor control mechanisms for L-DOPA, apomorphine and clonidine-induced growth hormone secretion in man. *Journal of Clinical Endocrinology and Metabolism*, **57**, 1145–1149.

DREW, G. M., GOWER, A. J. & MARRIOTT, A. S. (1979) Alpha adrenoceptors mediate clonidine induced sedation in rats. *British Journal of Pharmacology*, **67**, 135–141.

ERIKSSON, E., EDEN, S. & MODIGH, K. (1981) Up and down regulation of central post synaptic alpha₂ receptors reflected in the growth hormone response to clonidine in reserpine pretreated rats. *Psychopharmacology*, **77**, 327–31.

EDEN, S., ERIKSSON, E., MARTIN, J. B. & MODIGH, K. (1981) Evidence for a growth hormone releasing factor mediating alpha-adrenergic influence on growth hormone secretion in the rat. *Neuroendocrinology*, **33**, 24–27.

FICHTER, M. M., PIRKE, K. M. & HOLSBOER, F. (1984) Neuroendocrine disturbances in depression, anorexia and starvation. Proceedings of the 13th C.I.N.P., Florence, F90.

FRANTZ, A. G. & RABKIN, M. T. (1965) Effects of oestrogen and sex differences on secretion of human growth hormone. *Journal of Clinical Endocrinology and Metabolism*, **25**, 1470–1480.

FRAZER, A. (1975) Adrenergic responses in depression: implications for a receptor defect. In *Biological Psychiatry*, (ed. J. Mendels), pp. 7–26, New York; Wiley.

GLASS, I. B., CHECKLEY, S. A., SHUR, E. & DAWLING, S. (1982) The effect of desipramine upon central adrenergic function in depressed patients. *British Journal of Psychiatry*, **141**, 372–376.

GOLD, M. S., DONABEDIAN, P. K. & REDMOND, D. E. Jr. (1978) Clonidine induced increase in serum growth hormone: possible role of epinephrine-mediated synapses. *Psychoneuroendocrinology*, **3**, 187–194.

GRUEN, P. H., SACHAR, E. J., ALTMAN, N. & SASSIN, J. (1975) Growth hormone responses to hypoglycaemia in post-menopausal depressed women. *Archives of General Psychiatry*, **32**, 33–34.

HAEUSLER, G. (1974) Clonidine-induced inhibition of sympathetic nerve activity; no indication for a central presynaptic or an indirect sympathomimetic mode of action. *Naunyn Schmiedeberg's Archives of Pharmacology*, **286**, 97–111.

HAMILTON, M. (1967) Development of a rating scale for primary depressive illness. *British Journal of Social and Clinical Psychology*, **6**, 278–296.

HAMILTON, T. C., HUNT, A. A. E. & POYSER, R. H. (1980) Involvement of central α_2 adrenoceptors in the mediation of clonidine-induced hypotension in the cat. *Journal of Pharmacy & Pharmacology*, **32**, 788–789.

HONER, W., GLASS, I. B., THOMPSON, C., CORN, T. & CHECKLEY, S. A. (1984) The GH and other responses to clonidine in normal subjects at different times of day. *Psychoneuroendocrinology*, **9**, 279–284.

KAFKA, M. S., WIRZ-JUSTICE, A. & WALKER, D. (1981) Circadian and seasonal rhythms in alpha and beta receptors in rat brain. *Brain Research*, **287**, 409–419.

KATAKAMI, H., KATO, Y., MATSUSHITA, N., HIROTO, S., SHIMATSU, A. & IMURA, H. (1981) Involvement of alpha adrenergic mechanisms in growth hormone release induced by opioid peptides in conscious rats. *Neuroendocrinology*, **33**, 129–135.

——— KATO, Y., MATSUSHITA, N. & IMURA, H. (1984) Effects of neonatal treatment with monosodium glutamate on growth hormone release induced by clonidine and prostaglandin E_1 in conscious male rats. *Neuroendocrinology*, **38**, 1–5.

KOBINGER, W. & PICHLER, L. (1976) Centrally induced reduction in sympathetic tone — a post-synaptic α adrenoceptor-stimulating action of imidazolines. *European Journal of Pharmacology*, **40**, 311–320.

KRUHLICH, L., MAYFIELD, M. A., STEELE, M. K., McMILLEN, B. A., McCANN, S. M. & KOENIG, J. I. (1982) Differential effects of pharmacological manipulations at central α_1 and α_2 adrenergic receptors on the secretion of thyrotropin and growth hormone in male rats. *Endocrinology*, **110**, 796–803.

LAAKMANN, G. (1980) Beinflussung der Hypophysenvorderlappen-Hormonsekretion durch Antidepressive bei gesunden Probanden, neurotisch and endogen depressiven Patienten. *Der Nervenarzt*, **51**, 725–732.

LAL, S., GUYDA, H. & BIKADOROFF, S. (1977) Effect of methysergide and pimozide on apomorphine induced growth hormone secretion in man. *Journal of Clinical Endocrinology and Metabolism*, **44**, 766–770.

LECKMAN, J. F. & MAAS, J. W. (1984) Plasma MHPG: relationship to brain noradrenergic systems and emerging clinical applications. In *Neurobiology of Mood Disorders*, (eds. R. M. Post & J. C. Ballenger) pp. 529–532. Baltimore: Williams & Wilkins.

LOVINGER, R., HOLLAND, J., KAPLAN, S., GRUMMACH, M. M., BORYCZKA, A. T., SHACKLEFORD, R., SALMON, J., REID, I. A. & GANONG, W. F. (1976) Pharmacological evidence for stimulation of growth hormone secretion by a central noradrenergic system in dogs. *Neuroscience*, **1**, 443–450.

McWILLIAM, J. R. & MELDRUM, B. S. (1983) Noradrenergic regulation of growth hormone secretion in the baboon. *Endocrinology*, **112**, 234–239.

MATUSSEK, N., ACKENHAIL, M., HIPPIUS, H., MULLER, F., SCHRODER, H.Th., SCHULTES, H. & WASILEWSKI, B. (1980) Effect of clonidine on growth hormone release in psychiatric patients and controls. *Psychiatry Research*, **2**, 25–36.

——— ACKENHEIL, M. & HERZ, M. (1984) The dependence of the clonidine growth hormone test on alcohol drinking habits and the menstrual cycle. *Psychoneuroendocrinology*, **9**, 173–178.

MELTZER, H. Y., KOLAKOWSKAA, T., FANG, U. S., FOGG, L., ROBERTSON, A., LEWINE, R., STRAHILEVITZ, M. & BUSCH, D. (1984) Growth hormone and prolactin response to apomorphine in schizophrenia and the major affective disorders. *Archives of General Psychiatry*, **41**, 512–519.

MERIMEE, J. T. & FINEBERG, S. E. (1971) Studies of the sex based variation of human growth hormone secretion. *Journal of Clinical Endocrinology and Metabolism*, **33**, 896–902.

MIKI, N., ONO, M. & SHIZUME, K. (1984) Evidence that opiatergic and alpha-adrenergic mechanisms stimulate rat growth hormone release via growth hormone releasing factor (GRF). *Endocrinology*, **114**, 1950–1952.

NAIR, N. P. V., LAL, S., CERVANTES, P., YASA, R. & GUYDA, H. (1979) Effect of clozapine on apomorphine induced growth hormone secretion and serum prolactin concentrations in schizophrenia. *Neuropsychobiology*, **5**, 136–142.

POST, R. M., GORDON, E. K., GOODWIN, F. K. & BUNNEY, W. E. Jr. (1973) Central norepinephrine metabolism in affective illness: MHPG in the cerebrospinal fluid. *Science*, **9**, 1002–1003.

—— JIMERSON, D. C., BALLENGER, J. C., LAKE, C. R., UHDE, T. W. & GOODWIN, F. K. (1984) Cerebrospinal fluid norepinephrine and its metabolites in manic depressive illness. In *Psychobiology of Mood Disorders*, (eds. R. M. Post & J. C. Ballenger), pp. 539–553. Baltimore: Williams & Wilkins.

RISCH, S. C., JANOWSKY, D. S., PARKER, D., KALIN, N. H., ALOI, J., COHEN, R. M., JUDD, L. L., HUEY, L. Y. & MURPHY, D. L. (1984) Neuroendocrine abnormalities in affective disorders: possible cholinergic mechanisms. In *Neurobiology of Mood Disorders*, (eds. R. M. Post & J. C. Ballenger), pp. 652–663. Baltimore: Williams & Wilkins.

ROCKHOLD, R. W. & CALDWELL, R. W. (1979) Effect of lesions of the nucleus tractus solitairius on the cardiovascular actions of clonidine in conscious rats. *Neuropharmacology*, 18, 347–356.

ROTROSEN, J., ANGRIST, B., GERSHON, S., PAQUIN, J., BRAHCHEY, L., OLESHANSKY, M., HALPERN, F. & SACHAR, E. J. (1979) Neuroendocrine effects of apomorphine: characterisation of response patterns and application to schizophrenia research. *British Journal of Psychiatry*, 135, 444–456.

RUDOLPH, C. D., KAPLAN, S. L. & GANONG, W. F. (1980) Sites at which clonidine acts to affect blood pressure and the secretion of Renin, Growth Hormone and ACTH. *Neuroendocrinology*, 31, 121–128.

SAKUMA, M. & KNOBIL, E. (1970) Inhibition of endogenous growth hormone secretion by exogenous growth hormone infusion in the rhesus monkey. *Endocrinology*, 86, 890–894.

SCHILDKRAUT, J. J. (1965) The catecholamine hypothesis of affective disorders: a review of supporting evidence. *American Journal of Psychiatry*, 122, 509–522.

SCHMITT, H., SCHMITT, H. & FERNARD, S. (1972) New evidence for an α adrenergic component in the sympathetic centres: centrally mediated decrease in sympathetic tone by L-DOPA and its antagonism by piperoxane and yohimbine. *European Journal of Pharmacology*, 17, 293–296.

—— SCHMITT, H. & FERNARD, S. (1977) Action of α adrenergic blocking drugs on the sympathetic centres and their interactions with the central sympathetic-inhibitory effect of clonidine. *Arzneimittel-Forschung/Drug Research*, 23, 40–45.

SHARMA, J. N., SANDREW, B. B. & WANG, S. C. (1978) CNS site of action of clonidine induced hypotension: a microiontophoretic study of bulbar cardiovascular neurons. *Brain Research*, 151, 127–133.

SHIBASAKI, T., SHIZUME, K., NAKARA, M., MASUDA, A., JIBIKI, K., DEMURA, H., WAKABAYASHI, I. & LING, N. (1984) Age-related changes in plasma growth hormone response to growth hormone releasing factor in men. *Journal of Clinical Endocrinology and Metabolism*, 58, 212–213.

SIEVER, L. J., UHDE, T. W., SILBERMAN, E. K., JIMERSON, D. C., ALOI, J. A., POST, R. M. & MURPHY, D. L. (1982a) The growth hormone response to clonidine as a probe of noradrenergic receptor responsiveness in affective disorder patients and controls. *Psychiatry Research*, 6, 171–183.

—— UHDE, T. W., INSEL, T. R., ROY, B. F. & MURPHY, D. L. (1982b) Growth hormone response to clonidine unchanged by chronic clorgyline treatment. *Psychiatry Research*, 7, 139–144.

—— UHDE, T. W., JIMERSON, J. C., LAKE, C. R., SILBERMAN, E. R., POST, R. M. & MURPHY, D. L. (1984a) Differential inhibitory responses to clonidine in 25 depressed patients and 25 normal control subjects. *American Journal of Psychiatry*, 141, 733–741.

—— UHDE, T. W., JIMERSON, D. C., POST, R. M., LAKE, C. R. & MURPHY, D. L. (1984b) Plasma cortisol response to clonidine in depressed patients and controls: evidence for a possible alteration in noradrenergic-neuroendocrine relationships. *Archives of General Psychiatry*, 41, 63–71.

SLADE, A. P. & CHECKLEY, S. A. (1980) A neuro-endocrine study of the mechanism of action of ECT. *British Journal of Psychiatry*, 137, 217–221.

SPITZER, R. L., ENDICOTT, J. & ROBINS, E. (1977) Research Diagnostic Criteria (RDC) for a Selected Group of Functional Disorders. New York: New York Psychiatric Institute.

SUBRAHMANYAM, S. (1975) Role of biogenic amines in certain pathological conditions. *Brain Research*, 87, 355–362.

—— RAMAMURTHI, B. (1979) Estimation of CSF and urinary biogenic amines in functional brain disorders. In *Modern Concepts in Psychiatric Surgery*, (eds. E. R. Hitchcock, H. T. Ballentine & B. A. Mayerson) pp. 15–31. Amsterdam: Elsevier/North Holland.

SULSER, F., VETULANI, J. & MOBLEY, P. L. (1978) Mode of action of antidepressant drugs. *Biochemical Pharmacology*, **27**, 257–261.

TAKAHASHI, S., KONDO, H., YOSHIMURA, U. & OCHI, Y. (1974) Growth hormone response to administration of L-5HTP in manic depressive psychosis. In: *Psychoneuroendocrinology* (ed. N. Hotatani) pp. 32–38. Basel: S. Karger.

TADEPALLI, A. S. & MILLS, E. (1978) Contribution of supracollicular structures of the brain to the central depression of cardiovascular function by clonidine. *Journal of Pharmacology and Experimental Therapeutics*, **203**, 693–701.

TERRY, L. C. & MARTIN, J. B. (1981) Evidence for alpha adrenergic regulation of episode growth hormone and prolactin secretion in the undisturbed male rat. *Endocrinology*, **108**, 1869–1873.

TIMMERMANS, P. B. M. W. M., LAM, E. & VAN ZWIETEN, P. A. (1979) The interaction between prazosin and clonidine at alpha adrenoceptors in rats and cats. *European Journal of Pharmacology*, **55**, 57–66.

—— SCHOOP, A. M. C., KWA, H. Y. & VAN ZWIETEN, P. A. (1981) Characterisation of the α adrenoceptors participating in the central hypotensive and sedative effects of clonidine using yohimbine, rauwolscine and coryanthine. *European Journal of Pharmacology*, **70**, 7–15.

VAN ZWIETEN, P. A., LAM, E. & TIMMERMANS, P. B. M. W. M. (1978) The interaction between prazosin and clonidine. *Clinical Science & Molecular Medicine*, **55**, 259s–261s.

WARNKE, E. & HOEFKE, W. (1977) Influences of central pretreatment with 6 hydroxydopamine on the hypotensive effect of clonidine. *Arzneimittel-Forschung Drug Research*, **27**, 2311–2313.

WOLF, D. L. & MOHRLAND, J. S. (1984) Lateral reticular formation as a site for morphine- and clonidine-induced hypotension. *European Journal of Pharmacology*, **98**, 93–98.

ZANDBERG, P., DE JONG, W. & DE WIED, D. (1979) Effect of catecholamine-receptor stimulating agents in blood pressure after local application to the tractus solitarii of the medulla oblongata. *European Journal of Pharmacology*, **53**, 43–56.

7 Platelet binding and neuroendocrine responses in depression

C. L. E. KATONA; A. E. THEODOROU;
S. L. DAVIES; Y. YAMAGUCHI;
C. A. TUNNICLIFFE; A. S. HALE; R. W. HORTON;
J. S. KELLY; E. S. PAYKEL

As originally proposed by Schildkraut (1965), the monoamine hypothesis of depression suggested that the biochemical basis of depressive illness consisted of a reduction in monoamine neurotransmission. Antidepressant drugs were thought to correct this by increasing neurotransmitter availability at the synaptic cleft. This was achieved either by decreasing re-uptake of neurotransmitter by the presynaptic neuron, or by inhibiting neurotransmitter breakdown by monoamine oxidase. The monoamine hypothesis has been challenged on the basis that whereas neurotransmitter availability is enhanced within a matter of hours by both tricyclic and monoamine oxidase inhibitor (MAOI) antidepressants, the therapeutic response is slower. Furthermore, differences in monoamine turnover between depressed patients and control subjects have not been consistently demonstrated, and drugs such as amphetamine and cocaine, which effectively block monoamine re-uptake, are ineffective as antidepressants. In addition, atypical antidepressants such as mianserin and iprindole, though clinically effective, do not inhibit neurotransmitter uptake.

In view of these inconsistencies, research interest has concentrated increasingly on seeking changes in monoamine receptors associated with chronic administration of antidepressants in animals and in man, and in finding differences between depressed and control human subjects. There have been several studies of such receptors both in brain and on peripheral blood components whose membranes possess receptor sites with similar binding characteristics to those in brain, with the obvious advantage of *in vivo* accessibility. It has also proved possible to study the function of certain central receptor systems in terms of neuroendocrine or physiological response to systemic administration of selective agonists.

In animal studies the most consistent finding is of a decrease in beta-adrenoceptor binding in response to chronic administration of tricyclics, MAOI's, atypical antidepressants or electroconvulsive shock (ECS) (Sugrue, 1983). Increased lymphocyte beta-adrenoceptor binding capacity has been reported in depressed patients which normalised with successful treatment (Healy *et al*, 1983). The adequacy of such a mechanism alone to explain the mode of action of antidepressants has been challenged, since the relationship between a drug's therapeutic potency as an antidepressant and its ability to down-regulate beta-adrenoceptors following long-term administration to rats is inverse rather than direct (Willner, 1984). In animal studies antidepressants have also been shown to alter the number of alpha$_2$-noradrenergic (NA) and 5-hydroxytryptamine (5HT) receptors (Sugrue 1983). Although not as universally demonstrated as the effects on beta-noradrenergic receptors, these may be as important in the mechanism both of depression and of antidepressant treatment.

The research to be presented in this paper examines alpha$_2$ NA and 5HT receptors in man. We have studied alpha$_2$ NA receptors in platelet membranes, which have similar characteristics to those present in the brain (Daiguji *et al*, 1981a) using the selective antagonist ^{3}H-yohimbine. Platelet alpha$_2$ NA receptors in depressed patients have been variously reported to be increased, decreased or the same as in controls (Elliott, 1984). We have also examined central alpha$_2$ NA receptor function by measuring physiological and neuroendocrine responses to clonidine. The growth hormone response to clonidine has been found by several investigators to be reduced in depression (Checkley, Chapter 6). We have examined the 5HT system in the platelet using ^{3}H-imipramine binding. These binding sites have a close functional relationship to the 5HT uptake mechanism and have similar properties in brain and platelet (Briley *et al*, 1979). The number of ^{3}H-imipramine binding sites has, until recently, consistently been reported as reduced in depression (Elliott, 1984).

It is perhaps surprising that there have as yet been no reports of simultaneous measures of these variables in depressed patients and controls, or following a group of depressed patients through treatment. We report interim findings of a study of depressed patients and healthy volunteers in which, wherever possible, platelet ^{3}H-yohimbine and ^{3}H-imipramine binding, and responses to clonidine were measured at the same time, and the depressed patients were re-tested after a course of standardised antidepressant treatment. It should be emphasised that the study is still in progress and we are continuing to collect both depressed and control subjects.

Methods

Selection of sample

Clinical aspects of the studies were carried out from a 12-bedded affective disorders research unit at Springfield Hospital under the consultant charge of Professor E. S. Paykel. The majority of depressed patients studied were in-patients from the other wards at Springfield Hospital transferred to the research unit, or direct in-patient referrals from other centres. Four patients were studied on an out-patient basis. Selection criteria for inclusion in the study were as follows: (1) Research Diagnostic Criteria for Major Depressive Disorder (Spitzer & Endicott, 1978); (2) 17-item Hamilton Depression Rating Score (HDRS) $\geqslant 17$ (Hamilton 1967); (3) No major physical abnormality; (4) Drug-free for at least one week, except for short acting benzodiazepines; (5) Informed consent to participate in the study. Control subjects were physically fit, drug-free, gave informed consent to participate and had no past or present psychiatric illness.

Depressed patients were re-tested wherever possible following six weeks treatment with antidepressants (imipramine, maprotiline or BRL 14342, an antidepressant developed at Beecham Research Laboratories) or after six applications of electroconvulsive therapy (ECT). Concurrent drug treatment was limited to short-acting benzodiazepines. Demographic data was collected on all patients and controls, and patients were rated on the Newcastle scale for endogenicity (Carney *et al* 1965) and received weekly Hamilton Depression Ratings.

Platelet receptor binding assays

Blood (60ml) was withdrawn by antecubital venepuncture between 08:30 and 10:00 and placed immediately in tubes containing acid-citrate-dextrose anticoagulant (blood: anticoagulant 9:1 v/v). Platelet rich plasma was obtained by centrifugation at 190g for 20 min. Contaminating red cells were removed by a further centrifugation at 190g for 5 min. Platelets were pelleted (16,000g for 10 min at 4°C) and washed twice with 50mM Tris-HCl buffer pH 6.5 containing 110mM NaCl and 20mM EDTA. They were then lysed in 5mM Tris-HCl buffer pH 7.5 containing 5mM EDTA by homogenisation in a Potter-Elvejem homogeniser, centrifuged at 39,000g for 10 min, washed and finally resuspended in assay buffer (see below).

For ^{3}H-imipramine binding, aliquots of platelet membrane (50–100μg protein) were incubated with 6 ligand concentrations (0.3–9nM) for 60 min at 0°C in 50mM Tris-HCl buffer, pH 7.4 containing 120mM NaCl and 5mM KCl in a volume of 0.5ml. For ^{3}H-yohimbine binding, aliquots of platelet membranes (60–125μg protein) were incubated with 6 ligand concentrations (0.3–12nM) for 30 min at 25°C in 50mM Tris-HCl buffer, pH 7.1, in a volume of 0.25ml.

Membrane bound radioactivity was recovered by vacuum filtration through Whatman GF/C filters. Filters were washed rapidly four times with 4ml ice-cold incubation buffer and radioactivity determined by liquid scintillation spectrometry. Specific binding was defined as the radioactivity displaced by 100μM desipramine (^{3}H-imipramine) or 10μM phentolamine (^{3}H-yohimbine). Total and non-specific binding were determined in duplicate at each ligand concentration. The maximum numbers of binding sites (B_{max}) and the equilibrium dissociation constant (K_D) were estimated by least squares linear regression analysis of Scatchard plots. Only those assays in which the linear regression coefficient was > 0.90 were considered successful and included in the results section. Protein was determined by the method of Lowry *et al* (1951) using bovine serum albumin as standard.

Responses to clonidine

The procedure described by Glass *et al* (1982) was followed. Subjects aged > 60 and those with resting BP < 110/70mmHg were excluded. Subjects were fasted overnight and at 9a.m. the following morning they lay down on a bed and a 19G butterfly cannula was inserted in an antecubital fossa vein and connected via a 3-way tap to a slow infusion of normal saline. Baseline measurements of pulse, systolic and diastolic blood pressure (using a mercury sphygmomanometer), and sedation on a five point observer rated scale were taken every 15 min for one hour, together with 6ml blood samples. Blood was placed in lithium-heparin tubes and immediately centrifuged; the plasma was frozen at − 70°C pending growth hormone assay. At 10.00a.m., clonidine (1.3μg/kg made up to 10ml with saline) was infused through the 3-way tap over 10 min. Pulse, blood pressure and sedation measures, and plasma samples for growth hormone assay, were taken every 15 min for a further two hours from the start of the infusion. Patients remained supine for the duration of the test and were prevented from sleeping. Growth hormone was assayed in duplicate by a double antibody radioimmunoassay (Euro-Diagnostics, Holland). The lower limit of detection with 100μl plasma samples is about 0.25ng/ml. The within assay coefficients of variation were 12.3%, 7.3% and 4.9% at 2.5, 5 and 10ng/ml respectively and the interassay coefficients of variation were 12.0%, 3.5% and 4.0% at the same growth hormone concentrations. When possible growth hormone samples from control and depressed subjects were assayed in the same batch. Growth hormone concentrations were plotted against time and the effect of clonidine determined as the area under the post-clonidine curve minus baseline. Subjects with a growth hormone concentration of > 3ng/ml at the time of clonidine infusion were excluded from analysis. Reported changes in blood pressure, pulse and sedation were the maximal change compared to baseline values at 15 min before clonidine infusion.

Dexamethasone suppression test

Wherever possible the dexamethasone suppression test (DST) was administered to depressed subjects at baseline. DSTs were carried out after platelet binding assays and clonidine tests, using the method of Coppen *et al* (1983). Dexamethasone (1mg) was administered at 8p.m. and blood taken at 3.30p.m. the following day, immediately centrifuged, and the plasma frozen at $-70°C$ for subsequent cortisol estimation by radioimmunoassay (Amersham International). Non-suppression was defined as a post-dexamethasone cortisol concentration $>5.0\mu g/100ml$.

Results

A total of 42 depressed patients (30 females; 12 males) and 31 controls (20 females; 11 males) have been studied to date. The current control sample is younger (mean $\pm$ s.e.m. $= 37.7 \pm 2.0$ for females; 36.8 ± 4.3 for males) than the depressed group (46.1 ± 2.6 for females; 47.3 ± 3.0 for males). The mean HDRS score for the depressed sample at baseline was 23.7, indicating moderate to severe depression. All but two depressives were unipolar.

Platelet ^{3}H-yohimbine binding

Individual platelet ^{3}H-yohimbine binding values are shown in Fig. 1 and results are summarised in Table I. B_{max}, but not K_D, of ^{3}H-yohimbine binding was significantly correlated with age in the control group (Spearman's rho $= 0.40$, $p < 0.05$) but not in the depressives (rho $= 0.05$, n.s.). There were no significant differences in B_{max} or K_D between males and females in either group. There were no differences at baseline between the depressed and control samples. Within the depressed sample, severity (HDRS) did not correlate with B_{max} or K_D. There was a significant difference in the B_{max} of ^{3}H-yohimbine binding between those with a drug-free interval greater than two weeks (362 ± 17 fmoles/mg protein, $n = 19$) and those with a shorter drug-free interval (294 ± 23 fmoles/mg protein, $n = 20$; $p < 0.05$). Neither group differed significantly from controls. No significant differences were found when depressed subjects were divided in terms of endogenicity (Newcastle) or DST result. Treatment was not associated with consistent change in K_D or B_{max} of ^{3}H-yohimbine binding. There was a trend, just failing to reach statistical significance, for subjects who made a satisfactory clinical response (final HDRS < 10) to have a lower K_D after treatment than those who remained depressed (Table I).

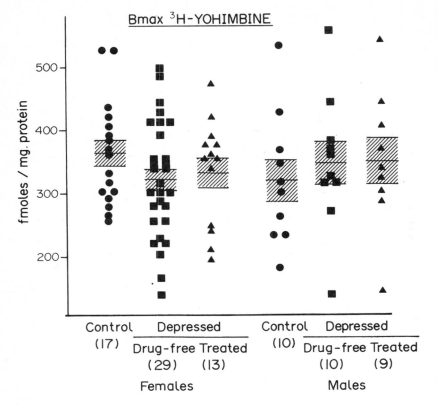

Fig. 1 — B_{max} of platelet ^{3}H-Yohimbine binding in control subjects and in depressed patients before and after treatment, each divided by sex. Hatched areas show means $\pm$ s.e.m.

Platelet ^{3}H-imipramine binding

Individual platelet ^{3}H-imipramine binding values are shown in Fig. 2 and results are summarised in Table II. There was no relationship between B_{max} or K_D and age in either group and no significant differences were found between males and females. Baseline depressed and control samples did not differ significantly in B_{max} or K_D. Within the depressed sample, there was a significant difference in the B_{max} of ^{3}H-imipramine binding between those with a drug-free interval greater than two weeks (1395 ± 66 fmoles/mg protein, $n = 16$) and those with a shorter drug free interval ($1149 + 53$ fmoles/mg protein, $n = 17$; $p < 0.01$). The latter were also significantly lower than the control group (1359 ± 47, fmoles/mg protein, $n = 28$, $p < 0.01$).

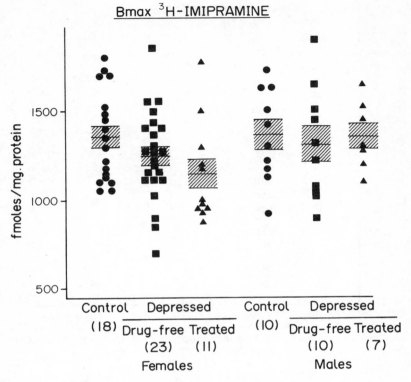

Fig. 2 — B_{max} of platelet ^3H-imipramine binding in control subjects and in depressed patients before and after treatment, each divided by sex. Hatched areas show means ± s.e.m.

Severity of depression did not correlate with B_{max} or K_D and significant differences were not seen when patients were divided in terms of endogenicity. The number of ^3H-imipramine binding sites in depressives with DST non-suppression was significantly lower than in controls, although within the depressed group the difference between DST suppressors and non-suppressors just failed to reach statistical significance. No significant differences were seen when depressed patients were divided in terms of endogenicity. Treatment was not associated with consistent change in B_{max} or K_D. There were insufficient successful assays following recovery to allow meaningful comparison between recovered and non-recovered depressives.

Responses to clonidine

Individual growth hormone (GH) responses are shown Fig. 3 and cardio-vascular and sedative responses in Table III. Nine out of 24 controls and

TABLE I
Platelet ^3H-Yohimbine binding

Group	Sub-group	n	B_{max}	K_D
Control	Total	27	346 ± 17	1.82 ± 0.15
	Male	10	320 ± 33	1.59 ± 0.21
	Female	17	361 ± 20	1.95 ± 0.20
Depressed	Total	39	327 ± 15	1.77 ± 0.09
(Baseline)	Male	10	347 ± 35	2.00 ± 0.19
	Female	29	320 ± 17	1.69 ± 0.10
	Endogenous	20	323 ± 18	1.83 ± 0.14
	Non-endogenous	19	331 ± 26	1.71 ± 0.13
	DST non-suppressor	12	325 ± 33	1.57 ± 0.19
	DST suppressor	13	312 ± 24	1.69 ± 0.12
Depressed	Before treatment	19	303 ± 21	1.63 ± 0.14
	After treatment	19	330 ± 20	1.50 ± 0.12
Non-recovered	Before treatment	14	313 ± 26	1.74 ± 0.16
	After treatment	14	331 ± 24	1.64 ± 0.14
Recovered	Before treatment	5	276 ± 34	1.32 ± 0.26
	After treatment	5	328 ± 37	1.12 ± 0.11

Values are means ± s.e.m. for the number of estimations (n).
B_{max} = fmoles/mg protein. K_D = nM.
Endogenous was defined as a Newcastle rating of > 5. DST non-suppression as a post dexamethasone cortisol > 5.0µg/100ml.
Recovery was defined as final HDRS < 10.
When comparing treatment the groups include only those subjects in whom binding assays were successfully carried out at base-line and at the end of treatment.

TABLE II
Platelet ^3H-Imipramine binding

Group	Sub-group	n	B_{max}	K_D
Control	Total	28	1359 ± 47	0.87 ± 0.05
	Male	10	1366 ± 82	0.82 ± 0.04
	Female	18	1355 ± 60	0.90 ± 0.07
Depressed	Total	33	1268 ± 47	1.03 ± 0.07
(Baseline)	Male	10	1312 ± 98	1.02 ± 0.09
	Female	23	1249 ± 53	1.03 ± 0.09
	Endogenous	19	1269 ± 56	1.05 ± 0.08
	Non-endogenous	14	1268 ± 82	0.99 ± 0.12
	DST non-suppressor	11	1167 ± 76*	0.97 ± 0.10
	DST suppressor	11	1330 ± 91	0.93 ± 0.08
Depressed	BEfore treatment	13	1199 ± 87	0.96 ± 0.09
	After treatment	13	1222 ± 75	1.06 ± 0.11
Non-recovered	Before treatment	11	1170 ± 99	0.92 ± 0.09
	After treatment	11	1204 ± 87	0.98 ± 0.10
Recovered	Before treatment	2	1362 ± 133	1.20 ± 0.24
	After treatment	2	1324 ± 120	1.48 ± 0.42

Legend as Table 1.
* $p < 0.05$ compared to total control group (t-test).

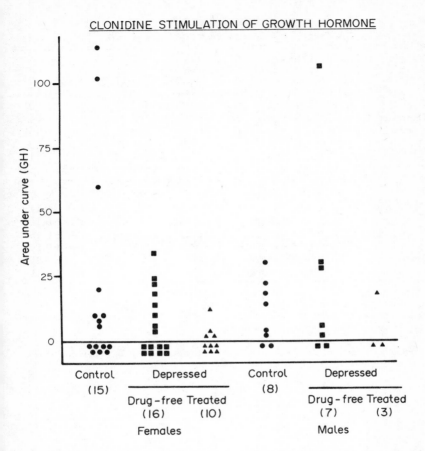

Fig. 3 — Area under curve of GH response to clonidine in control subjects and in depressed patients before and after treatment, each divided by sex. Values below the line indicate subjects in whom there was no detectable GH response to clonidine.

10 out of 23 depressives showed no GH response to clonidine and there was no significant difference between the two groups at baseline (Mann Whitney U-test). In neither group did GH response correlate significantly with age and there was no significant difference between males and females. Within the depressed group (Fig. 4), there was no significant difference between endogenous ($n = 12$) and non-endogenous ($n = 11$) depressives. DST non-suppressors ($n = 8$) showed significantly smaller GH responses than DST suppressors ($n = 9$; U-test $p < 0.01$). There was no correlation between drug-free interval and GH response in the depressed sample at baseline, but GH response following antidepressant treatment was significantly smaller than at baseline (paired t-test, $p < 0.02$). Pulse, blood pressure and sedation

TABLE III
Responses to clonidine and the effect of treatment

	Systolic blood pressure mmHg	Diastolic blood pressure mmHg	Pulse beats/min	Sedation
Control (23)	− 14.7 ± 2.6	− 12.3 ± 1.8	− 2.7 ± 3.3	1.8 ± 0.2
Depressed- drug free (15)	− 9.2 ± 4.5	− 6.7 ± 3.1	− 3.5 ± 3.0	1.6 ± 0.2
Depressed- treatment (12)	− 6.1 ± 4.2	− 3.8 ± 2.4	− 4.8 ± 3.8	1.4 ± 0.3

Results are presented as means ± s.e.m. of maximal changes from baseline in systolic blood pressure, diastolic blood pressure, pulse, and sedation. Sedation was measured on a five-point observer rated scale.

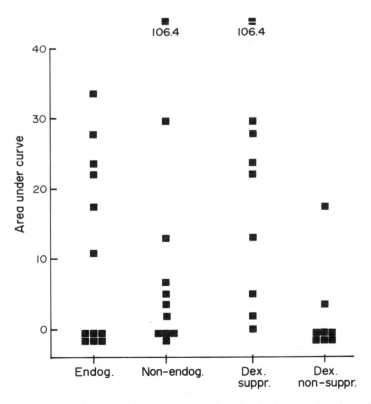

Fig. 4 — Area under curve of GH response to clonidine in depressed patients divided by endogenicity and DST result.

did not differ significantly between the control and depressed subjects at baseline; and within the depressed sample, treatment was not associated with significant changes in these responses.

There were no correlations between any of our measures of alpha$_2$ NA receptors that were consistent in both the depressed and control groups. There was a significant negative correlation between the B_{max} of ^{3}H-yohimbine binding and the GH response in the control sample (rho = -0.44, $p < 0.05$), but this was not apparent in the depressed sample (rho = -0.03, n.s.).

Discussion

Studies of alpha$_2$-noradrenergic binding in relation to depression have produced conflicting results. Platelet binding capacity of the non-selective antagonist ^{3}H-dihydroergocryptine (^{3}H-DHE) was lower in drug-free depressed females (Wood & Coppen 1981) and in recovered depressives maintained on lithium (Wood & Coppen 1983). However, Healy *et al* (1983) and Siever *et al* (1983) found increased platelet ^{3}H-DHE binding capacity in drug-free depressed patients, the former group also showing normalisation following antidepressant treatment in those who recovered but not where treatment had failed. Using the selective agonist ^{3}H-clonidine, Garcia-Sevilla *et al* (1981) identified two platelet receptor populations with low and high affinity for ^{3}H-clonidine, the former being present in significantly greater numbers in drug-free depressed patients than in controls. Antidepressant treatment was associated with normalisation of platelet ^{3}H-clonidine binding, irrespective of clinical response. These findings have recently been replicated (Doyle *et al* 1984).

Using the selective antagonist ligand ^{3}H-yohimbine, Daiguji *et al* (1981b) found no difference between 11 depressed patients drug-free for at least one week and controls; this was replicated by Stahl *et al* (1983) in 16 male patients drug-free for at least four weeks. Stahl *et al* (1983) also found no changes in the depressed patients following antidepressant treatment. Pimoule *et al* (1983) using ^{3}H-rauwolscine, an isomer of yohimbine with similar alpha$_2$ noradrenergic specificity, found no differences between 19 depressed patients drug-free for at least a week and controls and no effect associated with antidepressant treatment.

Our findings of no differences in B_{max} or K_D comparing relatively large groups of depressed patients and controls is in agreement with previous studies in which selective antagonist radioligands have been used. The lack of treatment effect on ^{3}H-yohimbine binding is similar to that reported in previous studies of depressed patients.

We have examined the possibility that the lack of overall differences between controls and depressed patients reflected the mixed population of endogenous and non-endogenous major depressives we have studied. There were, however, no differences or even trends when we divided our sample either by endogenicity or by DST results. We suggest that differences in findings to date between those studies in which selective antagonist radioligands and agonist or non-selective antagonist radioligands have been used, arises from differences in the population of platelet alpha$_2$ NA receptors labelled.

Several studies have examined platelet ^{3}H-imipramine binding in depressed patients. Briley *et al* (1980) found a lower binding capacity in 16 depressed patients than in controls. Similar findings in drug-free depressives have been reported by Raisman *et al* (1981), Paul *et al* (1981), Suranyi-Cadotte *et al* (1982) and Asarch *et al* (1980). The extent of the reduction in binding capacity ranged between 20% (Asarch *et al* 1980) and 54% (Briley *et al*, 1980).

Our findings of no difference between depressed patients and controls is at variance with all the above reports. It may be pertinent that our values for binding capacity both in controls and depressives are considerably higher than those in the above studies but similar to the values reported in three other studies, which also found no difference or in one case a small increase in binding capacity in depression (Mellerup *et al*, 1982; Baron *et al*, 1983; Gentsch *et al*, 1985). However, we found a 14% reduction in binding sites in those depressives showing DST non-suppression compared with controls but not in endogenous depressives. Lewis & McChesney (1985) have examined ^{3}H-imipramine binding of genetic, rather than clinical or neuroendocrine sub-groups and found decreased binding only in patients with bipolar and familial pure depressive diseases (Winokur, 1979).

Previous studies of the effects of treatment and of recovery have also been conflicting. Several studies have found no change in depressed patients following successful antidepressant treatment (Raisman *et al*, 1982; Paul *et al*, 1981; Mellerup *et al*, 1982) whereas Suranyi-Cadotte *et al* (1982; 1983) found that both treatment and recovery were associated with normalisation of previously reduced imipramine binding. Our findings show no change in ^{3}H-imipramine binding in patients tested at the end of a course of antidepressant treatment; unfortunately numbers were too small to draw valid conclusions as to the effect of recovery.

Four studies have found a consistent reduction in growth hormone response to clonidine in depressed subjects compared with controls (Matussek *et al*, 1980; Charney *et al*, 1981; Checkley *et al*, 1981; Siever *et al*, 1982), although these studies differ in the dose of clonidine and the route of administration. Our results are in contrast in showing no overall difference in growth hormone response in depressed patients. Like Siever *et al* (1982), we found that a considerable proportion of our control subjects showed minimal or no growth hormone response. Blunting of the growth hormone response to clonidine was reported to be more marked in endogenous depressives (Matussek *et al* 1980; Checkley *et al* 1984a). Our own results showed similar responses in endogenous and non-endogenous depression although blunted responses in depressives were virtually only found in subjects showing DST non-suppression.

We show a significantly reduced growth hormone response to clonidine in depressed patients following treatment, which is in keeping with the finding by Checkley and collaborators of a decreased growth hormone response to clonidine both in depressed patients and in volunteers given desipramine for three weeks (Glass *et al* 1982; Checkley *et al* 1984b). Our data do not permit comment on the growth hormone response to clonidine following recovery, though Siever *et al* (1982) report persistently blunted growth hormone response in drug-free recovered depressives.

Our findings of no difference in cardiovascular or sedative effects of clonidine between depressed patients and controls is largely in agreement with previous studies (Charney *et al* 1981; Checkley *et al* 1981) although Siever *et al* (1982) noted a blunted heart rate response to clonidine in depressed patients. The lack of treatment effect on cardiovascular and sedative responses in our subjects contrasts with the reduction in growth hormone response. This is not surprising in view of the effect of antidepressant treatment on other mechanisms pertaining to cardiovascular homeostasis and to the control of conscious level. The lack of inter-correlation between our several measures of alpha$_2$ NA receptors in brain and platelet suggests these various systems are differentially modulated.

Recent studies in which antidepressant drugs were taken by healthy volunteers have highlighted the importance of drug-free interval in platelet receptor studies in depression. Although platelet ^{3}H-yohimbine binding B$_{max}$ was unaffected, ^{3}H-imipramine binding B$_{max}$ was increased during three weeks administration of therapeutic doses of amitriptyline and remained elevated for up to 31 days after drug discontinuation (Braddock *et al* 1984). However, Poirier *et al* (1984) have reported a reduction in the number of platelet ^{3}H-imipramine binding sites following administration of clomipramine 50mg daily for one week. This persisted for at least 15 days after discontinuation.

Those depressed patients with a drug free interval of less than 2 weeks had fewer platelet binding sites for ^{3}H-imipramine and ^{3}H-yohimbine. This may reflect effects of recent withdrawal or persistent effects of recent treatment. The lack of change in platelet binding following the treatment we administered, supports the importance of the former. However, both these factors need to be considered in the evaluation of platelet binding studies since they may mask real effects of depression or its treatment.

In this interim report we describe decreased platelet ^{3}H-imipramine binding and decreased growth hormone responses to clonidine in depressed patients who showed DST non-suppression. Interestingly these changes were not apparent in the endogenous group of depressives as defined clinically. We are currently extending our study to achieve closer age matching; however, these effects are unlikely to be due to age differences between the groups since neither of the above receptor measures correlated significantly with age. Thus, a common neurochemical basis may underlie these three abnormalities in a sub-group of depressed patients.

Acknowledgements

We are indebted to the Wellcome Trust for financial support. We thank the patients and staff at Springfield Hospital for their generous co-operation and Mrs Anne Keable for typing the manuscript.

References

ASARCH, K. B., SHIH, J. C. & KULCSAR, A. (1980) Decreased ^{3}H-imipramine binding in depressed males and females. *Communications in Psychopharmacology*, **4**, 425–432.

BARON, M., BARKAI, A., GRUEN, R., KOWALIK, S. & QUITKIN, F. (1983) ^{3}H-imipramine platelet binding sites in unipolar depression. *Biological Psychiatry*, **18**, 1403–1409.

BRADDOCK, L. E., COWEN, P. J., ELLIOTT, J. M., FRASER, S. & STUMP, K. (1984) Changes in the binding to platelets of ^{3}H-imipramine and ^{3}H-yohimbine in normal subjects taking amitriptyline. *Neuropharmacology*, **23**, 2B, 285–286.

BRILEY, M. S., RAISMAN, R. & LANGER, S. Z. (1979) Human platelets possess high-affinity binding sites for ^{3}H-imipramine. *European Journal of Pharmacology*, **58**, 347–348.

—— LANGER, S. Z., RAISMAN, R., SECHTER, D. & ZARIFIAN, E. (1980) Tritiated imipramine binding sites are decreased in platelets of untreated depressed patients. *Science*, **209**, 303–305.

CARNEY, M. W. P., ROTH, M. & GARSIDE, R. F. (1965) The diagnosis of depressive syndromes and the prediction of ECT response. *British Journal of Psychiatry*, **140**, 659–674.

CHARNEY, D. S., HENINGER, G. R., STERNBERG, D. E., REDMOND, D. E., LECKMAN, J. F., MAAS, J. W. & ROTH, R. H. (1981) Presynaptic adrenergic receptor sensitivity in depression. The effect of long-term desipramine treatment. *Archives of General Psychiatry*, **38**, 1334–1340.

CHECKLEY, S. A., SLADE, A. P. & SHUR, E. (1981) Growth hormone and other responses to clonidine in patients with endogenous depression. *British Journal of Psychiatry*, **138**, 51–55.

—— GLASS, I. B., THOMPSON, C., CORN, T. & ROBINSON, P. (1984a) The GH response to clonidine in endogenous as compared with reactive depression. *Psychological Medicine*, **14**, 773–777.

—— CORN, T., GLASS, I. B. & THOMPSON, C. (1984b) Central alpha adrenoreceptor function following chronic desipramine treatment in depressed patients and normal subjects. F258 in Abstracts of 14th CINP Congress, Florence.

COPPEN, A., ABOU-SALEH, M., MILLN, P., METCALFE, M., HARWOOD, J. J. & BAILEY, J. (1983) Dexamethasone suppression test in depression and other psychiatric illness. *British Journal of Psychiatry*, **142**, 498–504.

DAIGUJI, M., MELTZER, H. Y. & U'PRICHARD, D. C. (1981a) Human platelet α_2-adrenergic receptors: labelling with ^{3}H-yohimbine, a selective antagonist ligand. *Life Sciences*, **28**, 2705–2717.

—— MELTZER, H. Y., TONG, C., U'PRICHARD, D. C., YOUNG, M., KRAVITZ, H. (1981b) α_2-Adrenergic receptors in platelet membranes of depressed patients: no change in number or ^{3}H-yohimbine affinity. *Life Sciences*, **29**, 2059–2064.

DOYLE, M. C., GEORGE, A. J. & RAVINDRAN, R. (1984) Platelet α_2 receptor characteristics in depression and dementia. P1986 in Abstracts of IUPHAR 9th International Congress of Pharmacology, London.

ELLIOTT, J. M. (1984) Platelet receptor binding studies in affective disorders. *Journal of Affective Disorders*, **6**, 219–239.

GARCIA-SEVILLA, J. A., ZIS, A. P., HOLLINGSWORTH, P. J., GREDEN, J. F. & SMITH, C. B. (1981) Platelet α_2-adrenergic receptors in major depressive disorder. *Archives of General Psychiatry*, **38**, 1327–1333.

GENTSCH, C., LICHTSTEINER, M., GASTPAR, M., GASTPAR, G. & FEER, H. (1985) ^{3}H-imipramine binding sites in platelets of hospitalized psychiatric patients. *Psychiatry Research*, **14**, 177–187.

GLASS, I. B., CHECKLEY, S. A., SHUR, E. & DAWLING, S. (1982) The effect of desipramine upon central adrenergic function in depressed patients. *British Journal of Psychiatry*, **141**, 372–376.

HAMILTON, M. (1967) Development of a rating scale for primary depressive illness. *British Journal of Social and Clinical Psychology*, **6**, 278–296.

HEALY, D., CARNEY, P. A. & LEONARD, B. E. (1983) Monoamine-related markers of depression: changes following treatment. *Journal of Psychiatric Research*, **17**, 251–260.

LEWIS, D. A. & McCHESNEY, C. (1985) Tritiated Imipramine binding distinguishes among subtypes of depression. *Archives of General Psychiatry*, **42**, 485–488.

LOWRY, O. H., ROSEBROUGH, N. J., FARR, A. L. & RANDALL, R. J. (1951) Protein measurement with the Folic phenol reagent. *Journal of Biological Chemistry*, **193**, 265–275.

MATUSSEK, N., ACHENHEIL, M., HIPPIUS, H., MÜLLER, F., SCHRODER, H.-TH., SCHULTES, H. & WASILEWSKI, B. (1980) Effect of clonidine on growth hormone release in psychiatric patients and controls. *Psychiatry Research*, **2**, 25–36.

MELLERUP, E. T., PLENGE, P. & ROSENBERG, R. (1982) ^{3}H-imipramine binding sites in platelets from psychiatric patients. *Psychiatry Research*, **7**, 221–227.

PAUL, S. M., REHAVI, M., SKOLNICK, P., BALLENGER, J. C. & GOODWIN, F. K. (1981) Depressed patients have decreased binding of ^{3}H-imipramine to platelet serotonin 'Transporter'. *Archives of General Psychiatry*, **38**, 1315–1317.

PIMOULE, C., BRILEY, M. S., GAY, C., LOO, H., SECHTER, D., ZARIFIAN, E., RAISMAN, R. & LANGER, S. Z. (1983) ^{3}H Rauwolscine binding in platelets from depressed patients and healthy volunteers. *Psychopharmacology*, **79**, 308–312.

POIRIER, M. F., LOO, H., BENKELFAT, C., SECHTER, D., ZARIFIAN, E., GALZIN, A. M., SHOEMAKER, H., SEGONZAC, A. & LANGER, S. Z. (1984) ^{3}H-imipramine binding and ^{3}H[5HT] uptake in human blood platelets: changes after one week chlorimipramine treatment. *European Journal of Pharmacology*, **106**, 629–633.

RAISMAN, R., SECHTER, D., BRILEY, M. S., ZARIFIAN, E. & LANGER, S. Z. (1981) High affinity ^{3}H-imipramine binding in platelets from untreated and treated depressed patients compared to healthy volunteers. *Psychopharmacology*, **75**, 368–371.

SCHILDKRAUT, J. J. (1965) The catecholamine hypothesis of affective disorders: a review of supporting evidence. *American Journal of Psychiatry*, **122**, 509–522.

SIEVER, L. J., UHDE, T. W., SILBERMAN, E. K., JIMERSON, D. C., ALOI, J. A., POST, R. M. & MURPHY, D. L. (1982) Growth hormone response to clonidine as a probe of noradrenergic receptor responsiveness in affective disorder patients and controls. *Psychiatry Research*, **6**, 171–183.

—— UHDE, T.W., JIMERSON, D. C., KAFKA, M. S., LAKE, C. R., TARGUM, S. & MURPHY, D. L. (1983) Clinical studies of monoamine receptors in the affective disorders and receptor changes with antidepressant treatment. *Progress in Neuro-Psychopharmacology and Biological Psychiatry*, **7**, 249–261.

SPITZER, R. L. & ENDICOTT, J. (1978) *Research Diagnostic Criteria for a Selected Group of Functional Disorders*. 3rd edition. New York, New York Psychiatric Institute.

STAHL, S. M., LEMOINE, P. M., CIARANELLO, R. D. & BERGER, P. A. (1983) Platelet α_2-adrenergic receptor sensitivity in major depressive disorder. *Psychiatry Research*, **10**, 157–164.

SUGRUE, M. F. (1983) Chronic antidepressant therapy and associated changes in central monoaminergic receptor functioning. *Pharmacology and Therapeutics*, **21**, 1–33.

SURANYI-CADOTTE, B. E., WOOD, P. L., VASAVAN NAIR, N. P. & SCHWARTZ, G. (1982) Normalization of platelet [^{3}H] imipramine binding in depressed patients during remission. *European Journal of Pharmacology*, **85**, 357–358.

—— WOOD, P. L., SCHWARTZ, G. & VASAVAN NAIR, N. P. (1983) Altered platelet ^{3}H-imipramine binding in schizo-affective and depressive disorders. *Biological Psychiatry*, **18**, 923–927.

WILLNER, P. (1984) The ability of antidepressant drugs to desensitise β-receptors is inversely correlated with their clinical potency. *Journal of Affective Disorders*, **7**, 53–58.

WINOKUR, G. (1979) Unipolar depression: is it divisible into autonomous subtypes? *Archives of General Psychiatry*, **36**, 47–52.

WOOD, K. & COPPEN, A. (1981) Platelet alpha-adrenoceptor sensitivity in depressive illness. *Advances in Biological Psychiatry*, **7**, 85–89.

—— (1983) Prophylactic lithium treatment of patients with affective disorders is associated with decreased platelet [^{3}H] Dihydroergocrytine binding. *Journal of Affective Disorders*, **5**, 253–258.

8 Vanadium and the sodium pump in manic depressive psychosis

G. J. NAYLOR

There have been reports of changes in water and mineral metabolism in manic depressive psychosis over many years. As early as 1914, Allers reported that the urinary output in depression was usually less than that in mania. In the late 1950's and early 1960's the activity in this field of interest increased. Coppen (1960) reported a reduced transport of sodium from plasma to CSF, a finding later confirmed by others (reviewed by Carroll, 1972). Coppen & Shaw, (1963) reported that as patients recovered from depression the residual sodium content (mainly intracellular) fell, a finding which has also been confirmed by others (e.g. Cox *et al*, 1971; Colt *et al*, 1982). Coppen *et al* (1966) also reported that the changes in residual sodium in mania were similar, not the opposite, to those in depression.

In general the sodium concentration within cells is low and potassium high, whereas in plasma and extra-cellular fluid the sodium concentration is high and potassium low. In simple terms, this distribution is maintained by an active (i.e. energy dependent) extrusion of sodium from the cell linked to an active uptake of potassium into the cell: this active process is balanced by sodium 'leaking' into the cell and potassium out of the cell. The enzyme Na-K ATPase is intimately involved in the sodium pump mechanism and it is inhibited by cardiac glycosides, e. g. digoxin or ouabain. A reduction in the activity of the pump leads to a rise in cellular sodium concentration. Therefore, the observation of raised intracellular sodium in depression could be explained by a reduction in active transport. Reduction in active membrane transport of sodium in depression has now been demonstrated in several tissues: from plasma to CSF (Coppen, 1960), from saliva (Glen *et al*, 1968), out of the erythrocyte (Naylor *et al*, 1970) and across the rectal mucosa (Peet, 1975).

It is the sodium transport of the erythrocyte that has been most intensively investigated in manic depressive psychosis.

Changes in the erythrocyte sodium pump in depression and in mania

Initial studies (Naylor, 1970) showed that as patients recovered from depression the erythrocyte sodium pump increased, i.e. measured as the rate at which sodium or potassium moved across the erythrocyte membrane. The next study (Naylor *et al*, 1973) confirmed this finding and showed that this increase in transport was probably secondary to an increase in the activity of Na-K ATPase, the enzyme which is intimately involved with the sodium pump. These findings have been confirmed (Choi *et al*, 1977; Glen, 1978; Nurnberger *et al*, 1982). Some workers report negative findings. Linnoila *et al*, (1983) found no correlation between erythrocyte Na-K ATPase and mood but they used only 8 patients, who were not a homogeneous group and there was little or no control of drug therapy. When patients are compared with controls although there is again some disagreement, it seems that depressed patients tend to have lower Na-K ATPase activity and lower sodium pump activity than normals but there is considerable overlap (Glen, 1978; Rybakowski *et al*, 1984; Nurnberger *et al*, 1982).

In mania there is less agreement about the changes that occur but on balance it appears likely that the changes are similar to those occuring in depression. When manic, sodium pump activity is reduced below normal and returns to normal with recovery. Hokin-Naeversen *et al*, (1974) reported that sodium pump activity of manic patients was lower than that of controls. Naylor *et al*, (1976b) reported that as manics recovered, sodium pump activity increased and that changes in severity correlated with changes in Na-K ATPase activity but they showed no significant difference between patients and controls. Rybakowski *et al*, (1983) and Dagher *et al*, (1984) reported that erythrocyte sodium transport in mania was lower than that of healthy controls. In contrast Nurnberger *et al* (1982) and Akagawa *et al* (1980) reported that Na-K ATPase in manics was higher than controls and higher than that of recovered manics, but six of the seven manic patients in Nurnberger's study were receiving lithium and Akagawa *et al*, only used four recovered patients.

Therefore, despite different experimental designs most studies of the sodium pump in manic depressive psychosis have suggested either that it is less active in patients (whether manic or depressed) than in healthy controls, or that it is reduced in patients when ill compared to when they are well.

The changes in erythrocyte sodium pump in manic depressive psychosis often occurred more quickly than could be accounted for by production of new erythrocytes. Since the erythrocyte has no nucleus and is a relatively inert cell, these changes were difficult to explain. It seemed possible either that the total *number* or the *activity* of Na-K ATPase molecules changed. This issue was resolved by simultaneously measuring the Na-K ATPase activity (i.e. activity of the sodium pump) and by measuring the number of Na-K ATPase molecules (i.e. number of pump sites) by binding of radioactive (tritiated) ouabain (Naylor *et al*, 1980). Ouabain is a cardiac glycoside and binds fairly specifically to Na-K ATPase. The activity of the Na-K ATPase per pump site was lower in depressed patients and severe manics than in recovered patients: the total number of pump sites remained largely unchanged.

Are the changes in the sodium pump of any significance?

The ideal clinical test of the importance of the sodium pump in the aetiology of manic depressive psychosis would be to observe the clinical effects of manipulating sodium pump activity. Unfortunately, this has not proved possible, e.g. attempts by Coppen (1965) to decrease the intracellular sodium were unsuccessful. An alternative but weaker strategy is to investigate the effect on the sodium pump of agents that are known to alter manic depressive illness.

Naylor *et al*, (1974) reported that in euthymic manic depressive subjects, lithium produced an increase in Na-K ATPase activity but no observable effect on the actual sodium transport. In a later study (Naylor *et al*, 1981) they showed that this increase in Na-K ATPase activity was not due to any change in the number of Na-K ATPase molecules. Several other workers have confirmed the increase in sodium pump activity with lithium (Glen, 1978, Hokin-Naeverson *et al*, 1976) but some failed to show such an effect, e.g. Nurnberger *et al*, (1982). Peet (1975) and Rask-Madsen *et al*, (1972) reported that lithium in manic depressive psychosis increased sodium transport across the rectal mucosa (measured by an increase in the rectal potential).

Three studies suggest these changes with lithium may be of clinical importance. Naylor *et al* (1976a) found that patients who responded best to lithium prophylaxis were those who, before treatment with lithium, had a low erythrocyte Na-K ATPase or whose Na-K ATPase rose most on treatment with lithium. Johnston *et al* (1980) reported that patients on lithium with a low Na-K ATPase tended to relapse more frequently over the subsequent 12 months. In the study of Naylor *et al* (1981) patients on lithium who had relapsed most frequently over the preceding five years tended to have low Na-K ATPase activity per pump site (Fig. 1).

Some reports suggest that inhibitors of Na-K ATPase (e.g. digoxin) may precipitate depression (Schouten & Van der Aa, 1984). In an attempt to test

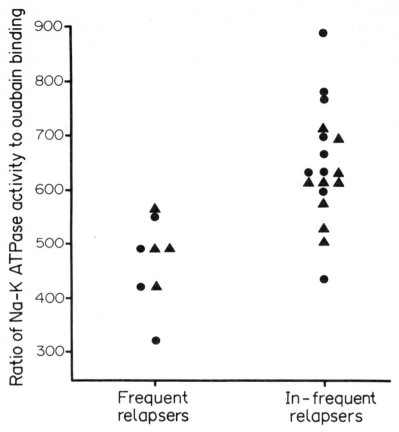

Fig. 1 — Distribution of ratio of Na-K ATPase to ouabain binding in bipolar patients, between those who had relapsed frequently and those who had relapsed infrequently in the previous five years: ● female, ▲ male (Naylor *et al*, 1981).

the hypothesis that increase in Na-K ATPase with lithium was essential to its therapeutic action in mania, Chambers *et al*, (1982) carried out a double blind trial of lithium, against lithium plus digoxin (an inhibitor of Na-K ATPase). The group of manic patients treated with lithium and digoxin did significantly worse over seven days than the group treated with lithium alone, i.e. inhibition of the sodium pump impaired the clinical response to lithium.

As indicated above, there is evidence that lithium may increase erythrocyte sodium pump activity in manic depressive subjects. However, this increase does not occur in normal humans or rats (Naylor *et al*, 1977). This suggests that control of the sodium pump may be abnormal in manic depressives. Further evidence comes from the correlations between the sodium pump activity and the erythrocyte sodium concentration. If the prime change occurs in the sodium pump activity, the cell sodium will change in the opposite direction, e.g. a decrease in pump leads to an increase in sodium concentration, hence the correlation is negative. If, however, the prime change is in the sodium concentration (perhaps by change in passive permeability or exchange, etc.) the sodium pump will change in the same direction (i.e. if sodium concentration increases, sodium pump increases — this is a simple self-regulating system) hence the correlation between the two will be positive. In normal subjects the correlation was significantly positive, whereas in manic depressive subjects it was significantly negative (Naylor *et al*, 1977), i.e. it appeared that in manic depressive subjects, in contrast to normal subjects, the prime change was in the sodium pump.

Nucleated cells possess an additional mechanism which regulates cell sodium concentration. As cell sodium concentrations increases, new pump sites are synthesised and inserted into the membrane (Boardman *et al*, 1975). This mechanism was investigated in the lymphocytes of manic depressive subjects. Naylor & Smith (1981b) reported that the ability of lymphocytes of manic depressive subjects to produce new pump sites in response to increase in cell sodium was lower than that of lymphocytes from normal controls. This mechanism, depending on the presence of a nucleus, is genetic and may be of importance in the predisposition to manic depressive psychosis.

Are there abnormalities of other membrane transport mechanisms in manic depressive illness?

Knowledge about membrance transport mechanisms has grown rapidly over the past 20 years and now there are many such systems described. In manic depressive illness change in several of these have been reported, e.g. Na-K co-transport (Dagher *et al*, 1984), sodium sodium exchange (or sodium lithium countertransport) (Ostrow *et al*, 1978), calcium ATPase (Choi *et al*, 1977; Linnoila *et al*, 1983) and calmodulin stimulated calcium ATPase (Meltzer & Kassir, 1983) although as usual there are also negative reports, e.g. of sodium lithium countertransport (Dagher *et al*, 1984).

It has also been reported that verapamil (a drug which alters movement of calcium ions across cell membranes) has some anti-manic properties (Giannini *et al*, 1984). Pettegrew *et al* (1982) reported abnormalities in membrane dynamics suggesting alterations in the hydrocarbon region of erythrocyte and lymphocyte membranes in patients with manic depressive illness. Hitzemann *et al* (1984) showed that membrane phosphatidyl choline content could be correlated with Na-Li counterflow.

It is, therefore, possible that there may be a fundamental change in membranes and that the change in sodium transport is but one manifestation of this.

Summary of sodium transport experiments

In mania and depression sodium transport is low and increases with recovery. The change is due to a change in the activity of the pump, not to the number of pump sites. This change can occur rapidly and the agent responsible is therefore presumably plasma born. The change in sodium pump appears to be of clinical importance. Lithium in manic depressives but not normals produces an increases in sodium pump activity but not the number of pump sites.

In 1970 Naylor *et al*, reported that the plasma of psychotic depressives was either more inhibitory or less stimulatory of sodium transport than that of the same patient on recovery. In 1973 Naylor *et al* wrote 'In depression there is probably an inhibition of Na-K ATPase by some as yet unknown factor.' In 1980 we suggested that the inhibitory factor could be the vanadate ion (Naylor & Smith, 1980; Dick *et al*, 1981).

Cantley *et al* (1977) reported that the vanadate ion was a potent inhibitor of the sodium pump. Vanadium is an element with atomic weight 51, which has been known for many years to be a trace element in humans and has relatively recently been shown to be an essential trace element in experimental animals (Hopkins & Nohr, 1974). In erythrocytes much of the intracellular vanadium is in the form of vanadyl ion (the $+4$ oxidation state) having been reduced from vanadate (the $+5$ oxidation state) (Cantley & Aisen, 1979). Vanadyl is much less inhibitory of Na-K ATPase than is vanadate and hence the oxidation reduction state of vanadium will influence its inhibitory effect.

From the above summary of the sodium transport changes in manic depressive psychosis one could make predictions about the putative inhibitory factor e.g. that the inhibitory factor levels should be higher when ill than on recovery and that lithium might reverse the effects of the factor on the sodium pump. Do these predictions hold true for vanadium?

Evidence for the involvement of vanadium in manic depressive psychosis

Tissue levels of vanadium

There is considerable debate about how best to estimate trace element status of individuals, e.g. Laker (1982) argued that hair was the best tissue but others disagree (e.g. Sturniolo *et al*, 1982). The tissue chosen depends on the element as well as on the availability of the tissue.

Dick *et al*, (1982) reported that the mean plasma vanadium level of a manic group and of a depressed group were significantly greater than that of a control group. Linnoila *et al* (1983) estimated the vanadium concentration in nine samples of washed erythrocyte membranes and found a non-significant negative correlation (-0.36) with the ratio of Na-K ATPase to

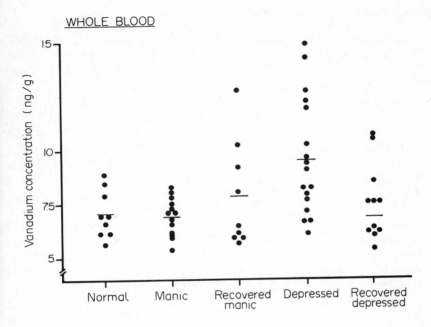

Fig. 2 — Vanadium concentration in whole blood of controls and patients (Naylor *et al*, 1984).

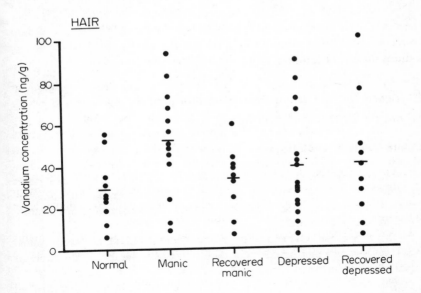

Fig. 3 — Vanadium concentration in hair of controls and patients (Naylor *et al*, 1984).

Mg ATPase activity. Both these reports are of doubtful value because the concentrations of vanadium reported were either at or below the sensitivity limits for the equipment. Naylor *et al* (in press) found a significant negative correlation between erythrocyte Na-K ATPase activity and serum vanadium of 58 depressed patients.

Naylor *et al* (1984) estimated the vanadium content of hair, whole blood and serum by neutron activation analysis in manic depressive patients and in controls (Fig. 2 and Fig. 3). In manic patients the vanadium level of hair was raised and fell with recovery but there was no significant change in the vanadium content of serum or whole blood. In contrast in the depressed patients the concentration of vanadium in whole blood and serum was significantly raised and fell with recovery. Some of the depressed patients had abnormally high concentration of vanadium in hair. The results suggest that changes in vanadium metabolism in mania are different to, but not simply the opposite of, those in depression.

Naylor *et al* (in press) in a further study reported that the 24 h urine vanadium excretion in depressed patients did not differ from that of normal controls although the mean serum level of vanadium in depressed patients was again higher than that of controls. Similarly Conri *et al* (1986) found serum vanadium levels to be significantly higher in depression than in healthy controls. Naylor *et al* (in press) in a third study using patients as their own controls (i.e. the same patients ill and recovered) reported that the vanadium concentration of hair, serum and whole blood fell with recovery from depression. In contrast Ali *et al* (1985) found no difference in vanadium concentration of whole blood between depressed patients, recovered patients and normal controls.

Therapeutic predictions

The hypothesis that raised body levels of vanadate are of aetiological significance in both depression and mania predicts that methods which decrease vanadate levels should be therapeutically beneficial.

Experimentally induced vanadium poisoning in animals can be reversed by large doses of ascorbic acid or by parenteral EDTA (sodium calcium edetate). Oral EDTA has been shown to decrease the gastro-intestinal absorption of vanadium and hence protect the animal from toxic oral doses (Hathcock *et al*, 1964). Ascorbic acid probably acts by reducing vanadate to the less metabolically active vanadyl ion. EDTA probably acts by chelating (binding) the vanadium.

Naylor & Smith (1981a) reported that in a double blind placebo controlled cross-over trial, a single 3g dose of ascorbic acid was therapeutically superior to placebo both in mania and in depression.

Naylor & Smith (1981a) carried out a double blind placebo controlled cross-over trial of a fixed vanadium intake with oral EDTA against a higher

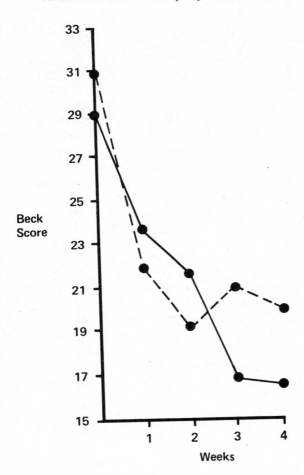

Fig. 4—Change in severity scores during treatment with ascorbic acid/EDTA
(— — —) or with amitriptyline (———) (Kay *et al*, 1984).

vanadium intake with no EDTA. Both manic and depressed patients were significantly better on the lower vanadium intake plus EDTA than during the control period.

Kay *et al* (1984) used a combination of these two methods. In a four week double blind trial in severely depressed females, oral EDTA plus ascorbic acid was as effective as amitriptyline, with a suggestion that the group receiving ascorbic acid and EDTA showed an earlier response (Fig. 4). However, in a similar trial in mania in which EDTA and ascorbic acid were compared with lithium, the patients on lithium showed a significantly better response.

Methylene blue catalyses the reduction of vanadate by NADH (reduced nicotinamide adenine dinucleotide) in the presence of FAD (flavin adenine dinucleotide). It is used in a similar manner in the treatment of methaemoglobinemia. There is an old literature reporting the antidepressant and antipsychotic effects of methylene blue (Bodoni, 1899; Ehringer *et al*, 1961; Rysanek *et al*, 1964; Allexsaht, 1938). Since it is excreted unchanged in the urine, the urine becomes blue and it is therefore difficult, if not impossible, to carry out a double blind trial of this drug. Naylor & Smith (1981c) reported a placebo controlled study of six manic depressives, all of whom had shown little or no response to other psychotropic medication: all six patients improved on methylene blue. Narsapur & Naylor (1983) reviewed their use of the drug. It had largely been given to patients who had failed to respond to other treatments: 14 of the 19 patients who had received oral methylene blue were judged to have shown definite improvement.

Naylor *et al* 1986 carried out a 2 year prophylactic trial in bipolar manic depressive illness, comparing 300 mg with 15 mg per day of methylene blue on a double blind cross-over basis. All patients were also maintained on lithium. During the year the patients were treated with 300 mg methylene blue per day they were significantly less depressed than during the year on 15 mg per day.

Thus there is some evidence that treatment strategies chosen only on the grounds that they affect vanadium metabolism are of therapeutic value in manic depressive psychosis. These studies were primarily undertaken to provide evidence for the hypothesis that vanadium is involved in manic depressive psychosis: they may or may not prove to be of value in routine clinical practice.

Possible relationship of vanadium to cerebral function

Many previous authors have commented on the possible relationship between neuronal electrophysiology and the sodium ion (Maas, 1972), e.g. that the action potentials of a nerve depends on the distribution of sodium across the membrane and that the sodium ions are involved both in the release and reuptake of noradrenaline at the synapse. It is known that in short term experiments inhibition of Na-K ATPase by ouabain leads to increased release of noradrenaline (Wu & Phillis, 1980). There is probably a $beta_2$ adrenoceptor linked ATPase involved in sodium transport (Clausen & Flatman, 1982), thus Na-K ATPase affects noradrenaline metabolism and noradrenaline affects Na-K ATPase activity. In addition to these possible interactions between effects of vanadium on sodium transport and neuronal action there are other properties of vanadium which may be of significance.

1. Vanadium reduces acetylcholine receptors.
2. Noradrenaline binds vanadium.

3. Vanadium catalyses the oxidation of catacholamines and 5-hydroxytryptophan.

Danielsson *et al* (1983) showed that orthovanadate induces a loss of muscarinic cholinergic binding sites in homogenates of the corpus striatum of rats.

Studies based on the amine hypothesis suggest that the urinary excretion of MHPG (3-methoxy, 4-hydroxy phenylglycol) which is perhaps some measure of the noradrenaline production in the CNS, is reduced in a subgroup of depressive patients (Maas *et al* 1972). Corrigan *et al* (in preparation) showed that MHPG excretion in psychotic depression correlated negatively with serum vanadium levels. Witkowska & Brzezinski (1979) showed that toxic doses of vanadium led to changes in cerebral monoamines in experimental animals.

Vanadate is bound by noradrenaline and in sufficient concentrations this will reverse the vanadium induced inhibition of Na-K ATPase. Whether the concentration of the noradrenaline is high enough at a nerve terminal for this to be of significance is uncertain. The total concentration of noradrenaline in nerve terminals is approximately 10–20 mmol/litre but most of this is in bound form. The concentration of free noradrenaline is perhaps around 100 to 200 μmols/litre (Tipton, 1973) and 250 μmols/litre of nordrenaline will produce 50% reversal of inhibition of Na-K ATPase (Quist & Hokin, 1978). This is, therefore, another possible way in which noradrenaline may affect sodium transport.

Martin *et al*, (1960) reported that several compounds of vanadium (both pentavalent and tetravalent) catalyse oxidation of catecholamines and 5-hydroxytryptophan. It is difficult to assess the *in vivo* significance of this effect partly because insufficient data was given in the original paper to calculate the catalytic rate, but also because of differences in pH, binding of vanadium, etc. If, however, vanadium compounds *in vivo* do contribute to the oxidation of monoamines, it could be of clinical importance.

It is clear, therefore, that there are many possible mechanisms by which vanadium may interact with CNS function.

Do established psychotropic drugs affect vanadium metabolism?

It has been reported that both lithium and carbamazepine reverse the inhibitory effect of vanadate on erythrocyte Na-K ATPase (Naylor *et al*, 1981; Naylor, 1985). However, McDonald *et al* (1982) were not able to replicate the effect of lithium on vanadate inhibited Na-K ATPase.

Many psychotropic drugs, particularly the phenothiazines and several monoamine oxidase inhibitors will catalyse the reduction of vanadate to the less active vanadyl ion but not as actively as methylene blue (Naylor *et al*, 1983). Vyskocil *et al* (1982), using electron spin resonance, showed that imipramine could directly reduce vanadate to vanadyl. Though these findings need confirming by other workers it seems likely that many of the psychotropic drugs used in manic depressive psychosis can affect vanadium metabolism.

Discussion

If vanadium plays an aetiological role in manic depressive psychosis as described, manic depressives must have some vulnerability to this since vanadium poisoning in normal subjects does not often lead to mood change, although melancholia has been described in vanadium poisoning (Witkowska & Brzezinski, 1979). A further point of interest is the difference in effect between ouabain and vanadate on cultured cells. Ouabain, a cardiac glycoside, is a potent inhibitor of Na-K ATPase and in cultured cells, e.g. HeLa cells, produces inhibition of the pump and marked changes in sodium and potassium concentration: in contrast vanadate, although also a potent inhibitor of the sodium pump, produces only minimal changes in sodium and potassium concentration in cultured cells (Wood, personal communication).

Again this suggests that if the electrolyte changes reported in manic depressive psychosis are due to vanadium, these subjects must be particularly sensitive to this. Naylor & Smith (1981b) reported that the cells of manic depressive patients were less able to produce new pump sites in response to changes in cell sodium and this would probably render them sensitive to any inhibition of the sodium pump. Increased sensitivity to vanadate could, however, occur by many other mechanisms, e.g. by increased penetration of vanadium into cells, or by alteration in the reduction of vanadate to vanadyl, etc.

This work on the sodium pump and vanadium in manic depressive psychosis illustrates the use of the erythrocyte as a tool for further investigation of affective illness, rather than as a model of a neurone. Many of the findings still await confirmation by other workers but there is sufficient evidence of the potential importance of this field for it to become a major area of research activity.

References

AKAGAWA, K., WATANABE, M. & TSUKADA, Y. (1980) Activity of erythrocyte Na-K ATPase in manic patients. *Journal of Neurochemistry*, **35**, 258–260.

ALI, S. A., PEET, M. & WARD, N. I. (1985) Blood levels of vanadium, caesium and other elements in depressive patients. *Journal of Affective Disorders*, **9**, 187–191.

ALLERS, R. (1914) Ergebnisse Stoffwechsel — patholgischer Untersuchungen bei Psychosen. III Das Manisch-depressive *Irresein*. *L. ges Neurol. Psychiat.*, **9**, 585–590.

ALLEXSAHT, W. J. (1938) The use of methylene blue in the treatment of catatonic dementia praecox patients. *Psychiatric Quarterly*, **12**, 245–252.

BOARDMAN, L. J., HUME, S. P., LAMB, J. F., McCOLL, D., NEWTON, J. P. & POLSON, J. M. (1975) In: *Developmental and Physiological Correlates of Cardiac Muscle*. (ed. M. Lieberman & T. Sano) pp. 127–138. New York: Raven Press.

BODONI, P. (1899) Sul passaggio del blue di metilene nei reni in varie forme di psicosi. *Rivista di Patologia Nervosa e Mentale*, **3**, 460–461.

CANTLEY, L. C. & AISEN, P. (1979) The fate of cytoplasmic vanadium. *Journal of Biological Chemistry*, **254**, 1781–1784.

——— JOSEPHSON, L., WARNER, R., YANAGISAVA, M., LECHENE, C. & GUIDOTTI, G. (1977) Vanadate is a potent (Na-K) ATPase inhibitor found in ATP derived from muscle. *Journal of Biological Chemistry*, **252**, 7421–7423.

CARROLL, B. J. (1972) Sodium and potassium transfer to cerebrospinal fluid in severe depression. In *Depressive Illness*, (ed. B. Davies, B. J. Carroll and R. M. Mowbray) pp. 247–257. Springfield, Illinois: Charles Thomas.

CHAMBERS, C. A., SMITH, A. H. W. & NAYLOR, G. J. (1982) The effect of digoxin on the response to lithium therapy in mania. *Psychological Medicine*, **12**, 57–60.

CHECKLEY, S. A., GLASS, I. B., THOMPSON, C., CORN, T. & ROBINSON, P. (1984) The GH response to clonidine in endogenous as compared with reactive depression. *Psychological Medicine*, **14**, 773–777.

CHOI, S. J., TAYLOR, M. A. & ABRAMS, R. (1977) Depression, ECT and erythrocyte adenosine-triphophatase activity. *Biological Psychiatry*, **12**, 75–81.

CLAUSEN, T. & FLATMAN, J. A. (1982) Beta$_2$ adrenoceptors mediate the stimulating effect of adrenaline on active electrogenic Na-K transport in rat soleus muscle. *British Journal of Pharmacology*, **68**, 749–755.

COLT, E. W. D., DUNNER, D. L., WANG, J., ROSS, D. C., PIERSON, R. N. & FIEVE, R. R. (1982) Body composition in affective disorder before, during and after lithium carbonate therapy. *Archives of General Psychiatry*, **39**, 577–581.

CONRI, C. L., SIMONOFF, M., FLEURY, B. & MOREAU, F. (1986) Does vanadium play a role in depressive state? *Biological Psychiatry* (in press).

COPPEN, A. (1965) Mineral metabolism in affective disorders. *British Journal of Psychiatry*, **111**, 1133–1142.

——— (1960) Abnormality of the blood-cerebro spinal fluid barrier of patients suffering from a depressive illness. *Journal of Neurology, Neurosurgery & Psychiatry*, **23**, 156–161.

——— SHAW, D. M. (1963) Mineral metabolism in melancholia. *British Medical Journal*, **2**, 1439–1444.

——— SHAW, D. M., MALLESON, A. & COSTAIN, R. (1966) Mineral metabolism in mania. *British Medical Journal*, **1**, 71–75.

COX, J. R., PEARSON, R. E. & SPEIGHT, C. J. (1971) Changes in sodium, potassium and body fluid spaces in depression and dementia. *Gerontology Clinics*, **13**, 233–245.

DAGHER, G., GAY, C., BROSSARD, M., FERAY, J. C., OLIE, J. P., GARAY, R. P., LOO, H. & MAYER, P. (1984) Lithium, sodium and potassium transport in erythrocytes of manic depressive patients. *Acta Psychiatrica Scandinavica*, **69**, 24–36.

DANIELSSON, E., UNDEN, A. & BARTFAI, T. (1983) Orthovanadate induces loss of muscarinic cholinergic binding sites. *Biochemical and Biophysical Research Communications*, **110**, 567–572.

DICK, D. A. T., DICK, E. G. & NAYLOR, G. J. (1981) Plasma vanadium concentration in manic depressive illness. *Journal of physiology*, **310**, 24P.

——— NAYLOR, G. J. & DICK, E. G. (1982) Plasma vanadium concentration in manic depressive illness. *Psychological Medicine*, **12**, 533–537.

EHRINGER, H., HORNYKIEWICZ, D. & LECHNER, K. (1961) Die Wirkung von Methylenblau auf die monoaminoxydase und den Katecholamin und 5-Hydroxytryptaminstoffwechsel des Gehirnes. *Archives of Experimental Pathology and Pharmacology*, **241**, 568–582.

GIANNINI, A. J., HOUSER, W. L., LOISELLE, R. H., GIANNINI, M. C. & PRICE, W. A. (1984) Antimanic effects of verapamil. *American Journal of Psychiatry*, **141**, 1602–1603.

GLEN, A. I. M. (1978) In *Lithium in Medical Practice* (ed. F. N. Johnson & S. Johnson). pp. 183–192. Lancaster: MTP Press.

—— ONGLEY, G. C. & ROBINSON, K. (1968) Diminished membrane transport in manic depressive psychosis and recurrent depression. *Lancet*, **2**, 241–243.

HATHCOCK, J. N., HILL, C. H. & MATRINE, G. (1964) Vanadium toxicity and distribution in chicks and rats. *Journal of Nutrition*, **82**, 106–110.

HITZEMANN, R., HIRSCHOWITZ, J. & GARVER, D. (1984) Membrane abnormalities in the psychoses and affective disorders. *Journal of Psychiatric Research*, **18**, 319–326.

HOKIN-NAEVERSON, M., BURCKHARDT, W. A. & JEFFERSON, J. W. (1976) Increased erythrocyte Na+ pump and Na–K ATPase activity during lithium therapy. *Research Communications in Chemical Pathology and Pharmacology*, **14**, 117–126.

—— SPIEGEL, D. A. & LEWIS, W. C. (1974) Deficiency of erythrocyte sodium pump activity in bipolar manic depressive psychosis. *Life Sciences*, **15**, 1739–1748.

HOPKINS, L. L. & MOHR, H. E. (1974) Vanadium is an essential nutrient. *Proceedings of the Federation of American Societies of Experimental Biology*, **33**, 1773–1775.

JOHNSTON, B. B., NAYLOR, G. J., DICK, E. G., HOPWOOD, S. E. & DICK, D. A. T. (1980) Prediction of clinical course of bipolar manic depressive illness treated with lithium. *Psychological Medicine*, **10**, 329–334.

KAY, D. S. G., NAYLOR, G. J., SMITH, A. H. W. & GREENWOOD, C. (1984) The therapeutic effect of ascorbic acid and EDTA in manic depressive psychosis: double blind comparisons with standard treatments. *Psychological Medicine*, **14**, 533–539.

LAKER, M. (1982) On determining trace element levels in man: the uses of blood and hair. *Lancet*, **2**, 260–262.

LINNOILA, M., MACDONALD, E., REINILA, M., LE ROY, A., RUBINOW, D. R. & GOODWIN, F. K. (1983) RBC membrane adenosine triphosphatase activities in patients with major affective disorders. *Archives of General Psychiatry*, **40**, 1021–1026.

MAAS, J. W. (1972) Adrenocortical steroid hormones, electrolytes and the disposition of the catecholamines with particular reference to depressive states. *Journal of Psychiatric Research*, **9**, 227–241.

—— FAWCETT, J. A. & DEKIRMENJIAN, W. (1972) Catecholamine metabolism, depressive illness and drug response. *Archives of General Psychiatry*, **26**, 252–262.

MACDONALD, D., LE ROY, A. & LINNOILA, M. (1982) Failure of lithum to counter-act vanadate induced inhibition of red blood cell membrane Na-K ATPase. *Lancet*, **2**, 774.

MARTIN, G. M., BENDITT, E. P. & ERIKSEN, N. (1960) Vanadium catalysis of the oxi-dation of catecholamines, dihydroxyphenylalanine and 5-hydroxyindoles. *Nature*, **186**, 884–885.

MELTZER, H. L. & KASSIR, S. (1983) Abnormal calmodulin-activated Ca ATPase in manic-depressive subjects. *Journal of Psychiatric Research*, **17**, 29–35.

NARSAPUR, S. L. & NAYLOR, G. J. (1983) Methylene blue: a possible treatment for manic depressive psychosis. *Journal of Affective Disorders*, **5**, 155–161.

NAYLOR, G. J. (1970) Cellular sodium and potassium metabolism and the symptoms in depressive illness. M.D. Thesis, Dundee.

—— (1985) Reversal of vanadate induced inhibition of Na-K ATPase. *Journal of Affective Disorders*, **8**, 91–93.

—— CORRIGAN, F. M., SMITH, A. H. W., CONNELLY, R. & WARD, N. I. Further studies of vanadium in depressive psychosis. *British Journal of Psychiatry* (in press).

—— DICK, D. A. T. & DICK, E. G. (1976a) Erythrocyte membrane cation carrier, relapse rate of manic depressive illness and prediction of response to lithium. *Psychological Medicine*, **6**, 257–263.

—— DICK, D. A. T., DICK, E. G., LE POIDEVIN, D. & WHYTE, S. F. (1973) Erythrocyte membrane cation carrier in depressive illness. *Psychological Medicine*, **3**, 502–508.

—— DICK, D. A. T., DICK, E. G. & MOODY, J. P. (1974) Lithium therapy and erythrocyte membrane cation carrier. *Psychopharmacologia*, **37**, 81–86.

—— DICK, D. A. T., DICK, E. G., WORRALL, E. P., PEET, M., DICK, P. & BOARDMAN, L. J. (1976b) Erythrocyte membrane cation carrier in mania. *Psychological Medicine*, **6**, 659–663.
—— DICK, D. A. T., JOHNSTON, B. B., HOPWOOD, S. E., DICK, E. G., SMITH, A. H. W. & KAY, D. (1981) Possible explanation for the therapeutic action of lithium and a possible substitute — (methylene blue).*Lancet*, **2**, 1175–1176.
—— MCNAMEE, H. B. & MOODY, J. P. (1970) The plasma control of erythrocyte sodium and potassium metabolism in depressive illness. *Journal of Psychosomatic Research*, **14**, 179–186.
—— MARTIN, B., HOPWOOD, S. E. & WATSON, Y. (1986) A 2 year double blind crossover trial of the prophylactic effect of methylene blue in manic depressive psychosis. *Biological Psychiatry* (in press).
—— SMITH, A. H. W. (1980) Vanadium, a possible aetiological factor in manic depressive illness. *IRCS Medical Science*, **8**, 446–447.
—— SMITH, A. H. W. (1981a) Vanadium, a possible aetiological factor in manic depressive illness. *Psychological Medicine*, **11**, 249–256.
—— SMITH, A. H. W. (1981b) Defective genetic control of sodium pump density in manic depressive psychosis. *Psychological Medicine*, **11**, 257–263.
—— SMITH, A. H. W. (1981c) Methylene blue: A new treatment for manic depressive psychosis. *IRCS Medical Science*, **9**, 1154–1155.
—— SMITH, A. H. W., BOARDMAN, L. J., DICK, D. A. T., DICK, E. G. & DICK, P. (1977) Lithium and erythrocyte membrane cation carrier studies in normal and manic depressive subjects. *Psychological Medicine*, **7**, 229–233.
—— SMITH, A. H. W., BRYCE-SMITH, D. & WARD, N. I. (1984) Tissue vanadium levels in manic-depressive psychosis. *Psychological Medicine*, **14**, 767–772.
—— SMITH, A. H. W., DICK, E. G., DICK, D. A. T., MCHARG, A. M. & CHAMBERS, C. A. (1980) Erythrocyte membrane cation carrier in manic depressive psychosis. *Psychological Medicine*, **10**, 521–525.
—— SMITH, A. H. W. & TROTTER, P. (1983) Catalysis of reduction of vanadate by psychotropic drugs. *Neuropharmacology*, **22**, 653–656.
NURNBERGER, J., JIMERSON, D. C., ALLEN, J. R., SIMMONS, S. & GERSHON, E. (1982) Red cell ouabain-sensitive Na-K adenosine triphosphatase: a state marker in affective disorder inversely related to plasma cortisol. *Biological Psychiatry*, **17**, 981–992.
OSTROW, D. G., PANDEY, G. N., DAVIS, J. M., HURT, S. W. & TOSTESON, D. C. (1978) A heritable disorder of lithium transport in erythrocytes of a subpopulation of manic-depressive patients. *American Journal of Psychiatry*, **135**, 1070–1078.
PEET, M. (1975) The potential difference across the rectal mucosa during depressive illness and lithium therapy. *British Journal of Psychiatry*, **127**, 144–148.
PETTEGREW, J. W., NICHOLS, J. S., MINSHEW, N. J., RUSH, A. J. & STEWART, R. H. (1982) Membrane biophysical studies in lymphocytes and erythrocytes in manic depressive illness. *Journal of Affective Disorders*, **4**, 237–247.
QUIST, E. E. & HOKIN, L. E. (1978) The presence of two Na-K ATPase inhibitors in equine muscle ATP: vanadate and a dithioerythritol dependent inhibitor. *Biochimica Biophysica Acta*, **213**, 741–747.
RASK-MADSEN, J., BAASTRUP, P. C. & SCHWARTZ, M. (1972) Lithium induced hyperpolarization of the human rectum *in vivo*. *British Medical Journal*, **2**, 496–498.
RYBAKOWSKI, J., POTOK, E. & STRZYZEWSKI, W. (1983) Decreased activity of ouabain-dependent sodium and potassium fluxes in erythrocytes during depression and mania. *Activitas Nervosa Superior*, **25**, 72–74.
—— POTOK, E., STRZYZEWSKI, W. & NOWAKOWSKA, C. (1984) Erythrocyte cation transport disturbances in patients with endogenous depression. *Clinical and Experimental Pharmacology and Physiology*, **11**, 319–326.
RYSANEK, K., VITEK, V. & VOJTECHOVSKY, M. (1964) Interpretation of the psychostimulating effect of methylene blue. *Activitas Nervosa Superior*, **6**, 74–76.
SCHOUTEN, J. & VAN DER AA, G. C. H. M. (1984) Een gedeprimeerde patiente ten gevolge van digitalis intoxicatie. *Tijdschrift voor Gerontologie en Geriatrie*, **15**, 63–66.
STURNIOLO, G. C., MARTIN, A., MASTROPAOLO, G., GURRIERE, G. & NACCARATO, R. (1982) Trace elements in human hair. *Lancet*, **2**, 608.

TIPTON, K. F. (1973) Biochemical aspects of monoamine oxidase. *British Medical Bulletin*, **29**, 116–119.

VYSKOCIL, P., PILAR, J., ZEMKOVA, N. & TEISINGER, J. (1982) Reduction of vanadate to vanadyl by methylene blue, imipramine and chlorpromazine in absence of NADH. *Lancet*, **1**, 1078–1079.

WITKOWSKA, D. & BRZEZINSKI, J. (1979) Alteration of brain noradrenaline, dopamine and 5-hydroxytryptamine levels during vanadium poisoning. *Polish Journal of Pharmacology*, **31**, 393–398.

WU, P. H. & PHILLIS, J. W. (1980) Characterization of receptor — mediated catecholamine activation of rat brain cortical Na-K ATPase. *International Journal of Biochemistry*, **12**, 353–359.

9 Recent advances in the treatment of depression

E. S. PAYKEL; A. S. HALE

This paper will review selected topics concerning the treatment of depression, with particular emphasis on recent growing points, areas where enough evidence has accumulated in the last few years to enable conclusions to be drawn from the literature and on problems of resistant depression.

Two major reservations must be underlined. The first concerns the range of treatments. Available treatments for depression span the full range of psychological, social and physical modalities. Supportive effects of hospital admission for the severely ill and of lengthy initial consultation, ventilation and assurance of continuing care for the out-patient may be very powerful influences. There is increasing evidence as to the efficacy of psychotherapy and cognitive therapy. While this review, in a biological psychiatry context, will only discuss drug treatment and electroconvulsive therapy (ECT), it should not be implied that other treatments are not important.

The second reservation concerns the range of patients. The vast majority of available evidence on the efficacy of antidepressant treatment concerns psychiatrically treated samples. These represent only the tip of the iceberg of treated depression. Annual admission rates for depression are of the order of 1:1000 of the general population while psychiatric referral rates were 3:1000 in two case register studies (Grad de Alarcon *et al*, 1975; Juel-Nielsen *et al*, 1961). In contrast the second National Morbidity Survey of 1971 (OPCS, 1974) found a one year consultation rate for depression in general practice of 35.5 per 1000. Eighty to ninety percent of depression is treated in general practice. Sireling *et al* (1985) found that, of patients treated in general practice with antidepressants, only half were major depressives on the Research Diagnostic Criteria (Spitzer & Endicott, 1977) and two thirds scored below 17 on the Hamilton Depression Rating Scale for depression, the usual minimum inclusion criterion for drug trials. Yet the vast majority of studies of antidepressant drugs have been undertaken in psychiatric in-patients or out-patients. There have been very few placebo controlled trials of anti-depressants in general practice, and although available evidence does suggest efficacy (Thomson *et al*, 1982) the proper place of drugs and the selection of patients who benefit remain unclear.

Electroconvulsive therapy (ECT)

There have been six recent double-blind controlled trials of ECT against simulated ECT reported from the UK. Lambourn & Gill (1978), in a relatively small sample found little difference between real and sham ECT. Johnstone *et al* (1980) found real ECT superior, but improvement on the sham treatment was impressive, and the advantage for real ECT had disappeared at one and six month follow up. They concluded that there was little evidence that the benefits of repeated convulsions are substantial or long lasting, but that benefits lie in speed of response. Freeman *et al* (1978) found two applications of real ECT superior to two of simulated ECT. West (1981) on a small sample found real ECT strongly superior. The placebo effect in this study was negligible, in contrast to the other five studies. Brandon *et al* (1984) found a large advantage for real ECT at two and four weeks after treatment, but this difference had disappeared by 12 weeks. Forty-three of their 138 subjects were minor depressives, for whom there was no difference between real and sham ECT. The most recently reported study is that of Gregory *et al* (1985). Their results suggest a clear superiority for real treatment. Janicak *et al* (1985) performed a meta-analysis of the results from many studies including several of the above. This technique examines magnitude of effect across studies and deals with some of the inadequacies of simply counting studies in evaluating conflicting data. They found real ECT to be clearly superior to sham treatment, the response rates being 72% and 40% respectively across studies.

It is instructive to enquire as to what the reasons may be for the discrepancies between studies. Gregory *et al* (1985) have suggested that the large study which although positive, showed only weak differences, that of Johnstone *et al* (1980), had a sample unrepresentative of those patients usually given ECT. This is difficult to prove or disprove. Two of the positive studies (Freeman *et al*, 1978; West, 1981) permitted concomitant use of antidepressants, which could lead to confounding of effects. Some studies permitted concurrent administration of benzodiazepines. This has been shown to reduce seizure duration (Standish-Barry *et al*, 1985) which has been suggested to be related to efficacy (Kranmer, 1983) although this is contested (Daniel, 1983).

Perhaps the most impressive difference is that the one negative study (Lambourn & Gill, 1978) used unilateral brief pulse ECT while the remaining positive studies used bilateral sine wave applications, or, in the case of Gregory *et al* (1985) groups with both unilateral and bilateral sine wave.

There have been a number of comparisons of bilateral and unilateral ECT. D'Elia and Raotma (1975) reviewed 21 comparative trials with random assignment. In 10 studies bilateral ECT was a little superior in efficacy, in nine bilateral and unilateral were equal while in two studies unilateral ECT was superior. The differences were small in degree but were significant. An additional more recent comparative trial by Abrams *et al* (1983) found bilateral ECT clearly and significantly superior. Studies comparing the antidepressant effect of unilateral and bilateral ECT are also reviewed by Janicak *et al* and compared by meta-analysis. They found a non-significant 6% difference in efficacy, although patients receiving non-dominant unilateral treatment commonly needed one or two extra treatments compared with those receiving a bilateral stimulus.

Memory impairment appears to be the common side effect to ECT treatment (Palmer, 1981; Gostin, 1981), hence the question of whether deficits are less severe or frequent with unilateral treatment, and whether any lasting deficits occur, are of crucial importance. The belief in lasting cognitive deficits following ECT is widespread among patients and psychiatrists, despite minimal supporting evidence. Evaluation of studies is bedevilled by the fact that depression itself produces memory impairment. Heshe *et al* (1978) showed short term retrograde memory impairment and some transient difficulty in retaining newly acquired information, which were worse following unilateral than bilateral ECT. Squire & Miller (1981) showed persistent minor deficits in ability to remember public events up to two years prior to treatment at six months after ECT. Freeman *et al* (1980) showed that complaints of lasting deficits were only partially explained by persistance of depressive symptoms. Most evidence however, is for deficits with comparatively long courses of bilateral ECT, given three times weekly. There is little convincing evidence for such deficits with unilateral non-dominant administration or indeed with bilateral treatment twice weekly (Weeks *et al*, 1980). Daniel & Crovitz (1982, 1983b) show bilateral treatment to produce both more amnesia and more post ictal confusion, than unilateral treatment. Fromm-Auch (1982) reviewed in detail evidence from 22 adequate studies of memory function following ECT, concluding that bilateral treatment impairs verbal and non-verbal memory whilst unilateral non-dominant treatment produces disturbance in non-verbal memory early in the course of treatment. There were no adequate studies showing long term difficulties in new learning. Squire & Slater (1983) conclude that self reports of amnesia for events following ECT are attributable to persistance of illness, whilst treatment effects are largely confined to a degree of retrograde amnesia for the period prior to treatments.

Since unilateral non-dominant ECT produces less memory disturbance it is a better first choice, but since overall it appears a little less efficacious than bilateral ECT, the latter is indicated in patients who have failed to respond, particularly if deluded or retarded (Abrams & Fink, 1984).

The second issue emerging from the controlled comparison is that of sine wave *vs* brief pulse electrical applications. In a controlled trial Robin & de Tissera (1982) compared sine wave ECT, high energy brief pulse applications, and low energy brief pulse ECT (the usual brief pulse form). The last was clearly less effective. Weiner (1982) also found sine wave application superior to brief pulse, although Welch *et al* (1982) found no difference.

The common factor may be the adequacy of seizures. Several authors have commented on the higher proportion of incompletely generalised seizures with unilateral ECT compared with bilateral. Such submaximal seizures seem less effective (Daniel & Crovitz, 1983a). Cronholm & Ottoson (1960), also found more submaximal or incomplete seizures with brief pulse ECT, which was less effective than unidirectional square waveform administration. Weiner *et al* (1982) showed a relationship of efficacy to the fit generalisation and to post-ictal EEG slow wave activity. Recovery is more rapid with brief pulse treatment, suggesting less generalisation of seizures. However, Robin & de Tissera (1982) found no difference in fits in spite of a difference in efficacy. Daniel & Crovitz (1983) have presented some evidence that amnesia is more common following administration of sinusoidal waveforms than with the lower energy brief pulse techniques. This is consistent with findings of Cronholm & Ottoson (1963).

With regard to who responds the evidence is quite unequivocal. Eight predictor studies reviewed by Paykel (1979) found patients at the psychotic or endogenous extreme reponded better than did neurotic depressives. Only two studies failed to do so. The Northwick Park predictor study (1983) found the best ECT response in deluded patients, with a tendency for retarded patients also to do well. Other double blind trials of ECT have also shown better response in deluded depressives (Brandon *et al*, 1984; Abrams & Fink, 1984). The evidence also strongly suggests that among in-patients ECT is preferable to drugs. Among nine comparative trials (non-blind) comparing ECT with tricyclic antidepressants (Paykel, 1979), six found ECT better overall, two studies found equal effects, and one study found the drug faster although with ultimately equal effects. Studies in milder or more neurotic patients might, however, give quite different results. There is accumulating evidence that deluded depressives respond poorly to tricyclic antidepressants (Glassman *et al*, 1975; Avery & Lubrano, 1979; Perry *et al*, 1982) and thus go on to receive ECT.

Tricyclic antidepressants

The tricyclics have now been available for 25 years. They are well studied drugs and there is no doubt of their overall superiority to placebo. Ten years ago Morris & Beck (1974) reviewed trials of the six tricyclics then available in the USA. There were 93 studies of which 62 showed drugs superior to placebo and 31 failed to do so. This is far in excess of chance expectation of 5% significance. There is the problem of the negative studies. Some are due to small samples, particularly with the variability in outcome common in depression, some to unresponsive subjects, low doses, short treatment periods. Undoubtedly part of the problem also lies in limited efficacy. The spontaneous outcome of depression is often quite good, with added non-specific treatment effects from support and hospital admission. Improvement in placebo groups includes all these elements. The element which the drugs add is on average limited, although very marked in some patients. The proportion of the total variance in antidepressant trials which is attributable to drug effects is often quite low, around 10%. Janick *et al* (1985) estimated a 27% advantage for active drug over placebo in their meta-analysis. Put another way an additional 20–30% of recoveries occur above those which might occur without the drug.

From the early studies it has been believed that endogenous depressives respond better to tricyclics than do nonendogenous patients. However, the evidence is not very clear-cut, even in the earlier studies (Paykel, 1979). In recent years there have been many reports referred to earlier that depressives with delusions do badly with tricyclics and much better with ECT. Rao & Coppen (1979) found best response to amitriptyline in the middle range of the Newcastle Scale rather than at the most endogenous extreme. A number of studies have shown tricyclics superior to placebo in out-patient neurotic depressives, anxiety states (Paykel, 1979), phobic and obsessional neuroses (Marks, 1983). There is some evidence that effects in obsessional disorders are independent of antidepressant effects (Mavissakalian *et al*, 1985) and that clomipramine may be superior to other tricyclic drugs (Thoren *et al*, 1980; Ananth *et al*, 1981). In Morris & Beck (1974) out-patient studies tended more to give positive results than did in-patient studies. Probably the best response is in depression of moderate severity and endogenous symptoms, with quite a good response in neurotic depressives and poor response in many severe psychotic depressives, a sub group of endogenous depression.

Dosage may be an issue in trials and in clinical practice. Practice in the USA now tends to use doses higher than in this country, with doses up to 300mg daily of amitriptyline not uncommon in in-patients. Cases of resistant depression may respond when the dose is increased to the 200–300mg/day range (Kotin *et al*, 1973; Schatsburg *et al*, 1983). Several studies have compared the efficacy of 150mg and 300mg of a tricyclic in endogenous depressives. Significantly better response rates were found with the higher dose (Watt *et al*, 1972; Simpson *et al*, 1976; Klein & Davis, 1969). Studies attempting to relate tricyclic plasma levels to response have reported that up to half of depressed patients have inadequate levels on doses of lower than 225mg/day (Simpson *et al*, 1982; Glassman *et al*, 1977; Reisby *et al*,

1977). Schucklit *et al* (1971) and Nelson *et al* (1982) report that some patients seem to require doses in excess of 400mg/day before improvement is seen. Much effort has been devoted to investigating the clinical utility of the assay of serum tricyclic and metabolite levels. Three small studies suggested a linear relationship between outcome and serum levels of amitriptyline and nortriptyline (the desmethylated derivative). Three larger studies found a curvilinear relationship, sometimes interpreted as a therapeutic window effect. Nine large studies found no relationship. These studies are reviewed by Razavi & Mendlewicz (1982) and Rowan *et al* (1984). Nelson *et al* (1982) found a threshold effect at 115ng/ml with desipramine. Faravelli *et al* (1982) found a relationship between serum level and outcome for clomipramine and its desmethyl metabolite and outcome, but interestingly, also a relationship between early recovery despite low serum levels, and later relapse. Monitoring of serum levels may be of use in the elderly, in patients with cardiac disease, and in patients unresponsive to treatment as a measure both of absorption and compliance (Barnes & Braithwaite, 1978), but for most patients serum level monitoring appears to be of doubtful utility. In clinical practice, the onset of side effects may be a more useful guide to the activity of the drug in a given patient.

Regarding length of treatment, superiority over placebo starts to appear at about three weeks in controlled trials, and may disappear again by three months due to differential drop out and to non-drug improvement including natural remission (Klerman & Cole, 1965). Often superiority of active drug over placebo is not significant until the fifth or sixth week of treatment (Quitkin *et al*, 1984; Rowan *et al*, 1982). Quitkin *et al* (1984b) suggest that true drug responders should be identified by response later than the second week of medication which persists. In their trials, patients receiving placebo were more likely to respond within the first three weeks and to relapse prior to the fourth week of treatment.

Newer drugs

There are at present 17 antidepressants of tricyclic structure, related pharmacology, or apparently similar clinical effects, available on the UK market and several others have appeared and been withdrawn. This is many more than in the USA. Pharmacologically the majority are still amine re-uptake inhibitors, selective or non-selective to varying degrees. An older drug which has only minor use, iprindole, and two more important newer drugs mianserin and trazodone, have rather different or obscure actions. The older tricyclics have a number of limitations: limited overall efficacy, delay in improvement, side effects and toxicity. There is a need also for drugs which are clinically more selective, particularly for the depressives who do not respond well to current treatment. Unfortunately the newer drugs fail to overcome these limitations. There is no convincing evidence that any of the newer drugs is overall more efficacious or acts more quickly than the old. Indeed, for some of them, the evidence that they are as effective as the older drugs is not yet conclusive.

Differences in pharmacology might suggest different effects but have so far also proved disappointing. Most of the newer drugs are re-uptake inhibitors, although they may be more selective. The drugs which have different pharmacology, such as mianserin, do not seem to have clinical effects which are much different: something quite remarkable in the view of the different proposed modes of action or selective effects on different neurotransmitters. However, data available for the most recent drugs are still sparse.

The next few years are likely to see the introduction of a number of new selective serotonin re-uptake inhibitors, similar in effect to zimelidine but freer of toxicity. There was relatively little evidence of any group definable in clinical terms to be preferentially responsive to zimelidine, but one study of it and another of the selective uptake inhibitor fluvoxamine, has suggested less effects on retarded depression and more on anxiety (Åberg-Wisted, 1982; Norton *et al*, 1984). This would be in keeping with the evidence that clomipramine is superior to nortriptyline in obsessional disorders (Thoren *et al*, 1980).

The main advantage of the newer drugs is regarding toxicity. The common unwanted tricyclic anticholinergic and sedative effects are usually at the level of minor irritants but do limit doses in general practice and major urinary problems can occur. Cardiotoxicity is mainly a problem in those with previous cardiac disorders, or in overdoses. The tricyclics have become an important cause of suicide (Crome & Newman, 1979). The newer drugs do clearly produce less anticholinergic effects and cardiotoxicity. The advantages are not all one sided: mianserin causes considerable sedation and can cause agranulocytosis (Curson & Hale, 1979): the selective serotonin uptake inhibitors produce nausea and zimelidine produced worse effects. The newer drugs are expensive and the efficacy rests on a less solid base. As clinical experience increases and costs fall there is likely to be a swing towards them but the advantage at present is unfortunately only a relatively small one.

Monoamine oxidase inhibitors

The monoamine oxidase (MAO) inhibitors were introduced before the tricyclic antidepressants but their place is smaller; one reason being the risk of interactions with other substances and another, doubts regarding efficacy.

Early large controlled trials incorporating both a tricyclic antidepressant and an MAO inhibitor and found the first superior to placebo but the second ineffective. Phenelzine has been the best studied drug. Among 13 published controlled comparisons with placebo four have been negative, three doubtfully positive and six positive (Paykel, 1979; Paykel *et al*, 1982a). All the negative studies were carried out on in-patients whereas five of the six positive studies were in out-patients. The doubtfully positive studies were mainly in mixed samples. The most likely explanation is that severely ill inpatients are a non-responsive group and that responders lie somewhere among out-patients. The paper by Tyrer (1976) crystallises well known views. He has suggested that, rather than being regarded as true antidepressants, the MAO inhibitors should be regarded as 'delayed psycho-stimulants' with effects predominantly in a spectrum including agoraphobia, anxiety neurosis and mixed anxiety depression rather than pure depression. The term atypical depression is often used to describe this.

However, the picture is not clear-cut. The concept of atypical depression is imprecise, incorporating anxiety, reversed functional shift symptoms and other features of neurotic depression. In our study (Paykel *et al*, 1982a), although anxious depressives tended to do better on phenelzine than amitriptyline, the difference was very small. The evidence that tricyclics are effective in anxiety disorders has already been discussed. Even the conclusion that MAO inhibitors are ineffective in severe depressives needs re-evaluation, since most were early studies with low doses and short treatment periods. Many clinicians believe that tranylcypromine is effective in severe depressives. Delineation of responsive subgroups on previous history of response (Pare & Mack, 1971), family history or ultimately, on biochemistry may have more to offer than does symptom picture.

It is clear that dosages of MAO inhibitors have tended to be too low in the past. There has been some disagreement as to the role of acetylator phenotype for hydrazine MAOIs but three of eight studies have shown strong effects and in our own study (Paykel *et al*, 1982b), on a dose of 60–75 mg phenelzine daily was only strongly superior to placebo in slow acetylators, suggesting that fast acetylators need even larger doses. Doses of 45 mg daily for four weeks appear borderline (Tyrer, 1976) and a larger dose or longer treatment period is required, preferably at least six weeks with dose pushed to the level where there is either response or dose related side effects such as hypotension or ankle oedema. For phenelzine this not uncommonly requires 75 mg daily and sometimes 90 mg daily.

The most active research area in relation to MAO inhibitors at the moment lies in the possibility of new drugs being developed. One of these, eldepryl, a selective MAO B inhibitor appears to lack the cheese reaction but, unfortunately, it is doubtful whether it has antidepressant efficacy. This is not surprising since it is MAO A which deaminates serotonin and noradrenaline. There are under development several selective MAO A inhibitors which are rapidly reversible and which may interact to a lesser extent with tyramine. Meanwhile, the MAO inhibitors tend clinically to be second choice because of side effects.

Anticonvulsants

Shortly after the introduction of the tricyclic carbamazepine as an anti-epileptic, reports began to appear that it produced improvement in character and behavioural disorders in epileptic patients. Bonduelle *et al* (1962), Rett (1962; 1963) and others suggested improvement after starting patients on carbamazepine, in the traits of sluggish thought and action, and perseveration, which were then attributed to the 'epileptoid character'. A beneficial effect was also noticed on lability of mood and on depression, anxiety and hypochondriacal complaints (Dehing, 1968). Ketz (1964) however, reported worsening of psychotic symptoms in some patients. Dalby (1971) conducted an open study of 50 epileptic patients. He reported that in 44% of patients carbamazepine was prophylactic against aggression and disturbed mood. This action was evident within two weeks of starting treatment. He suggested that such changes in affective symptoms were independent of improvements in control of fits and that beneficial changes in 'sticky' personality traits were secondary to changes in mood. He reported similar findings in a controlled trial (Dalby, 1975). Thompson *et al* (1980) and Janke *et al* (1983) have reported that carbamazepine produces an elevation in mood, energy and activity levels in normal subjects, accompanied by an anxiolytic effect.

Following these observations trials were conducted with carbamazepine in patients with affective illness. Takezaki & Hannoka (1971) showed some beneficial effect in an open clinical trial with bipolar patients. Okuma *et al* (1973) reported improvement in open trials of the addition of carbamazepine in patients failing to respond to lithium, tricyclics and neuroleptics. Okuma *et al* (1979) found carbamazepine equal in efficacy to chlorpromazine in a double blind trial in acute mania and Ballinger & Post (1980) found it efficacious compared with placebo substitution in seven of nine manic patients. Double blind controlled trials in both phases of bipolar affective disorder and in unipolar depressives have suggested that carbamazepine alone is an effective treatment in the acutely ill patient (Post *et al*, 1978; 1980; Post 1982; Okuma *et al*, 1979). Okuma *et al* (1981) and Post *et al* (1983) showed marked superiority of carbamazepine over placebo in a one year assessment of prophylaxis in bipolar patients. Carbamazepine appears more effective in severe than mild depressives (Post & Uhde, 1983) and a 2–3 week time lag in onset of antidepressant action has been reported although improvement in sleep pattern occurs within the first week of treatment. Overall, the evidence for the utility of carbamazepine is much more compelling in bipolar than unipolar illness, especially where rapid cycling occurs (Okuma *et al*, 1973) as the use of antidepressant medication in this group of patients may induce such rapid cycling (Potter *et al*, 1982). Dosages used vary between 400 and 2000 mg daily, with blood levels between 4 and 12 ug/ml. Plasma level monitoring is desirable in view of risk of toxicity. Post *et al* (1983) found no relationship between plasma or CSF carbamazepine levels and efficacy. There is as yet no evidence for a therapeutic window or threshold effect. However, they demonstrated a closer relationship between clinical response and plasma levels of the -10, 11 epoxide metabolite.

Inoue *et al* (1981) and Lipinski & Pope (1982) have reported a synergy between carbamazepine and lithium in patients unresponsive to either drug alone. The latter paper also suggested that this combination was beneficial in rapid cycling bipolar patients with four or more cycles per year. However, Ghose (1978), Chaudhty & Walters (1983) and Shukla *et al* (1984), have reported neurotoxicity with the combination. This occurred with mean lithium levels of only 0.88 mmoles/1 and carbamazepine levels of 8.7mmoles/1. However, many of the patients had a prior history of central nervous system or systematic disease. It must also be borne in mind that carbamazepine, like lithium, may induce hypothyroidism (Aanderud & Strandjord, 1980). Neurotoxicity has also been reported with carbamazepine combined with neuroleptics.

Lambert *et al* (1975) reported acute and prophylactic effects of the valproic acid metabolite dipropylacetamide in open studies with bipolar patients. Emrich *et al* (1980) showed acute effects for valproic acid in double blind studies, including a group resistant to lithium. Doses used were 800–1800 mg/day with plasma levels of 48–102 ug/ml. Emrich *et al* (1982) showed prophylaxis in an open trial lasting 18–36 months.

Valproic acid is less well investigated than carbamazepine, and toxicity is greater. Trimble (1977) has shown valproate to produce psychomotor slowing, and worsening of cognitive performance and depression, none of which were seen with carbamazepine. Carbamazepine certainly seems to have a place in the treatment of bipolar affective disorder, and probably in unipolar disorder.

Long-term treatment

The long-term outcome of modern treatment of depression is not clear. Although most depressives improve fairly rapidly, a moderate proportion show incomplete remission with persisting symptoms and social disability. At least 20% relapse within a year, and at least 50% have a later episode. Emphasis has been shifting towards these longer term problems. Two different situations need to be distinguished: routine antidepressant continuation after acute treatment, and long-term maintenance. Four studies have now been published of the effects of early withdrawal within two months of patients responding to tricyclics versus continuation for six months to a year (Mindham *et al*, 1973; Paykel *et al*, 1975; Coppen *et al*, 1978; Stein *et al*, 1980). All found early withdrawal followed by a substantial relapse rate, varying from 29% to 69%, which was at least halved by continuation. It should be standard practice to recommend continuation where the response looks genuinely related to the drug. Very abrupt withdrawal from tricyclic antidepressants may also precipitate a withdrawal phenomenon (Kramer *et al*, 1961; Shatan, 1966; Dilsaver & Greden, 1984). There are also studies indicating the value of antidepressant continuation for six months after ECT (Paykel, 1979). There is not yet clear-cut evidence that the same rules apply to MAO inhibitors.

For long-term maintenance there are now eight controlled studies showing lithium superior to placebo in bipolars and seven in unipolars (Paykel, 1979; Coppen *et al*, 1981; Kane *et al*, 1982; MRC, 1981). There is also possible evidence of a withdrawal phenomenon following abrupt lithium cessation (Small *et al*, 1971; Lapierre *et al*, 1980; Klein *et al*, 1981; Margo & McMahan, 1982). The question remains as to the place of antidepressants in long-term maintenance. In bipolars two controlled trials have found tricyclics no better than placebo and inferior to lithium partly because of increased mania, (Prien *et al*, 1973; Kane *et al*, 1982). In unipolars the evidence is more evenly split. Two studies have shown tricyclics superior to placebo and equal to lithium (Prien *et al*, 1973; MRC, 1981) as opposed to one which found no superiority to placebo (Kane *et al*, 1982) and three finding inferiority to lithium (Kane *et al*, 1982; Coppen *et al*, 1978b, 1981). One additional study (Bialos *et al*, 1982) showed a high rate of relapse following discontinuation of amitriptyline after long-term maintenance.

These studies may unduly favour lithium. Clinically there are some bipolars who do not respond, although carbamazepine may be a better second choice than tricyclics. Many unipolars do well on tricyclics antidepressants and most psychiatrists have quite a number of patients on long-term tricyclics or MAO inhibitors. Most maintenance studies have in any case been in the more severe rather than milder depressives, in whom lithium may be of less value.

Resistant depression

Only a relatively small group of depressives are resistant to standard treatments, although a more common situation is that of partial, incomplete remission with residual symptoms. For severe resistant depression the first strategy must be a thorough reassessment. This will include review of the diagnosis, including the possibility of hypothyroidism and organic brain disorder: it is not uncommon however to find an apparent organic element in resistant depression in the elderly which remains ambiguous after investigation and may clear after effective treatment of depression. It is important to consider perpetuating factors in the social environment and family. Particularly in chronic depression it is not uncommon to find that family dynamics have changed so that the depressed member is effectively excluded from any useful role in a family which has learned to function without him or her. In these circumstances brief family therapy may be necessary as recovery occurs so that both a role and a non-dependent way of functioning can be recreated; without this, early relapse is likely. Reassessment of perpetuating factors in the personality is also important but it can sometimes be very difficult to reach a firm distinction between a dependent personality and long term secondary effects of illness. Again, as with first line treatment, it is important to consider all modalities including social support and environmental manipulation, cognitive therapy and psychotherapy.

From the point of view of physical treatments, the first task, often a surprisingly difficult one, is to obtain a detailed treatment history. Our preference, with in-patients, is to withdraw all drugs and reassess the picture in their absence. Where there is any doubt as to previous treatment, full courses pushed to high dosage should be tried of a tricyclic antidepressant and/or MAO inhibitor. If ECT has not been given in the last six months a course of bilateral treatment should be tried: ECT may sometimes be effective in a later phase of illness when it has not been earlier.

Failing response, the next step is likely to be drug combinations. Although MAO inhibitor tricyclic combinations have been reported to produce hypertension, hyperpyrexia, delirium, seizures and coma (Lancet, 1965) the risk of serious problems seems mainly in sequential prescribing of high doses, in particular the addition of a tricyclic to established treatment with an MAOI (Ananth & Luchins, 1977). Continuous administration does not appear to produce significantly more adverse effects than a tricyclic or MAOI alone (Schuklit et al, 1971; Young et al, 1979). The best procedure is to allow a drug free interval of at least one week and then start both drugs together at a low dosage, increasing slowly. Amitriptyline and trimipramine appear to be the tricyclics least likely to produce side effects in combination with MAOIs, while clomipramine should be avoided. Phenelzine and isocarboxazid are probably preferable to tranylcypromine. Questions remain as to the efficacy of such combinations. Two major trials comparing the combination of tricyclic and MAOI with individual antidepressant drugs (Young et al, 1979; Razani et al, 1983) have failed to find the combination superior to the individual constituents. Both studies were of first line treatment rather than in the more usual situation of resistant patients where there might be a higher incidence of responders only to combined treatment. However, Davidson *et al* (1978) found ECT superior to combined antidepressants in resistant cases. Nevertheless it is clinical experience that some otherwise resistant patients do well on the combination.

A more valuable combination, and probably the first choice where single treatments fail, would appear to be the addition of lithium to antidepressants. De Montigny *et al* (1981, 1983) reported dramatic clinical improvement in open studies within 48 h of the addition of lithium in patients who had not responded to three weeks of tricyclic treatment, and postulated potentiation of serotoninergic neurotransmission. Heninger *et al* (1983) carried out a double-blind trial comparing the addition of lithium and placebo in patients failing to improve on tricyclic or mianserin. Again there was a considerable effect, although the improvement took between six and twelve days rather than being immediate. Our own experience is similar. The effect does appear to involve potentiation, since it is much more dramatic than any active antidepressant effect of lithium given alone; evidence of acute antidepressant effect for lithium, at least outside bipolars, is dubious, in contrast to the situation for prophylaxis. There is anecdotal support, which our own experience confirms, for a similar effect of combining lithium with an MAO inhibitor in resistant depression (Zall, 1971; Himmelhoch *et al*, 1972; Nelson & Byck, 1982). Price *et al* (1985) found tranylcypramine to potentiate lithium in patients who were largely resistant to the synergistic benefit of a lithium-tricyclic combination.

L-tryptophan appears to have little antidepressant effect by itself (D'Elia *et al*, 1978, 1983) but there is reasonable evidence of potentiation at least in combination with MAO inhibitors. Evidence of potentiation in controlled trials was found by Coppen *et al* (1963), Pare (1963), Glassman & Platman (1969) and Guitierrez & Lopez-Ibor (1971) but not by Coppen *et al* (1967). For tricyclics evidence is less clear but Walinder *et al* (1976) found potentiation of clomipramine and Thomson *et al* (1982) suggestive but not conclusive evidence of potentiation of amitriptyline. Zimeldine potentiation was not found by Walinder *et al* (1981). Three other studies (Pare, 1963; Shaw *et al*, 1972; Lopez-Ibor *et al*, 1973) did not find potentiation of other tricyclics. There have been recent reports of neurotoxicity presenting as delirium in cases of MAOI and L-tryptophan combination (Thomas & Rubin, 1984; Pope *et al*, 1985) with doses of MAOIs within the usual range, and tryptophan dosages of 1–6 g/day. The authors have similar experience of neurotoxicity with a combination of clomipramine and tryptophan disappearing with tryptophan discontinuation. The mechanism of this toxicity remains unclear.

Eccleston (1981), Shaw (1983) and Bridges (1983) report experience using a combination of lithium, L-tryptophan and clomipramine. They suggest a subgroup of very resistant depressives who will respond only to all three drugs but to neither pair. Barker & Eccleston (1984) have reported a similar regime with phenelzine in place of the tricyclic. These reports are all anecdotal. Systematic evaluation is difficult as the number of patients requiring combination therapy is small.

A further combination therapy sometimes advocated, especially for the treatment of deluded depressives, is that of a combination of tricyclic antidepressants with antipsychotic neuroleptics. Many studies show that deluded depressives respond poorly to tricyclic antidepressants alone (Glassman *et al*, 1975; Minter & Mandel, 1979; Avery & Lubrano, 1979). Fifteen studies gave a total of 33.9% response to various tricyclics in deluded depressives. Studies of the use of antipsychotics alone in depression are generally poor with 6 small studies giving a 41.7% response rate which may be an overestimate. However, in six small studies of a combination of adequate doses of tricyclic drugs with antipsychotic medication, the response rate overall was 80.6% (Spiker *et al*, 1985), comparable to the efficacy of ECT in a similar patient population (Avery & Winokur, 1977; d'Elia *et al*, 1983; Janicek *et al*, 1985). However, none of the studies above had random treatment assignment, and there is no adequate trial comparing the effects of ECT and tricyclics in the same population of deluded depressives. The value of ECT in depressives with mood-congruent delusions is more clearly established. The addition of antipsychotic medication may be of more value where there are mood-congruent delusions.

There is also evidence that triodothyronine strongly potentiates tricyclic antidepressants (Goodwin *et al*, 1982). This effect is more apparent with tricyclic resistant than drug naive patients. The risk of cardiac toxicity makes this combination more risky and it has received little use. Psychosurgery retains a small place when all has failed in intractable cases (Bartlett *et al*, 1981).

In practice it is easiest to add lithium to an established antidepressant and it may be worth while to add tryptophan in addition although in our experience effects of the latter are not dramatic. If this is unsuccessful, withdrawal may be followed by a tricyclic-MAO inhibitor combination with later addition of lithium. For the cycling bipolar who has not responded to lithium, antidepressants are best avoided as evidence suggests that cycling may be worsened, and addition of carbamazepine is most likely to be helpful.

References

AANDERUD, S. & STRANDJORD, E. R. (1980) Hypothyroidism induced by anti-epileptic therapy. *Acta Neurologica Scandinavica*, **61**, 330–332.
ABRAMS, R., TAYLOR, M. A., FABER, R., TS'O, T. O. T., WILLIAMS, R. A. & ALMY, G. (1983) Bilateral verses unilateral electroconvulsive therapy-efficacy in melancholia. *American Journal of Psychiatry*, **140**, 463–465.

—— FINK, M. (1984) The present status of unilateral ECT — some recommendations. *Journal of Affective Disorders*, **7**, 245–247.

ANANTH, J. & LUCHINS, D. (1977) A review of combined tricyclic and MAOI therapy. *Comprehensive Psychiatry*, **18**, 221–230.

ANANTH, J., PECKNOLD, J. C. & VAN DER STEEN, N. (1981) Double-blind comparative study of clomipramine and amitriptyline in obsessive neurosis. *Program. Neuropsychopharmacology*. **5**, 257–262.

ÅBERG-WISTED, A. C. (1982) A double-blind study of Zimelidine, a serotonin reuptake inhibitor and desipramine, a noradrenergic reuptake inhibitor, in endogenous depression. 1. Clinical findings. *Acta Psychiatrica Scandinavica*, **66**, 50–65.

AVERY, D. & WINOKUR, G. (1977) The efficacy of electroconvulsive therapy and antidepressants in depression. *Biological Psychiatry*, **12**, 507–523.

—— & LUBRANO, A. (1979) Depression treated with imipramine and ECT; the de Carolis study reconsidered. *American Journal of Psychiatry*, **136**, 559–562.

BALLINGER, J. C. & POST, R. M. (1980) Carbamazepine in manic depressive illness — a new treatment. *American Journal of Psychiatry*, **137**, 782–790.

BARKER, W. A. & ECCLESTON, D. (1984) The treatment of chronic depression: an illustrative case. *British Journal of Psychiatry*, **144**, 317–319.

BARNES, T. R. E. & BRAITHWAITE, R. (1978) Chapter in: *Current Themes in Psychiatry*, Vol. 1. (ed. R. N. Gaind & B. L. Hudson) London, Macmillan Press.

BARTLETT, J., BRIDGES, P. & KELLY, D. (1981) Contemporary indications for psychosurgery. *British Journal of Psychiatry*, **138**, 507–511.

BIALOS, D., GILLER, E., JATLOW, P., DOCHERTY, J. & HARKNESS, L. (1982) Recurrence of depression after discontinuation of long-term amitriptyline treatment. *American Journal of Psychiatry*, **139**, 225–228.

BONDUELLE, M., BOURYGUES, P., SALLOU, C. & CHEMALY, R. (1962) Bilan de l'experimentation clinique de l'anti-epileptique G32883 (5 carboxyol -5-H-dibenzo (b,f) azepine). *III Congres du College International de Neuropsychopharmacology*, pp. 312–316. Amsterdam, Elsevier.

BRANDON, S., COWLEY, P. MCDONALD, C., NEVILLE, P., PALMER, R. & WELLSTOOD-EASON, S. (1984) Electroconvulsive therapy: results in depressive illness from the Leicestershire trial. *British Medical Journal*, **288**, 22–25.

BRIDGES, P. K. (1983) '. . . and a small dose of an antidepressant might help'. *British Journal of Psychiatry*, **142**, 626–629.

CHAUDHTY, R. P. & WALTERS, B. G. (1983) Lithium and carbamazepine interaction: possible neurotoxicity. *Journal of Clinical Psychiatry*, **44**, 30–31.

COPPEN, A., SHAW, D. M. & FARRELL, J. P. (1963) Potentiation of antidepressive effect of a monoamine oxidase inhibitor by tryptophan. *Lancet*, **1**, 79–81.

—— SHAW, D. M., HERZBERG, B. & MAGGS, R. (1967) Tryptophan in the treatment of depression. *Lancet*, **2**, 1178–1180.

—— GHOSE, K. & MONTGOMERY, S. (1978) Amitriptyline plasma concentration and clinical effect. *Lancet*, **1**, 63–66.

—— ABOU-SALEH, M. T. & MONTGOMERY, S. (1978b) Continuation therapy with amitriptyline in depression. *British Journal of Psychiatry*, **133**, 28–33.

—— ABOU-SALEH, M. T., MILLN, P., BAILEY, J., METCALF, M., BURNS, B. & ARMOND, A. (1981) Lithium continuation therapy following electroconvulsive therapy. *British Journal of Psychiatry*, **139**, 284–287.

CROME, P. & NEWMAN, R. (1979) Fatal tricyclic antidepressant poisoning. *Journal of the Royal Society of Medicine*, **72**, 649–653.

CRONHOLM, B. & OTTOSON, J. O. (1960) Experimental studies in the therapeutic action of electroconvulsive therapy in endogenous depression. *Acta Psychiatrica Scandinavica* suppl. **145**, 69–101.

CURSON, D. A. & HALE, A. S. (1979) Mianserin and agranulocytosis *British Medical Journal*, **1**, 378–379.

D'ELIA, G. & RAOTMA, H. (1975) Is unilateral ECT less effective than bilateral ECT? *British Journal of Psychiatry*, **126**, 83–89.

—— HANSSON, L. & RAOTMA, H. (1978) L-trytophan and 5-hydroxytryptophan is the treatment of depression. A review. *Acta Psychiatrica Scandinavica*, **27**, 239–252.

—— OTTOSSON, J. O. & STROMGREN, L. S. (1983) Present practice of electroconvulsive therapy in Scandanavia. *Archives of General Psychiatry*, **40**, 577–581.

DALBY, M. M. (1971) Antiepileptic and psychotropic effects of carbamazepine (Tegretol) in the treatment of psychomotor epilepsy. *Epilepsia*, **12**, 325–334.

—— (1975) Behavioural effects of carbamazepine. In: *Complex Partial Seizures and their Treatment*. (ed. J. K. Penry & D. D. Daly) New York, Raven Press.

DANIEL, W. F. & CROVITZ, H. F. (1982) Recovery of orientation after electroconvulsive therapy. *Acta Psychiatrica Scandinavica*, **66**, 421–428.

—— (1983) ECT seizure duration and alleviation of depression. *British Journal of Psychiatry*, **143**, 523.

—— CROVITZ, H. F. (1983a) Acute memory impairment following electroconvulsive therapy. 1. Effects of electrical stimulus waveform and number of treatments. *Acta Psychiatrica Scandanavica*, **67**, 1–7.

—— CROVITZ, H. F. (1983b) Acute memory impairment following electroconvulsive therapy. II. Effects of electrode placement. *Acta Psychiatrica Scandanavica*, **67**, 57–68.

DAVIDSON, J., MCLEOD, M. N. & BLUM, R. (1978) Acetylation phenotype, platelet monoamine oxidase inhibition and the effectiveness of phenelzine in depression. *American Journal of Psychiatry*, **135**, 467–469.

DE MONTIGNY, C., GRUNBERG, F., MAYER, A. & DESCHENES, J. P. (1981) Lithium induces rapid relief of depression in tricyclic antidepressant drug non-responders. *British Journal of psychiatry*, **138**, 252–256.

—— COURNOYER, G., MORISSETTE, R., LANGLOIS, R. & CAILLE, G. (1983) Lithium carbonate addition in tricyclic antidepressant resistant unipolar depression. *Archives of General Psychiatry*, **40**, 1327–1334.

DEHING, J. (1968) Studies on the psychotropic of Tegretol. *Acta Neurologica & Biologica*, **68**, 895–905.

DILSAVER, S. C. & GREDEN, J. F. (1984) Antidepressant withdrawal phenomena. *Biological Psychiatry*, **19**, 237–256.

ECCLESTON, D. (1981) Monoamines in affective illness: is there a place for 5HT? *British Journal of Psychiatry*, **138**, 257–258.

EMRICH, H. M., VON ZERSSEN, D., KISSLING, W., MOLLER, H. S. & WINDORFER, A. (1980) Effects of sodium valporate on mania. The GABA hypothesis of affective disorders. *Archive Psychiatrica Nervenkrank*, **229**, 1–16.

—— VON ZERSSEN, D., KISSLING, W. & MOLLER, H. S. (1982) Antimanic action of propranolol and of sodium valporate. Presented at the *13th C.I.N.P. Congress*, Tel Aviv.

FARAVELLI, C., BALLERINI, A., BROADHURST, A. D. & DAS, M. (1982) Relevance of plasma levels during clomipramine treatment of primary depression. *Journal of Affective Disorders*, **4**, 163–165.

FREEMAN, C. P. L., BASSON, J. V. & CRIGHTON, A. (1978) A double blind controlled trial of electroconvulsive therapy (ECT) and simulated ECT in depressive illness. *Lancet*, **2**, 738–740.

—— WEEKS, D. & KENDELL, R. E. (1980) Patients who complain. *British Journal of Psychiatry*, **137**, 17–25.

FROMM-AUCH, D. (1982) Comparison of unilateral and bilateral E.C.T. — Evidence for selective memory impairment. *British Journal of Psychiatry*, **141**, 608–613.

GHOSE, K. (1978) Effect of carbamazepine in polyuria associated with lithium therapy. *pharmakopsychiatrica Neuropsychopharmakologica*, **11**, 241–245.

GLASSMAN, A. H. & PLATMAN, S. R. (1969) Potentiation of a monoamine oxidase inhibitor by tryptophan. *Journal of Psychiatric Research*, **7**, 83–88.

—— KANTOR, S. J. & SHOSTAK, M. (1975) Depression, delusions and drug response. *Archives of General Psychiatry*, **132**, 716–719.

—— PEREL, J. M., SHOSTAK, M., KANTOR, S. J. & FLEISS, J. L. (1977) Clinical implications of imipramine plasma levels for depressive illness. *Archives of General Psychiatry*, **134**, 197–204.

GOODWIN, F. K., PRANGE, A. J. & POST, R. M. (1982) L-triiodothyronine converts tricyclic antidepressant non-responders to responders. *American Journal of Psychiatry*, **139**, 37–42.

GOSTIN, L. O. (1981) A jurisprudential and ethical examination of electroconvulsive therapy. in: *Electroconvulsive Therapy* (ed. R. L. Palmer), 288–302. Oxford University Press.

GRAD DE ALARCON, J., SAINSBURY, P. & COSTAIN, W. R. (1975) Incidence of referred mental illness in Chichester and Salisbury. *Psychological Medicine*, **5**, 32–54.

GREGORY, S., SHAWCROSS, C. R. & GILL, D. (1985) The Nottingham E.C.T. study: A double-blind comparison of bilateral, unilateral and simulated E.C.T. in depressive illness. *British Journal of Psychiatry*, **146**, 520–524.

GUITIERREZ, J. L. A. & LOPEZ-IBOR, A. J. J. (1971) Tryptophan and a M.A.O.I. (Nialamide) in the treatment of depression. *International Pharmacopsychiatry*, **6**, 92–97.

HENINGER, G. R., CHARNEY, D. S. & STERNBERG, D. E. (1983) Lithium carbonate augmentation of antidepressant treatment — an effective prescription for treatment of refactory depression. *Archives of General Psychiatry*, **40**, 1335–1342.

HESHE, J. & THEILGAARD, A. (1978) Unilateral and bilateral E.C.T. *Acta Psychiatrica Scandanavica* suppl. 275.

HIMMELHOCH, J. M., DETRE, T. & KUPFER, D. J. (1972) Treatment of previously intractable depression with tranylcypromine and lithium. *Journal of Nervous and Mental Diseases*, **155**, 216–20.

INOUE, K., ARIMA, S. & TANAKA, K. (1981) A lithium and carbamazepine combination in the treatment of bipolar disorder — a preliminary report. *Folia Psychiatrica Japan*, **35**, 465–76.

JANICAK, P. G., DAVIS, J. M., GIBBONS, R. D., ERICKSEN, S., CHANG, G. & GALLAGHER, D. (1985) Efficacy of E.C.T. — a meta-analysis. *American Journal of Psychiatry*, **142**, 297–302.

JANKE, W., EHRHARDT, K. J. & MUNCH, U. (1983) Behavioural effects of carbamazepine after single and repeated administration in emotionally labile subjects. *Neuropsychobiology*, **10**, 217–227.

JOHNSTONE, E. C., DEAKIN, J. F. W., LAWLER, P., FRITH, C. D., STEVENS, M., MCPHERSON, K. & CROW, T. J. (1980) The Northwick Park Electroconvulsive Therapy Trial. *Lancet*, **2**, 317–370.

JUEL-NEILSEN, M., BILLE, M., FLYGENRING, J. & HELGASON, T. (1961) Frequency of depressive states within geographically delimited population groups. 3. Incidence. (The Aarhus County Investigation). *Acta Psychiatrica Scandinavica* (Suppl. 162) 69–80.

KANE, J. M., QUITKIN, F. M., RIFKIN, A., RAMOS-LORENZI, J. R., NAYARAK, D. D. & HOWARD, A. (1982) Lithium carbonate and imipramine in the prophylaxis of unipolar and bipolar II illness. *Archives of General Psychiatry*, **39**, 1065–1069.

KETZ, E. (1964) Tegretol — ein neurartiges antiepileptikum. *Praxis*, **53**, 264–269.

KLEIN, D. F. & DAVIS, J. M. (1969) *Diagnosis and Drug Treatment of Psychiatric Disorders* Baltimore, Williams & Wilkins Co.

KLEIN, H. E., BROUCEK, B. & GREIL, W. (1981) Lithium withdrawal triggers psychotic states. *British Journal of Psychiatry*, **139**, 255–256.

KLERMAN, G. L. & COLE, J. O. (1965) Clinical pharmacology of imipramine and related antidepressant compounds. *Pharmacology Review*, **17**, 101–141.

KOTIN, J., POST, R. M. & GOODWIN, F. K. (1973) Drug treatment of depressed patients referred for hospitalization. *American Journal of Psychiatry*, **130**, 1139–1141.

KRAMER, J. C., KLEIN, D. P. & FINK, M. (1961) Withdrawal symptoms following discontinuation of imipramine therapy. *American Journal of Psychiatry*, **118**, 549–550.

KRANMER, B. A. (1983) Seizure parameters in depressed patients receiving electroconvulsive therapy; a study. *Comprehensive Psychiatry*, **24**, 259–261.

LAMBERT, P. A., CARRAZ, G., BORSELLI, S. & BOUCHARDY, M. (1975) Le dipropylacetamide dans le traitment de la psychose maniaco-depressive. *Encephale*, **1**, 25–31.

LAPIERRE, Y. D., GAGNON, A. & KOKKINIDIS, L. (1980) Rapid recurrence of mania following lithium withdrawal. *Biological Psychiatry*, **15**, 859–864.

LAMBOURN, J. & GILL, D. (1978) A controlled comparison of simulated and real ECT. *British Journal of Psychiatry*, **138**, 514–519.

LANCET (1965) Combining the antidepressant drugs. *Lancet*, **2**, 118.

LIPINSKI, J. F. & POPE, H. G. (1982) Possible synergistic action between carbamazepine lithium carbonate in the treatment of three acutely manic patients. *American Journal of Psychiatry*, **139**, 948–949.

LOPEZ-IBOR, A. J. J., AYUSO-GUTIERREZ, J. L. & MONTEJO-IGLESIAS, M. L. (1973) Tryptophan and amitryptiline in the treatment of depression: a double-blind study *International Pharmacopsychiatry*, **8**, 145–150.

MARGO, A. & MCMAHON, P. (1982) Lithium withdrawal triggers psychosis. *British Journal of Psychiatry*, **141**, 407–410.

MARKS, I. (1983) Are there anticompulsive or antiphobic drugs? Review of the evidence. *British Journal of Psychiatry*, **143**, 338–347.

MAVISSAKALIAN, M., TURNER, S. M., MICHELSON, L. & JACOB, R. (1985) tricyclic antidepressants in obsessive-compulsive disorder: Antiobsessional or antidepressant agents? II. *American Journal of Psychiatry*, **142**, 572–576.

MINDHAM, R. H. S., HOWLAND, C. & SHEPHARD, M. (1973) An evaluation of continuation therapy with tricyclic antidepressants in depresive illness. *Psychological Medicine*, **3**, 5–17.

MINTER, R. E. & MANDEL, M. R. (1979) The treatment of psychotic major depressive disorder with drugs and electroconvulsive therapy. *Journal of Nervous and Mental Diseases*, **167**, 726–733.

MORRIS, J. B. & BECK, A. T. (1974) The efficacy of antidepressant drugs. A review of research (1958–1972) *Archives of General Psychiatry*, **30**, 667–674.

MRC (1981) Continuation therapy with lithium and amitriptyline in unipolar-depressive illness: a controlled trial. *Psychological Medicine*, **2**, 409–416.

NELSON, C. J. & BYCK, R. (1982) Rapid response to lithium in phenelzine non-responders. *British Journal of Psychiatry*, **141**, 85–86.

—— JATLOW, P., QUITKIN, D. M. & BOWERS, M. B. Jr. (1982) Desipramine plasma concentrations and antidepressant response. *Archives of General Psychiatry*, **39**, 1419–1422.

NORTHWICK PARK ECT TRIAL (1984) Predictors of response to real and simulated ECT. *British Journal of Psychiatry*, **144**, 227–237.

NORTON, K. R. W., SIRELING, L. I., BHAT, A. V., RAO, B. & PAYKEL, E. S. (1984) A double-blind comparison of Fluvoxamine, Imipramine and Placebo in depressed patients. *Journal of Affective Disorders*, **7**, 297–308.

OKUMA, T., KISHIMOTO, A., INOUE, K., MATSUMOTO, H. K., OGURA, A., MATSUSHITA, T., NAKLAO, T. & OGURA, C. (1973) Antimanic and prophylactic effects of carbamazepine on manic depressive illness. *Folia Psychiatrica Japan*, **27**, 283–297.

—— MANAGA, K., OTSUKI, S., SARAI, K., TAKAHASHI, R., HAZAMA, H. & WATANABE, M. (1979) Comparison of antimanic efficacy of carbamazepine and chlorpromazine: a double-blind controlled study. *Psychopharmacology*, **66**, 211–217.

—— INANAGA, K., OTSUKI, S., SARAI, K., TAKAHASHI, R., HAZAMA, H., MORI, A. & WATANABE, M. (1981) A preliminary double-blind study of the efficacy of carbamazepine in the prophylaxis of manic-depressive illness. *Psychopharmacology*, **73**, 95–96.

OPCS (1974) Morbidity statistics from General Practice 1970–71: Second National Study. Studies on medical and population subjects. No. 26. London, HMSO.

PALMER, R. L. (ed.) (1981) *Electroconvulsive Therapy: An Appraisal*. Oxford University Press.

PARE, C. M. B. (1963) Some clinical aspects of antidepressant drugs in: *The Scientific Basis of Drug Therapy in Psychiatry* (ed. J. Marks & C. B. M. Pare) Oxford, Pergamon Press.

—— MACK, J. W. (1971) Differentiation of two Genetically specific types of depression by the response to antidepressant drugs. *Journal of Medical Genetics*, **8**, 306–309.

PAYKEL, E. S., DIMASCIO, A., HASWELL, D. & PRUSOFF, B. A. (1975) Effects of maintenance of amitriptyline and psychotherapy on symptoms of depression. *Psychological Medicine*, **5**, 67–71.

—— (1979) Predictors of treatment response in *Psychopharmacology of Affective Disorders* (ed. E. S. Paykel, & A. Coppen) Oxford University Press.

—— ROWAN, P. R., PARKER, R. R. & BHAT, A. V. (1982a) Response to phenelzine and amitriptyline in subtypes of outpatient depression. *Archives of General Psychiatry*, **39**, 1041–1049.

—— WEST, P. S. & ROWAN, P. R. (1982b) Influence of acetylator phenotype on anti-depressant effects of phenelzine. *British Journal of Psychiatry*, **141**, 243–248.

PERRY, P. S., MORGAN, D. E., SMITH, R. E. & TSUANG, M. T. (1982) Treatment of unipolar depression accompanied by delusions. *Journal of Affective Disorders*, **4**, 195–200.

POPE, H. W., JONAS, J. M., HUDSON, J. I., & KAFKA, M. P. (1985) Toxic reactions to the combination of monoamine oxidase inhibitors and tryptophan. *American Journal of Psychiatry*, **142**, 491–492.

POST, R. M., BALLENGER, J. C., REUS, V. I., LAKE, C. R., LERNER, P. & BUNNEY, W. E. Jr. (1978) Effects of carbamazepine in mania and depression. Presented at scientific proceedings of the 13th annual meeting of the *American Psychiatric Association New Research Abstracts* No. 7.

—— BALLENGER, J. C., HARE, T. A., BUNNEY, W. E. Jr. (1980) Lack of effect of carbamazepine gamma-amino butyric acid levels in cerebrospinal fluid. *Neurology*, 30, 1008–1011.

—— (1982) Use of the anticonvulsant carbamazepine in primary and secondary affective illness. Clinical and theoretical implications. *Psychological Medicine*, 12, 701–704.

—— UHDE, T. W., BALLENGER, J. C., CHATTERJI, D. C., GREENE, R. F. & BUNNEY, W. E. (1983) Carbamazepine and its 10-11 epoxide metabolite in plasma and C.S.F. relationship to antidepressant response. *Archives of General Psychiatry*, 40, 693–696.

—— UHDE, T. W. (1983) Treatment of mood disorders with antiepileptic medication: clinical and theoretical implications. *Epilepsia*, 24, (Suppl. 2) 97–108.

POTTER, W., MURPHY, D. & WEHR, T. (1982) Clorgine, a new treatment for patients with refractory cycling disorder. *Archives of General Psychiatry*, 39, 505–510.

PRICE, L. H., CHARNEY, D. S. & HENINGER, G. R. (1985) Efficacy of lithium-ranylcypromine treatment in refractory depression. *American Journal of Psychiatry*, 142, 619–623.

PRIEN, R. F., KLETT, C. J. & CAFFEY, E. M. (1973) Lithium carbonate and imipramine in prevention of affective episodes. *Archives of General Psychiatry*, 29, 420–425.

QUITKIN, F. M., RABKIN, J. G., ROSS, D. & MCGRATH, P. J. (1984a) Duration of antidepressant drug treatment. What is an adequate trial. *Archives of General Psychiatry*, 41, 238–245.

—— RABKIN, J. G., ROSS, D. & STEWARD, J. W. (1984b) Identification of true drug response to antidepressants. Use of pattern analysis. *Archives of General Psychiatry*, 41, 782–786.

RAO, R. & COPPEN, A. (1979) Classification of depression in response to amitriptyline therapy. *Psychological Medicine*, 9, 321–325.

RAZANI, J., WHITE, J., SIMPSON, G., SLOANE, R. B., REBAL, R. & PALMER, R. (1983) The safety and efficacy of combined amitriptyline and tranylcypramine antidepressant treatment. *Archives of General Psychiatry*, 40, 657–661.

RAZAVI, D. & MENDLEWICZ, J. (1982) Tricyclic antidepressant plasma levels: the state of the art and clinical prospects. *Neuropsychobiology*, 8, 73–85.

REISBY, N., GRAM, L. F., BECH, P., NAGY, A., PETERSEN, G. O. & ORMAN, J. (1977) Imipramine-clinical effects and pharmacokinetic variability. *Psychopharmacology*, 54, 263–272.

RETT, A. (1962/63) Zur Beurteilungder Wirkung von Anticonvulsiva im Kindersalter — ein Klinisher und entwicklungsphysiologisches Problem. *Neue ost Zeitung Kindecheilk*, 7, 178–191.

ROBIN, A. & DE TISSERA, S. (1982) A double blind comparison of the therapeutic effects of low and high energy electroconvulsive therapy. *British Journal of Psychiatry*, 141, 357–366.

ROWAN, P. R., PAYKEL, E. S., PARKER, R. R. (1982) Phenelzine and amitriptyline: effects on symptoms of neurotic depression. *British Journal of Psychiatry*, 140, 475–483.

—— PAYKEL, E. S., MARKS, V., MOULD, G., BHAT, A. (1984) Serum levels and response to amitriptyline in depressed outpatients. *Neuropsychobiology*, 12, 9–15.

SCHATSBURG, A. F., COLE, J. D. & COHEN, B. M. (1983) Survey of depressed patients who failed to respond to treatment. In *The Affective Disorders* (ed. J. M. Davis & J. W. Maas) Washington DC, American Psychiatric Press.

SCHUKLIT, M., ROBINS, E., FEIGNER, J. (1971) Tricyclic antidepressants and monoamine oxidase inhibitors — combined therapy in the treatment of depression. *Archives of General Psychiatry*, 24, 509–514.

SHATAN, C. (1966) Withdrawal symptoms after abrupt termination of Imipramine. *Canadian Psychiatric Association Journal*, 11, (Suppl.), 5150–5158.

SHAW, D. M. (1983) Resistant depression. In *Affective Disorders: Latest Developments*. Proceedings of The Boots Company Symposia, Nottingham, U.K.

—— JOHNSON, A. L. MCSWEENEY, D. A. (1972) Tricyclic antidepressants and tryptophan in unipolar affective disorder. *Lancet*, 1, 1245.

SHUKLA, S., GOODWIN, C. D., LONG, E. B. & MILLER, M. G. (1984) Lithium-carbamazepine neurotoxicity and risk factors. *American Journal of Psychiatry*, 141, 1604–1606.

SIMPSON, G. M., LEE, J. H., CUCULIC, Z. & KELLNER, R. (1976) Two dosages of imipramine in hospitalized endogenous and neurotic depressives. *Archives of General Psychiatry*, 33, 1093–1102.

172 *Biology of antidepressant drugs*

—— WHITE, K. L., BOYD, J. L., COOPER, T. B., HALARIS, A., WILSON, I. C., RAMAN, E. J. & RUTHER, E. (1982) Relationship between plasma antidepressant levels and clinical outcome from inpatients receiving imipramine. *American Journal of Psychiatry*, **139**, 358–366.

SIRELING, L. I., PAYKEL, E. S., FREELING, P., RAO, B. M. & PATEL, S. P. (1985) Depression in General Practice: case thresholds and diagnosis. *British Journal of Psychiatry*, **147**, 113–118.

SMALL, J. G., SMALL, I. F. & MOORE, D. F. (1971) Experimental withdrawal of lithium in recovered manic depressive patients. A report of five cases. *American Journal of Psychiatry*, **127**, 1555–1558.

SPIKER, D. G., WEISS, J. C., DEALY, R. S., GRIFFIN, S. J., HANIN, I., NEIL, J., PEREL, J. M., ROSSI, A. J. & SOLOFF, P. F. (1985) The pharmacological treatment of delusional depression. *American Journal of Psychiatry*, **142**, 430–36.

SPITZER, R. L. & ENDICOTT, J. (1977) *Schedule for Affective Disorders and Schizophrenia* 3rd ed. New York Biometrics Research, New York State Psychiatric Institute.

SQUIRE, L. R. & MILLER, P. L. (1981) Retrograde amnesia and bilateral electroconvulsive therapy. *Archives of General Psychiatry*, **38**, 89–95.

—— SLATER, P. C. (1983) Electroconvulsive therapy and complaints of memory dysfunctiion — a prospective 3 year follow up study. *British Journal of Psychiatry*, **142**, 1–8.

STANDISH-BARRY, H. M. A. S., DEACON, V. & SNAITH, R. P. (1985) The relationship of concurrent bendoiazepine administration to seizure duration in ECT. *Acta Psychiatrica Scandinavica*, **71**, 269–71.

STEIN, M. K., RICKELS, K. & WEISSE, C. C. (1980) Maintenance therapy with amitriptyline: a controlled trial. *American Journal of Psychiatry*, **137**, 370–371.

TAKEZAKI, H. & HANNOKA, M. (1971) The use of carbamazepine in the control of manic depressive psychosis and other manic depressive states. *Journal of Clinical Psychiatry*, **13**, 173–183.

THOMAS, J. M. & RUBIN, E. H. (1984) Case report of a toxic reaction from a combinatiion of Tryptophan and Phenelzine. *American Journal of Psychiatry*, **141**, 281–283.

THOMSON, J., RANKIN, H., ASHCROFT, G. W., YATES, G. M., McQUEEN, J. K. & CUMMINGS, S. W. (1982) The treatment of depression in general practice: a comparison of L-tryptophan amitriptyline and a combination of L-tryptophan and amitriptyline with placebo. *Psychological Medicine*, **12**, 741–752.

THOMPSON, P., HUPPERT, F. & TRIMBLE, M. (1980) Anticonvulsant drugs, cognitive function and memory. *Acta Neurologica Scandinavica* (Suppl. 80) **62**, 75–81.

THOREN, P., ASBERG, M., CRONHOLM, B., JORNESTEDT, L. & TRASKMAN, L. (1980) Clomipramine treatment of obsessive-compulsives. I. A controlled trial. *Archives of General Psychiatry*, **37**, 1281–1285.

TRIMBLE, M. (1977) The effect of anticonvulsants on mental symptoms and behaviour in *Tegretol in Epilepsy* (ed. F. D. Roberts) Macclesfield, Geigy.

TYRER, P. (1976) Towards rational therapy with monoamine oxidase inhibitors. *British Journal of Psychiatry*, **128**, 354–360.

WALINDER, J., SKOTT, A., CARLSSON, A., NAGY, A. & ROOS, B. E. (1976) Potentiation of the antidepressant action of clomipramine by tryptophan *Archives of General Psychiatry*, **33**, 1384–1389.

—— CARLSSON, A., PERSSON, R. (1981) 5HT reuptake inhibitors plus tryptophan in endogenous depression. *Acta Psychiatrica Scandinavica* (Suppl. 290) **63**, 179–190.

WATT, D. C., CRAMMER, J. L. & ELKES, A. (1972) Metabolism, anticholinergic effects and therapeutic effects on outcome of desmethylimipramine in depressive illness. *Psychological Medicine*, **2**, 397–405.

WEEKS, D., FREEMAN, C. P. L. & KENDELL, R. E. (1980) ECT, enduring cognitive deficits? *British Journal of Psychiatry*, **137**, 26–37.

WEINER, R. D., ROGERS, H. J., DAVIDSON, J. & MILLER, R. D. (1982) Evaluation of the central nervous system risks of E.C.T. *Psychopharmacology*, **18**, 31–34.

WELCH, C. A., WEINER, R. D. & WEIR, D. (1982) Efficacy of ECT in the treatment of depression — waveform and electrode placement considerations. *Psychopharmacology*, **18**, 31–34.

WEST, E. C. (1981) Electric convulsion therapy in depression: a double blind controlled trial. *British Medical Journal*, **282**, 355–357.

YOUNG, J. P. R., LADER, M. H. & HUGHES, W. C. (1979) Controlled trial of trimipramine, monoamine oxidase inhibitors and combined treatment in depressed outpatients. *British Medical Journal*, **279**, 1315–1317.

ZALL, H. (1971) Lithium carbonate and isocarboxazid — an effective drug approach in severe depression. *American Journal of Psychiatry*, **127**, 1400–1403.

10 Antidepressants and monoamines: actions and interactions

A. RICHARD GREEN; GUY M. GOODWIN

The concept that changes in monoamine function might underlie the mechanism of action of antidepressant drugs has been with us for around 30 years. The idea evolved with observations on the changes in monoamine biochemistry which were elicited by the drugs in the brains of experimental animals and while it is still generally considered that the drugs probably act by altering monoamine function, it is still unclear which of the various changes seen in animals might have therapeutic importance. Much effort seems to have been expended on trying to show that all treatments produce a common biochemical change. Implicitly, therefore, it is perhaps assumed that depressive states have a common core pathophysiological change which treatment directly remedies. While there is some logic in this approach, it seems to us that the assumption should be more explicit and that it is unreasonable to ignore the possibility that differences seen in the action of drugs are equally important. Given, for example, the very different mechanisms of action of anti-arrhythmic drugs we should not necessarily anticipate that all antidepressants have a common mode of biochemical action. Furthermore, depressive illness is not clinically a homogeneous phenomenon and there are increasing grounds for offering different treatments depending on the clinical picture (see Paykel, 1985). Indeed, the differences might give us clues as to why one treatment is successful while another fails in a particular patient.

In order to discuss the changes in monoamine biochemistry or function produced by antidepressant treatments it is easiest to discuss their actions on 5-hydroxytryptamine (5HT) and noradrenaline separately before showing that these two neurotransmitter systems are functionally interrelated and thus cannot be considered definitively in isolation.

It is now fair to say that the original hypothesis for the mechanism of action of antidepressants, the so-called catecholamine (Schildkraut, 1965) and indoleamine hypothesis (Lapin & Oxenkrug, 1969; Curzon, 1969) are not supported by much of the current clinical and experimental evidence.

There is little relationship between the time of onset of antidepressant action and the speed with which the drugs inhibit monoamine uptake and indeed, no correlation between inhibition of amine uptake and antidepressant action (Ghose & Coppen, 1977).

This review, therefore, will predominantly focus on the longer term effects of the drugs (around 14 days administration) rather than the acute effects.

Antidepressants and 5HT biochemistry and function

Tricyclic antidepressant drugs inhibit the uptake of 5HT and noradrenaline into the presynaptic nerve ending but have little effect on dopamine uptake. They do not inhibit uptake of the two monoamines equally; some, such as clomipramine, being more potent as 5HT uptake inhibitors, while others, such as desipramine, show greater selectivity towards noradrenaline uptake inhibition (see Iversen & Mackay, 1979; Green & Nutt, 1983). Recently newer drugs have been examined which have marked selectivity as 5HT uptake inhibitors. These include zimeldine and fluvoxamine and there is good evidence that these more selective drugs have antidepressant properties (e.g. Åberg-Wistedt *et al*, 1984).

Recently, most attention has been paid to the consequences of administering antidepressant drugs for 2/3 weeks for changes in 5HT receptors. 5HT receptors have been divided, primarily on the basis of ligand receptor binding techniques, into $5HT_1$ and $5HT_2$ sub-types (Peroutka & Snyder, 1979), although there have been suggestions that the $5HT_1$ sub-type might be further sub-classified (Pedigo *et al*, 1981). Receptor binding methods do not, of course, indicate whether a site has a function. Without demonstration of function a drug binding site remains just that and not a receptor. Fortunately, drugs showing selectivity as agonists or antagonists at $5HT_1$ and $5HT_2$ sites are now being developed and evaluated and there are clear indications that these binding sites of both $5HT_1$ and $5HT_2$ sub-type are indeed functional receptor sites (e.g. Goodwin & Green, 1985; Goodwin *et al*, 1985a).

Peroutka and Snyder (1980) demonstrated that repeated administration of a variety of antidepressant drugs decreased the number of $5HT_2$ binding sites in frontal cortex of rats. This was followed by reports that repeated daily electro-convulsive shock (ECS) increased the number of these receptors (Kellar *et al*, 1981; Vetulani *et al*, 1981). Subsequent investigations showed that the number of $5HT_2$ receptor sites increased when ECS was given in a manner very similar to the clinical administration of ECT; that is, intermittent administration during anaesthesia (Green *et al*, 1983b). There was clearly, therefore, an apparent paradox in that most antidepressant treatments appeared to down-regulate the $5HT_2$ receptor whilst ECS, undoubtedly a very successful treatment for severe depressive illness, up-regulated the receptor. One problem in evaluating the data was that different protocols had been used, particularly in timing the examination of receptor number after the last drug treatment. We decided, therefore, to re-evaluate the effect of antidepressant drugs on $5HT_2$ receptor number, examining this biochemical parameter while the animals were still on drug treatment and after withdrawal, and at the same time examining a functional $5HT_2$ receptor-mediated response.

Peroutka *et al* (1981) had suggested that the head-twitch response in mice which follows administration of 5HT precursors or agonists is $5HT_2$ receptor-mediated and recent evidence (Goodwin & Green, 1985) using some of the new selective $5HT_1$ and $5HT_2$ agonists and antagonists has considerably strengthened this proposal. Therefore, we examined the effects of repeated ECS on both $5HT_2$ receptor number and the functional response of this receptor in the same animals. The reports that repeated ECS increased 5HT-induced head-twitch behaviour (Lebrecht & Nowak, 1980; Green *et al*, 1983a) were confirmed (Table I; Goodwin *et al*, 1984). An increase in $5HT_2$ receptor number (B_{max}) was also observed in the frontal cortex of ECS-treated mice (Table I).

In contrast to the ECS data, repeated administration of tranylcypromine (a monoamine oxidase inhibitor), desipramine (a relatively selective noradrenaline uptake inhibitor) and zimeldine (a relatively selective 5HT uptake inhibitor) resulted in a decrease in $5HT_2$ receptor number in the frontal cortex and a decrease in the head-twitch response (zimeldine data shown in Fig. 1) while the animals were still on drug treatment. Mianserin (a so-called atypical or second generation antidepressant) which does not inhibit monoamine uptake also decreased the behavioural response and the $5HT_2$ receptor number but did so in one day of drug administration (Goodwin *et al*, 1984).

TABLE I

Effect of repeated electroconvulsive shock (ECS) on 5-hydroxytryptophan (5HTP)-induced head-twitch and $5HT_2$ receptor binding

	Behaviour Total head-twitches per 2 min	$5HT_2$ receptor binding B_{max}	K_D
Control	5.9 (8)	207 ± 28 (3)	1.57 ± 0.23 (3)
ECS	14.2 (8)**	248 ± 25 (7)*	1.48 ± 0.92 (7)

Groups of mice received ECS during halothane anaesthesia or halothane alone (controls). Results are shown as mean head-twitch response and mean $\pm$ s.e. mean for binding data (B_{max}: fmol mg^{-1} protein; K_D:nM) with number of observations in parentheses. Different from control: *$p < 0.05$; **$p < 0.01$.
Reproduced from Goodwin *et al* (1984) with permission of Macmillan Journals.

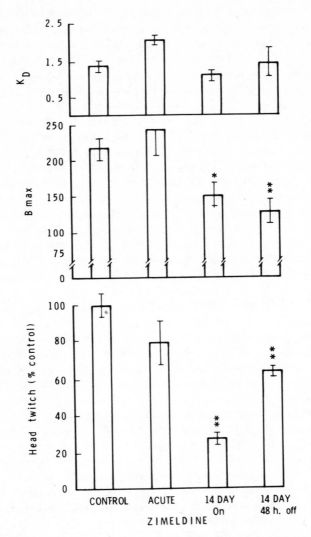

Fig. 1—The parameters of specific [3]-spiperone binding (K_D:nM; B_{max}:fmol mg^{-1} protein), together with head-twitch response revoked by 5-methoxy-N, N-dimethyltryptamine (20 mg kg^{-1} i.p.) expressed as a percentage of untreated controls run simultaneously. Zimeldine given as loading dose (20 mg kg^{-1} i.p.) then orally (20 mg kg^{-1} per day). Binding and behaviour determined in control (untreated) condition, 24 h and 14 d after starting drug treatment and 48 h after discontinuing chronic (14 d) treatment. Results shown as mean of at least 8 observations (behaviour) and 3 observations (binding); s.e. mean shown by vertical lines. Different from control groups: *$p < 0.05$, **$p < 0.01$.

Reproduced from Goodwin *et al* (1984) with permission of Macmillan Journals.

The fact, therefore, that a range of diverse antidepressant drugs all decreased $5HT_2$ receptor number and the $5HT_2$ receptor-mediated behavioural response while repeated ECS increased both these parameters, precludes the formulation of any simple hypothesis linking changes in $5HT_2$ receptor number and function with antidepressant activity. A further point is that like repeated ECS, repeated administration of both diazepam (Green *et al*, 1985a) and baclofen (Metz *et al*, 1985) also results in increased cortical $5HT_2$ receptor number and $5HT_2$-mediated head-twitch behaviour and neither of these drugs has been reported to have antidepressant properties.

In general there are few indications that antidepressants have any effects on $5HT_1$ receptor binding (Peroutka & Snyder, 1980). However, functional studies have been hampered by the lack of $5HT_1$ selective drugs. Recent studies in our laboratory have suggested that the hypothermic response to the 5HT agonist 8-hydroxy-2-(di-N-propylamino)tetralin (8-OH-DPAT) may be a $5HT_1$ receptor-mediated effect in both rats (Goodwin & Green, 1985) and mice (Goodwin *et al*, 1985a) and studies suggest that antidepressants attenuate this response (Goodwin *et al*, 1985b).

Antidepressants and noradrenaline

As stated earlier, most tricyclic antidepressant drugs inhibit, to some degree, noradrenaline uptake and there are now available drugs with high selectivity for inhibiting noradrenaline uptake, like maprotiline and nomifensine, although the latter is unusual in that it has significant activity as a dopamine uptake inhibitor as well.

By far the most consistent change induced in monoamine biochemistry and function is that produced in cortical beta-adrenoceptors. Vetulani *et al* (1976) observed that repeated administration of tricyclic antidepressants, monoamine oxidase inhibitors and ECS resulted in a decrease in the sensitivity of noradrenaline-sensitive adenylate cyclase. Most antidepressant treatments on longer term administration to rats also decrease the number of beta-adrenoceptors in the cortex (Banerjee *et al*, 1977; Wolfe *et al*, 1978; and see Sulser & Mobley, 1981), although some drugs, such as zimeldine and mianserin, decrease the activity of noradrenaline-sensitive adenylate cyclase but not beta-adrenoceptor number (Sulser & Mobley, 1981). Recently the beta-adrenoceptor agonist drugs salbutamol and the more liposoluble clenbuterol have been reported to have antidepressant properties (Simon *et al*, 1984) and it is worth noting that the latter drug has also been demonstrated to decrease beta-adrenoceptor number in rat brain cortex (Nimgaonkar *et al*, 1985).

Beta-adrenoceptors in the cortex are generally considered to be post-synaptic (Fig. 3). In contrast, the alpha$_2$-adrenoceptors can be both pre-

and postsynaptic (U'Prichard *et al*, 1979) although most attention has focused on the presynaptic receptor when considering the action of antidepressant drugs. The reason for this is that this receptor is thought to control noradrenaline synthesis and release, both peripherally and centrally (Fig. 3) (see Langer, 1977). The pre- and postsynaptic location of this receptor has, almost certainly, resulted in the conflicting data on the effects of antidepressant drugs on the receptor number examined using ligand receptor binding techniques. Attempts have been made, therefore, to try and examine a functional response which would reflect changes in the sensitivity of the presynaptic alpha$_2$-adrenoceptor. In the periphery it has shown that chronic antidepressant drug administration resulted in greater noradrenaline overflow during nerve stimulation, a change which would occur if the alpha$_2$-adrenoceptor was less sensitive (Crews & Smith, 1978).

In studies on the central nervous system, the drug clonidine, which acts at low dose preferentially on the presynaptic alpha$_2$-adrenoceptor as an agonist (Anden *et al*, 1976), has been used extensively. Sugrue (1981), for example, has shown that longer term administration of several antidepressant drugs attenuates the decrease in brain MOPEG-SO$_4$ concentration induced by clonidine injection, implying that clonidine was less able to decrease noradrenaline synthesis because it was acting on a subsensitive

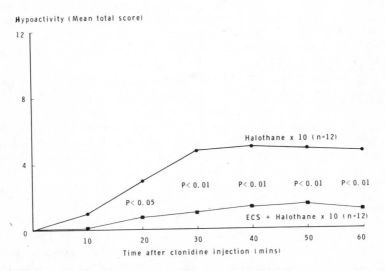

Fig. 2 — Effect of repeated ECS on clonidine-induced hypoactivity in rats. Rats were given either an ECS during halothane anaesthesia (■) or halothane alone (●) once daily for 10 days. Hypoactivity measured after clonidine (0.1 mg/kg) 24 h after the last treatment.

Reproduced from Heal *et al* (1981) with permission of Elsevier.

TABLE II

Effect of repeated ECS on clonidine-induced changes in rat brain MOPEG-SO$_4$ concentration

	MOPEG-SO$_4$ concentration (pmol/g whole brain)	
	Saline-treated	Clonidine-treated
Untreated controls	443 ± 14 (8) ← $p < 0.001$ →	197 ± 22 (5)
Halothane × 10	416 ± 19 (4) ← $p < 0.001$ →	238 ± 21 (8)
	↑ N.S. ↓	↑ $p < 0.02$ ↓
ECS × 10	453 ± 76 (5) N.S.	362 ± 35 (9)

Rats were given a single ECS or halothane once daily for 10 days as described in Methods. 24 h after the final treatment both of these groups plus a group of untreated controls were injected with clonidine (0.25 mg/kg) or saline. 60 min later brain MOPEG-SO$_4$ concentrations were determined. Results are shown as mean $\pm$ S.E. with the number of observations shown in parentheses. Data were analysed using Student's unpaired t-test. N.S. = Not significantly different. Reproduced from Heal *et al* (1981) with permission of Elsevier.

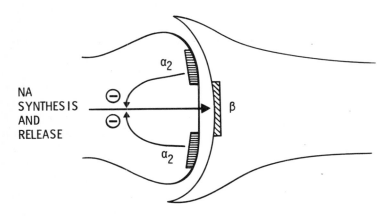

Fig. 3 — Speculative drawing of the relationships between alpha$_2$- and beta-adrenoceptors at the nerve ending. For details, see text.

alpha$_2$-adrenoceptor. Interestingly, repeated ECS has been found by Heal *et al* (1981) to have the same effect (Table II). Low dose clonidine injection also induces a specific type of sedation or hypoactivity and, in line with the MOPEG-SO$_4$ data, some tricyclic antidepressants, mianserin and ECS (Fig. 2) also attenuate the sedation response (Sugrue, 1982; Heal *et al*, 1981; 1983).

It appears, therefore, that a variety of antidepressant treatments are able to decrease the sensitivity of the, presumed, presynaptic $alpha_2$-adrenoceptor. In contrast, a recent study of a functional $alpha_1$-adrenoceptor response, the locomotor response to central injection of phenylephrine has indicated that there are no obvious changes in the function of this receptor following repeated ECS or tricyclic antidepressant drug administration (Heal, 1984).

A major difficulty with these studies is that the receptor changes cannot be considered in isolation. A decrease in the sensitivity of the $alpha_2$-adrenoceptor would be expected to lead to greater transmitter overflow and an increase in the synaptic cleft concentration of the neurotransmitter. Re-uptake inhibition would have the same effect. In contrast, a decrease in beta-adrenoceptor number would diminish the post-synaptic response. It is unknown whether any one of these changes can dominate the overall trans-synaptic function of noradrenaline or whether, less interestingly, these changes merely 'balance out'. A problem in trying to answer this point has been that we do not have a clear understanding of the function of noradrenaline release in brain. However, one recent approach which has proved useful has been to study melatonin production in the pineal since this is under central control via peripheral beta-adrenoceptors. In the rat (Axelrod, 1974) and in man (Cowen *et al*, 1983a) the production of melatonin is dependent upon the activity in the pineal gland of junctions between noradrenaline nerve terminals and post-synaptic pinealocytes carrying beta-adrenoceptors. There is a marked circadian pattern in this activity with melatonin synthesis occurring at night (Axelrod, 1974). In the rat it has been shown that isoprenaline injection leads to a marked increase in melatonin formation during the daylight hours and furthermore, that chronic administration of tricyclic antidepressants attenuates this rise (Cowen *et al*, 1983b; Heydorn *et al*, 1982) consistent with down-regulation of beta-adrenoceptor number and function. This is not a viable approach in man because of the effects of isoprenaline on the cardiovascular system. Nevertheless, in man there is a marked night-time rise and this can be blocked by administration of beta-adrenoceptor antagonists, such as atenolol (Cowen *et al*, 1983a). We have recently investigated the effect of repeated desmethylimipramine treatment on the rise of night-time melatonin content of plasma in normal volunteers (Cowen *et al*, 1985). During the first few days of desmethylimipramine administration there was a marked enhancement of the midnight concentration of plasma melatonin indicating, presumably, an increase in noradrenergic function due to inhibition of noradrenaline re-uptake by the drug. On continued treatment this change was steadily attenuated (Fig. 4) and we interpret this finding as an indication of a decrease in the sensitivity of beta-adrenoceptors during the time of drug administration. It is worth noting that at no time did the response become

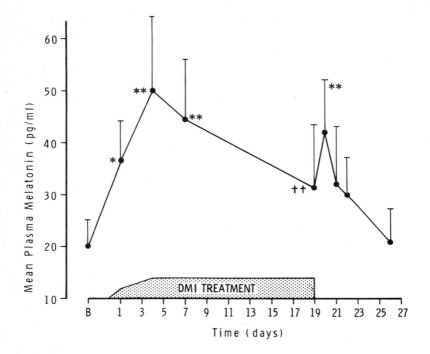

Fig. 4—Mean (± s.e. mean) midnight plasma melatonin concentration in 10 normal subjects before (B), during and after 19 days DMI treatment. For treatment schedule see Methods. Midnight melatonin concentration varied significantly during sampling period. $p < 0.005$, (one-way analysis of variance). Significantly greater than B, *$p < 0.025$, **$p < 0.01$. ††Significantly less than day 4, $p < 0.01$, and day 7, $p < 0.025$ (Fisher's LSD test).
Reproduced from Cowen *et al* (1985) with permission of Blackwell Scientific Publications.

subsensitive (Fig. 4). On drug withdrawal there was a rapid return to normal night-time increases in melatonin content of the plasma.

These results suggest, therefore, that adaptive changes do occur in noradrenaline synapses in man during chronic desipramine treatment but do not, as has been proposed by Vetulani and others, decrease noradrenaline transmission below normal levels. Instead, noradrenaline function is initially enhanced before homeostasis is restored in the presence of the drug. This is certainly true in normal subjects, but of course requires investigation in depressed patients.

Neurotransmitter interactions

The previous sections have considered, in isolation, the effects of antidepressant treatments on monoamine biochemistry and function. However, it is now becoming increasingly clear that altering the function of one neurotransmitter can affect the ability of antidepressant treatments to elicit changes in other neurotransmitter systems.

Repeated ECS enhances the behavioural responses of rodents to 5HT agonists and increases $5HT_2$ receptor number in the cortex (see earlier). It also enhances the behavioural responses of rodents to dopamine mimetic drugs, such as amphetamine and apomorphine (Modigh, 1975; Green *et al*, 1977). In 1980, Green & Deakin demonstrated that a chemical lesion of the noradrenaline pathways in rat brain did not alter the behavioural responses of rats to either a 5HT agonist (quipazine) or a dopamine agonist (apomorphine) compared to sham-lesioned controls despite the marked decrease in noradrenaline content in the brains of the lesioned

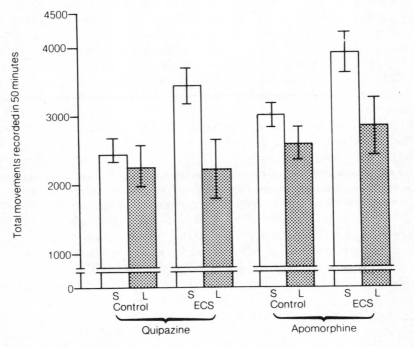

Fig. 5 — The effect of a lesion of the noradrenergic system of rat brain (L) or a sham lesion (S) on the responses of rats to a 5HT agonist (quipazine) or a dopamine agonist (apomorphine). Subsequent administration of electroconvulsive shock (ECS) can be seen to enhance the behaviour of S- but not L-treated rats.
Reproduced from Green & Deakin (1980) with permission of Nature.

animals. However, while repeated ECS administration to the sham-lesioned rats resulted in the expected enhancement of both 5HT- and dopamine-mediated behavioural responses, no enhancement was seen in the animals with the noradrenaline lesion (Fig. 5). Recently, Goodwin & Heal (1985) have confirmed these findings using a different chemical lesioning drug. Pretreatment of rats with the noradrenaline synthesis inhibitor alpha-methyl-p-tyrosine also prevented the enhanced 5HT-induced behaviour (Green *et al*, 1980). The reason for the failure of ECS to enhance 5HT-mediated behaviour in the animals with decreased noradrenaline function appears to be that $5HT_2$ receptor number does not increase (Green *et al*, 1983b). Noradrenaline, therefore, appears to play a permissive role in allowing ECS to increase both 5HT and dopamine function. It is not yet established whether beta-adrenoceptor down-regulation is involved in the effect.

A converse interaction has also now been demonstrated in several studies. Brunello *et al* (1982) and Janowsky *et al* (1982) both showed that a lesion of 5HT pathways to the cortex did not in itself alter the beta-adrenoceptor density in the cortex. However, when these lesioned animals were given repeated desipramine, the beta-adrenoceptor no longer down-regulated as occurs in normal rats given this drug. Dumbrille-Ross and Tang (1983) showed that repeated imipramine administration also failed to decrease beta-adrenoceptor density in the cortex of rats with lesions of 5HT pathways. Brunello *et al* (1982) discussed these observations in terms of 5HT neurones playing a permissive role in the down-regulation of beta-adrenoceptors by desipramine.

Recently we have examined whether intact 5HT innervation was necessary for the occurrence of a decrease in the number of beta-adrenoceptors in the cortex in response to the administration of two entirely different antidepressant treatments, namely, repeated ECS and the beta-adrenoceptor agonist clenbuterol (Nimgaonkar *et al*, 1985).

It was confirmed that repeated desipramine administration decreased beta-adrenoceptor number in intact and sham-lesioned rats but not in rats with a lesion of 5HT pathways (Fig. 6). However, in addition it was observed that the 5HT lesion also abolished the ability of repeated ECS and injection of clenbuterol to decrease beta-adrenoceptor density (Fig. 6).

The data with desipramine clearly indicate that the down-regulation of beta-adrenoceptors by desipramine is not merely the consequence of an increase in synaptic cleft concentration of noradrenaline occasioned by uptake inhibition. This view is strengthened by the ability of ECS to decrease beta-adrenoceptor number, since ECS does not inhibit noradrenaline re-uptake (Hendley, 1976; Minchin *et al*, 1983). Furthermore, even a beta-adrenoceptor agonist (clenbuterol) did not decrease beta-adrenoceptor number in the absence of intact 5HT function. Whether the down-regulation of beta-adrenoceptors cannot occur in the absence of intact 5HT innervation

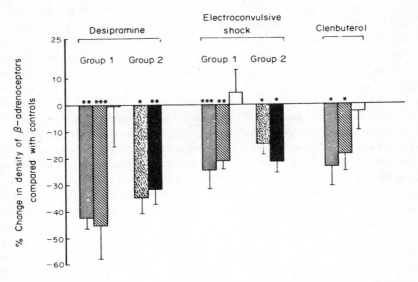

5-HT modulation of β-adrenoceptors

Fig. 6 — Effect of depletion of 5HT on down-regulation of beta-adrenoceptors induced by antidepressants in cerebral cortex of rat. Results show for each treatment from left to right: 1st group, untreated, sham-lesioned, lesioned, 2nd group, saline-injected, PCPA-treated. Different from appropriate controls: $*p<0.05$, $**p<0.25$, $***p<0.005$ (Student's t-test). Results expressed as mean percentage change for control group with s.e. mean shown as bars for 3–7 experiments. No difference in K_D was observed between any of the treatment conditions compared to controls. Reproduced from Nimgaonkar *et al* (1985) with permission of Pergamon Press.

to the cortex or whether the process merely takes longer to occur requires further experimentation.

A further point to be noted in Fig. 6 is that when the 5HT concentration was decreased to that observed after the lesion by use of the 5HT synthesis inhibitor p-chlorophenylalanine, both ECS and desipramine treatment produced a down-regulation of the beta-adrenoceptor number in the cortex. This implies that it is not 5HT itself which is playing a permissive role in the beta-adrenoceptor number decrease but rather some other compound present in the 5HT terminals which is removed by the lesion but not the 5HT synthesis inhibitor (Nimgaonkar *et al*, 1985).

General conclusions

Repeated administration of antidepressant treatments to experimental animals produces a variety of changes in monoamine biochemistry and function. The problem remains, however, of deciding whether any of the changes seen have significance in terms of the mechanism of therapeutic action. Some of the changes seen could be an adaptive change of the neurotransmitter system in an effort to maintain homeostasis. Furthermore, it is naive to assign a change in the function of a neurotransmitter system on the basis of a change at one part of the synapse; for example, that beta-adrenoceptor down-regulation will result in a decrease in noradrenergic transmission.

While it is likely that more selective drugs will be developed, it is not certain that they will give greater insight into the mechanisms involved in their therapeutic action because of the complexity of interaction occurring between monoamine systems. Beta adrenoceptor agonists, for example, do decrease beta-adrenoceptor number, as might be expected for any agonist. However, they require 5HT innervation to be intact (see earlier) and they also enhance 5HT-mediated behavioural responses (e.g. Cowen *et al*, 1982; Nimgaonkar *et al*, 1983; Green *et al*, 1983a; Green *et al*, 1986). These interactions may be important to the mechanism of action of the drugs but make it difficult to propose a therapeutic approach which will have selectivity of action on a single neurotransmitter and therefore perhaps a lower incidence of unwanted side effects.

Lastly, interpretation of treatment effects in animals will always be heavily dependent upon a comparison with clinical phenomena produced by the same treatments in patients and volunteers. At present there is relatively little detailed description of how different drugs alter individual depressive symptoms in different patient groups and with what speed of onset. We are convinced that greater insight into the pathophysiology of depressive illness can proceed from an improved understanding of the mechanisms of treatment effects. However, clinical studies and basic research must increasingly be designed and performed in parallel to allow this approach a clear chance of success.

References

ÅBERG-WISTEDT, A., ROSS, S. B., JOSTELL, K.-G. & SJÖQVIST, F. (1984) A double blind study of zimelidine, a serontonin uptake inhibitor in endogenous depression: clinical and biochemical findings. *Advances in Biochemical Psychopharmacology*, **39**, pp. 439–447. (eds. E. Usdin, M. Asberg, L. Bertilsson & E. F. Sjöqvist.) New York: Raven Press.

ANDEN, N.-E., GRABOWSKA, M. & STRÖMBON, U. (1976) Different alpha-adrenoceptors in the central nervous system mediating biochemical and functional effects of clonidine and receptor blocking agents. *Naunyn-Schmiedeberg's Archives of Pharmacology*, **292**, 43–52.

AXELROD, J. (1974) The pineal gland: a neurochemical transducer. *Science*, **184**, 1341–1348.

BANERJEE, S. P., KUNG, L. S., RIGGI, S. J. & CHANDA, S. K. (1977) Development of beta-adrenergic receptor subsensitivity by antidepressants. *Nature*, **268**, 455–456.

BRUNELLO, N., BARBACCIA, M. L., CHUANG, D. M. & COSTA, E. (1982) Down-regulation of beta-adrenergic receptors following repeated injections of desmethylimipramine: permissive role of serotonergic axons. *Neuropharmacology*, **21**, 1145–1149.

COWEN, P. J., GRAHAME-SMITH, D. G., GREEN, A. R. & HEAL, D. J. (1982) Beta-adrenoceptor agonists enhance 5-hydroxytryptamine-mediated behavioural responses. *British Journal of Pharmacology*, **76**, 265–270.

—— FRASER, S., SAMMONS, R. & GREEN, A. R. (1983a) Atenolol reduces plasma melatonin concentration in man. *British Journal of Clinical Pharmacology*, **15**, 579–581.

—— GRAHAME-SMITH, D. G., GREEN, A. R. & STANFORD, C. (1983b) The effect of chronic antidepressant administration on beta-adrenoceptor function of the rat pineal. *British Journal of Pharmacology*, **78**, 89–96.

—— GREEN, A. R., GRAHAME-SMITH, D. G. & BRADDOCK, L. E. (1985) Plasma melatonin during desmethylimipramine treatment: evidence for changes in noradrenergic transmission. *British Journal of Clinical Pharmacology*, **19**, 799–805.

CREWS, F. T. & SMITH, C. B. (1978) Potentiation of responses to adrenergic nerve stimulation in isolated rat atria during chronic tricyclic antidepressant administration. *Science*, **202**, 322–324.

CURZON, G. (1969) Tryptophan pyrrolase — a biochemical factor in depressive illness. *British Journal of Psychiatry*, **115**, 1367–1374.

DUMBRILLE-ROSS, A. & TANG, S. W. (1983) Noradrenergic and serotonergic input necessary for imipramine induced changes in beta but not S_2 receptor densities. *Psychiatric Research*, **9**, 207–215.

GHOSE, K. & COPPEN, A. (1977) Noradrenaline, depressive illness and the action of amitriptyline. *Psychopharmacology*, **54**, 57–60.

GOODWIN, G. M. & GREEN, A. R. (1985) A behavioural and biochemical study in mice and rats of putative agonists and antagonists for $5HT_1$ and $5HT_2$ receptors. *British Journal of Pharmacology*, **84**, 743–753.

—— & HEAL, D. J. (1985) DSP-4 lesioning abolishes the enhanced monoamine-mediated behaviour following repeated electroconvulsive shock. *British Journal of Pharmacology*, **84**, 53P.

—— GREEN, A. R. & JOHNSON, P. (1984) $5HT_2$ receptor characteristics in frontal cortex and $5HT_2$ receptor-mediated head-twitch behaviour following antidepressant treatment to mice. *British Journal of Pharmacology*, **83**, 235–242.

—— DE SOUZA, R. J. & GREEN, A. R. (1985a) The pharmacology of the hypothermic response in mice to 8-hydroxy-2-(di-N-propylamino)tetralin (8-OH-DPAT): a model of presynaptic $5HT_1$ function. *Neuropharmacology* **24**, 1187–1194.

—— DE SOUZA, R. J. & GREEN, A. R. (1985b) Presynaptic serotonin receptor-mediated response in mice attenuated by antidepressant drugs and electroconvulsive shock. *Nature*, **317**, 531–533.

GREEN, A. R. & DEAKIN, J. F. W. (1980) Brain noradrenaline depletion prevents ECS-induced enhancement of serotonin- and dopamine-mediated behaviour. *Nature*, **285**, 232–233.

—— & NUTT, D. J. (1983) Antidepressants. In *Psychopharmacology* I/1 (eds. D. G. Grahame-Smith & P. J. Cowen). Amsterdam: Elsevier/Excerpta Medica.

—— COSTAIN, D. W. & DEAKIN, J. F. W. (1980) Enhanced 5-hydroxytryptamine and dopamine-mediated behavioural responses following convulsions. III. The effects of monoamine antagonists and synthesis inhibitors on the ability of electroconvulsive shock to enhance responses. *Neuropharmacology*, **19**, 907–914.

—— HEAL, D. J. & GRAHAME-SMITH, D. G. (1977) Further observations on the effect of repeated electroconvulsive shock on the behavioural responses of rats produced by increases in the functional activity of brain 5-hydroxytryptamine and dopamine. *Psychopharmacology*, **52**, 195–200.

—— JOHNSON, P., LAURENCE, B. E. & NIMGAONKAR, V. L. (1983a) Antidepressant treatments: effects in rodents on dose-response curves of 5-hydroxytryptamine- and dopamine-mediated behaviours and $5HT_2$ receptor number in frontal cortex. *British Journal of Pharmacology*, **80**, 377–385.

—— JOHNSON, P. & NIMGAONKAR, V. L. (1983b) Increased 5HT receptor number in brain as a probable explanation for the enhanced 5-hydroxytryptamine-mediated behaviour following repeated electroconvulsive shock administration to rats. *British Journal of Pharmacology*, **80**, 173–177.

—— MOUNTFORD, J. A. & NIMGAONKAR, V. L. (1985a) Some anticonvulsant drugs alter monoamine-mediated behaviour in mice in ways similar to electroconvulsive shock: implications for antidepressant therapy. *British Journal of Pharmacology*, **82**, 337–346.

—— GOODWIN, G. M., DE SOUZA, R. J. & HEAL, D. J. (1986) The beta-adrenoceptor agonists clenbuterol and salbutamol enhance the hypothermic action of 8-hydroxy-2-(di-N-propylamino)tetralin (8-OH-DPAT) by a central mechanism. *Neuropharmacology* **25**, 21–24.

HEAL, D. J. (1984) Phenylephrine-induced activity in mice as a model of central alpha₁-adrenoceptor function. Effects of acute repeated administration of antidepressant drugs and electroconvulsive shock. *Neuropharmacology*, **23**, 1241–1251.

—— AKAGI, H., BOWDLER, J. M. & GREEN, A. R. (1981) Repeated electroconvulsive shock attenuates clonidine-induced hypoactivity in rodents. *European Journal of Pharmacology*, **75**, 231–237.

—— LISTER, S., SMITH, S. L., DAVIES, C. L., MOLYNEUX, S. G. & GREEN, A. R. (1983) The effects of acute and repeated administration of various antidepressants on clonidine-induced hypoactivity in mice and rats. *Neuropharmacology*, **22**, 983–992.

HENDLEY, E. D. (1976) Electroconvulsive shock and norepinephrine uptake kinetics in rat brain. *Psychopharmacology Communications*, **2**, 17–25.

HEYDORN, W. E., BRUNSWICK, D. J. & FRAZER, A. (1982) Effect of treatment of rats with antidepressants on melatonin concentrations in the pineal gland and serum. *Journal of Pharmacology and Experimental Therapeutics*, **222**, 534–542.

IVERSEN, L. L. & MACKAY, A. V. P. (1979) Pharmacodynamics of antidepressants and antimanic drugs. In *Psychopharmacology of Affective Disorders* (ed. E. S. Paykel & A. Coppen). Oxford: Oxford University Press.

JANOWSKY, A., OKADA, F., MANIER, D. H., APPLEGATE, C. D., SULSER, F. & STERANKA, L. R. (1982) Role of serotonergic input in the regulation of the beta-adrenergic receptor-coupled adenylate cyclase system. *Science*, **218**, 900–901.

KELLAR, K. J., CASCIO, C. S., BUTLER, J. A. & KURTZKE, R. W. (1981) Differential effects of electroconvulsive shock and antidepressant drugs on serotonin-2-receptor in rat brain. *European Journal of Pharmacology*, **69**, 515–518.

LANGER, S. Z. (1977) Presynaptic receptors and their role in the regulation of transmitter release. *British Journal of Pharmacology*, **60**, 481–497.

LAPIN, I. P. & OXENKRUG, G. F. (1969) Intensification of the central serotonergic processes as a possible determinant of the thymoleptic effect. *Lancet*, **1**, 132–136.

LEBRECHT, U. & NOWAK, J. Z. (1980) Effect of single and repeated electroconvulsive shock on serotonergic system in rat brain. II. Behavioural studies. *Neuropharmacology*, **19**, 1049–1053.

METZ, A., GOODWIN, G. M. & GREEN, A. R. (1985) Baclofen administration to mice increases 5HT₁-mediated head-twitch behaviour and 5HT receptor number in frontal cortex. *Neuropharmacology*, **24**, 357–360.

MINCHIN, M. C. W., WILLIAMS, J., BOWDLER, J. M. & GREEN, A. R. (1983) The effect of electroconvulsive shock on the uptake and release of noradrenaline and 5-hydroxytryptamine in rat brain slices. *Journal of Neurochemistry*, **40**, 765–768.

MODIGH, K. (1975) Electroconvulsive shock and postsynaptic catecholamine effects: increased psychomotor stimulant action of apomorphine and clonidine in reserpine pretreated mice by repeated ECS. *Journal of Neural Transmission*, **36**, 19–32.

NIMGAONKAR, V. L., GREEN, A. R., COWEN, P. J., HEAL, D. J., GRAHAM-SMITH, D. G. & DEAKIN, J. F. W. (1983) Studies on the mechanisms by which clenbuterol, a beta-adrenoceptor agonist enhances 5HT-mediated behaviours and increases brain 5HT metabolism in the rat. *Neuropharmacology*, **22**, 739–749.

—— GOODWIN, G. M., DAVIES, C. L. & GREEN, A. R. (1985) Down-regulation of beta-adrenoceptors in rat cortex by repeated administration of desipramine, electroconvulsive shock and clenbuterol requires 5HT neurones but not 5HT. *Neuropharmacology*, **24**, 279–283.

PAYKEL, E. S. (1985) Recent advances in therapy. *British Journal of Psychiatry*, (This volume).

PEDIGO, N. W., YAMAMURA, H. I. & NELSON, D. L. (1981) Discrimination of multiple [³H]-5-5hydroxytryptamine binding sites by the neuroleptic spiperone in rat brain. *Journal of Neurochemistry*, **36**, 220–226.

PEROUTKA, S. J. & SNYDER, S. H. (1979) Multiple serotonin receptors: differential kinding of [³H]-hydroxytryptamine, [³H]-lysergic acid diethylamide and [³H]spiroperidol. *Molecular Pharmacology*, **16**, 687–699.

—— & SNYDER, S. H. (1980) Long term antidepressant treatment decreases spiroperidol-labelled serotonin receptor binding. *Science*, **210**, 88–90.

—— LEBOVITZ, R. M. & SNYDER, S. H. (1981) Two distinct serotonin receptors with different physiological functions. *Science*, **212**, 827–829.

SCHILDKRAUT, J. J. (1965) The catecholamine hypothesis of affective disorders: a review of the supporting evidence. *American Journal of Psychiatry*, **122**, 509–522.

SIMON, P., LECRUBIER, Y., JOUVENT, R., PUECH, A. & WIDLOCHER, D. (1984) Beta-receptor stimulation in the treatment of depression. *Advances in Biochemical Psychopharmacology*, **39**, 293–299. (eds. E. Usdin, M. Åsberg, L. Bertilsson, & F. Sjöqvist.) New York: Raven Press.

SUGRUE, M. F. (1981) Effects of acutely chronically administered antidepressants on the clonidine-induced decrease in rat brain 3-methoxy-4-hydroxyphenylethyleneglycol sulphate content. *Life Sciences*, **28**, 377–384.

—— (1982) A study of the sensitivity of rat brain alpha$_2$-adrenoceptors during chronic antidepressant treatments. *Naunyn-Schmiedeberg's Archives of Pharmacology*, **320**, 90–96.

SULSER, F. & MOBLEY, P. L. (1981) Regulation of central noradrenergic receptor functions: new vistas on the mode of action of antidepressant treatments. In *Neuroregulators: basic and clinical aspects*. (eds. E. Usdin, J. M. Davis & W. E. Bunney). Chichester: John Wiley & Sons.

U'PRICHARD, D., BECHTEL, W., ROUST, B. & SNYDER, S. H. (1979) Multiple apparent alpha noradrenergic receptor binding sites in rat brain: effect of 6-hydroxydopamine. *Molecular Pharmacology*, **16**, 47–60.

VETULANI, J., STAWARZ, R., DINGELL, J. V. & SULSER, F. (1976) A possible common mechanism of action of antidepressant treatments. Reduction in the sensitivity of noradrenergic cyclic AMP generating system in the rat limbic forebrain. *Naunyn-Schmiedeberg's Archives of Pharmacology*, **293**, 109–114.

—— LEBRECHT, U. & PILC, A. (1981) Enhancement of responsiveness of the central serotonergic system and serotonin-2-receptor density in rat frontal cortex by electroconvulsive treatments. *European Journal of Pharmacology*, **76**, 81–85.

WOLFE, B. B., HARDEN, T. K., SPORN, J. R. & MOLINOFF, P. B. (1978) Presynaptic modulation of beta-adrenergic receptors in rat cerebral cortex after treatment with antidepressants. *Journal of Pharmacology and Experimental Therapeutics*, **207**, 446–457.

11 Antidepressant drugs and the autonomic nervous system

E. SZABADI; C. M. BRADSHAW

The three major classes of antidepressants (tricyclic antidepressants, monoamine oxidase inhibitors, 'novel' or 'atypical' antidepressants) are widely used in the treatment of depression, and their clinical effectiveness is well established (see Paykel & Coppen, 1979). The ideal antidepressant drug would only have a central mood-elevating ('antidepressant') effect without affecting the functions of peripheral tissues. Most of the currently available antidepressants, however, have profound effects on the peripheral autonomic nervous system, and thus on the activity of tissues receiving an autonomic innervation. The effects of antidepressant drugs on the peripheral autonomic nervous system are responsible for many of the therapeutically irrelevant side-effects of these drugs which can cause discomfort to the patient, adversely affect patient compliance, and put the patient's life at risk.

Apart from their great clinical importance, the peripheral autonomic effects of antidepressants are also of theoretical significance since the actions of these drugs on peripheral autonomic neurones can give us insights into the possible actions of these drugs at analogous sites in the central nervous system. This possibility arises from the fact that the two kinds of autonomic effector neurones, i.e. the cholinergic and (nor)adrenergic neurones, also occur in the central nervous system, and there is a large body of evidence indicating that the peripheral and central neurones are indistinguishable in terms of their biochemical and physiological properties, and also that the post-junctional receptors linked to them have very similar pharmacological properties (see McGeer et al, 1978; Szabadi et al, 1978; 1985). Indeed, the discovery of the blockade of the uptake of noradrenaline into sympathetically innervated tissues in the periphery (e.g. spleen, nictitating membrane) by tricyclic antidepressant drugs (see Iversen & Mackay, 1979) led to the search for a similar effect in the brain, and finally to the formulation of the first biological theory (the 'catecholamine theory') of affective disorders (Schildkraut, 1965). According to this theory tricyclic antidepressants exert their therapeutic effect by blocking the (re)uptake of noradrenaline into central noradrenergic nerve terminals, thereby causing an enhancement of the effects of noradrenaline released from these terminals. Conversely, a change in central (nor)adrenergic mechanisms should be accompanied by corresponding changes in the periphery, providing suitable peripheral markers for the central actions of these drugs. Thus, the recently discovered reduction in central beta-adrenoceptor numbers and biochemical responses mediated by them following chronic treatment with antidepressants (see Charney *et al*, 1981; Sugrue, 1983) are expected to be reflected in similar changes in peripheral beta-adrenoceptors.

Sites of action of antidepressants in the autonomic nervous system

Most of the known peripheral autonomic effects of antidepressants are exerted at the level of the peripheral autonomic junction (Fig. 1).

Cholinergic neuroeffector junction

The most important effect of tricyclic antidepressants at the *cholinergic junction* is the blockade of post-junctional muscarinic cholinoceptors, which results in the antagonism of the effects of released acetylcholine and thus in the

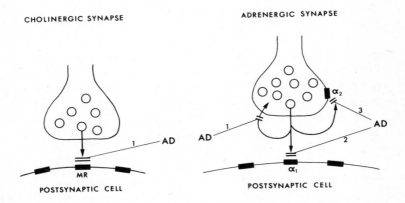

Fig. 1 — Possible sites of action of antidepressants at the autonomic neuroeffector junction. *Cholinergic synapse: (1) tricyclic and some 'novel' antidepressants (AD) block post-junctional muscarinic receptors (MR). Adrenergic synapse*: tricyclic and some 'novel' antidepressants (1) block the uptake of released noradrenaline, resulting in the potentiation of transmission, (2) block post-junctional alpha$_1$-adrenoceptors resulting in antagonism of transmission, (3) block release-modulating prejunctional alpha$_2$-adrenoceptors resulting in enhancement of transmission. Please note that the action of monoamine oxidase inhibitors is not shown in this simplifed diagram.

blockade of cholinergic autonomic neurotransmission. This effect is often referred to as the 'atropine-like' effect of the antidepressants and is generally held responsible for most of the troublesome side-effects of these drugs. The blockade of muscarinic receptors by the tricyclic antidepressants is well documented both in receptor binding (e.g. Snyder & Yamamura, 1977; Richelson & Nelson, 1984) and in functional pharmacological (Atkinson & Ladinsky, 1972; Bevan *et al*, 1975) experiments. There are great differences between the affinities of different antidepressants for the muscarinic receptor, amitriptyline showing the highest affinity, and some of the 'novel' or 'atypical' antidepressants (e.g. trazodone, nomifensine) showing a very low affinity for this receptor (Richelson & Nelson, 1984).

Adrenergic neuroeffector junction

Synaptic disposal of noradrenaline

Most antidepressants inhibit the synaptic disposal of noradrenaline either (1) by inhibiting the mitochondrial enzyme monoamine oxidase (monoamine oxidase inhibitors) or (2) by blocking the uptake of noradrenaline into the presynaptic nerve terminal (tricyclic and some 'atypical' antidepressants). The result of these effects is potentiation of the post-junctional effects of endogenously released or exogenously administered noradrenaline (see Iversen & Mackay, 1979).

Adrenoceptors

Adrenoceptors are classified on the basis of the relative potencies of agonists and antagonists, as alpha- and beta-adrenoceptors; more recently subclasses (alpha$_1$, alpha$_2$, beta$_1$, beta$_2$) of these receptor types have been identified (see Szabadi *et al*, 1978; 1985). Both alpha- and beta-adrenoceptors can occur both pre- and post-junctionally: while the pre-junctional receptors may modify the release of noradrenaline, the post-junctional receptors mediate the response of the tissue to noradrenaline.

Alpha-adrenoceptors   Alpha$_1$-adrenoceptors are located mainly post-junctionally, and are the major receptor type responsible for adrenergic smooth muscle contraction (dilator muscle of the iris, vascular smooth muscle, vas deferens). Many tricyclic antidepressants (e.g. amitriptyline, doxepin, trimipramine), and some 'atypical' antidepressants (e.g. mianserin, trazodone) have considerable affinities for these receptors (Richelson & Nelson, 1984). The blockade of alpha$_1$-adrenoceptors results in a reduction of noradrenergic neurotransmission and in the antagonism of the effects of exogenously administered noradrenaline and other alpha$_1$-adrenoceptor agonists. Alpha$_2$-adrenoceptors are located mainly on the pre-junctional terminal and their activation by the released noradrenaline is believed to result in the feedback inhibition of the release of noradrenaline (Starke, 1978). While tricyclic antidepressants have a relatively low affinity for this receptor, some of the novel antidepressants (e.g. mianserin, trazodone) are effective blockers of alpha$_2$-adrenoceptors (Richelson & Nelson, 1984). The blockade of prejunctional alpha$_2$-adrenoceptors is expected to result in an enhanced release of noradrenaline, and thus in the facilitation of noradrenergic neurotransmission (see Starke, 1978).

<u>Beta-adrenoceptors</u>   Beta$_1$-adrenoceptors are the receptor type responsible for the positive chronotropic and inotropic effects of adrenaline and noradrenaline in the heart, whereas beta$_2$-adrenoceptors are involved in mediating relaxation of bronchial and vascular smooth muscle. It has been suggested that there may be differences between the locations of the two beta-receptor subtypes, beta$_1$-receptors occurring post-junctionally, and beta$_2$-receptors extra-junctionally; thus beta$_1$-receptors would be activated by synaptically released noradrenaline, while beta$_2$-receptors would be stimulated by circulating adrenaline (Ariëns & Simonis, 1983). Release-modulating pre-junctional beta-adrenoceptors have also been described, and these receptors are thought to facilitate the release of noradrenaline (Langer & Dubocovich, 1978).

Antidepressants of different classes have only a very low affinity for beta-adrenoceptors. More recently, however, it has been shown that long-term administration of antidepressants of different classes results in a reduction in the number of beta-adrenoceptors and in some biochemical responses (e.g. enhancement of cyclic AMP production) mediated by beta-adrenoceptors in the brain of experimental animals (see Charney *et al*, 1981; Sugrue, 1983). It is not known, however, how long-term antidepressant administration affects beta-adrenoceptors in the periphery. It is noteworthy that the administration of antidepressants is not associated with an increase in asthma attacks in patients (for review see Van der Kolk *et al*, 1978); this would argue against a reduction in the effectiveness of beta$_2$-adrenoceptors in the airways. It should be noted, however, that the reduction in beta-adrenoceptor numbers and in the pharmacological responses mediated by them may be confined to beta$_1$-adrenoceptors while beta$_2$-adrenoceptors may be relatively resistant to this effect of the antidepressants (Minneman *et al*, 1979).

In conclusion, the antidepressants have complex actions at the noradrenergic synapse: their pre-junctional effects (inhibition of monoamine oxidase and noradrenaline uptake, blockade of release-modulating alpha$_2$-adreno-ceptors) resulting in potentiation, and their post-junctional effect (blockade of alpha$_1$-adrenoceptors) resulting in antagonism of transmission and of the effects of exogenously administered noradrenaline. The net effect of any particular antidepressant will reflect the action of the drug at all these sites.

Other possible sites

Apart from the cholinergic and adrenergic neuroeffector junctions, anti-depressants may also act at some other sites within the autonomic nervous system. The local anaesthetic effect of tricyclic antidepressants (see Gyermek, 1966) may impair conduction in *peripheral autonomic fibres* contributing to the diminution of some autonomic functions resulting from post-junctional muscarinic receptor and/or alpha$_1$-adrenoceptor blockade. In addition to post-junctional muscarinic receptors, tricyclic antidepressants may also block muscarinic receptors in *sympathetic ganglia* (see Volle & Hancock, 1970) causing a decrease in postganglionic sympathetic outflow. Indeed, it has been shown that the blockade of ganglionic muscarinic receptors is likely to contribute to the reduction in sweat gland activity in human subjects observed following the systemic administration of muscarinic receptor antagonists (Longmore *et al*, 1985a). Apart from blocking ganglionic muscarinic receptors, tricyclic antidepressants may impair ganglionic transmission by potentiating the inhibitory effect of noradrenaline on sympathetic ganglion cells (Cairncross *et al*, 1967; Kadzielawa *et al*, 1968; for a recent review of adrenergic mechanisms in *sympathetic ganglia*, see Brown & Caulfield, 1978). Monoamine oxidase inhibitors may also cause sympathetic ganglion blockade by potentiating the inhibitory effect of noradrenaline on ganglionic transmission; indeed, this mechanism has been used to explain, at least in part, the orthostatic hypotension produced by monoamine oxidase inhibitors (Nickerson & Ruedy, 1975). Finally, antidepressants may influence autonomic functions by a *central* action. Thus the miosis found after the administration of amitriptyline may, at least in part, reflect the sedation production by the drug (Peck *et al*, 1979; Bye *et al*, 1979).

Pharmacodynamic assessment of the effects of antidepressants on the autonomic nervous system

The effect of a systemically administered antidepressant on the autonomic nervous system can be assessed either by measuring the baseline activity of an autonomically innervated tissue or by measuring changes in responses evoked by appropriate cholinoceptor and adrenoceptor stimulants.

Stimulation of muscarinic receptors

A number of selective and potent muscarinic receptor agonists are available apart from acetylcholine. Thus carbachol, a synthetic analogue of acetylcholine, is often used to stimulate cholinoceptors on sweat glands and pilocarpine is used routinely to activate muscarinic receptors in the smooth muscle of the iris; methacholine has been used to activate muscarinic receptors in vascular smooth muscle and salivary glands (Davies & Palmai, 1964).

Stimulation of alpha$_1$-adrenoceptors

Adrenoceptor stimulants can be divided into three groups on the basis of their affinities for the post-junctional alpha$_1$-adrenoceptor and the pre-junctional uptake site (Trendelenburg, 1972); (1) noradrenaline, the natural transmitter, has affinity for both sites; (2) directly acting synthetic sympathomimetic amines, such as phenylephrine and methoxamine, have affinities only for the post-junctional alpha$_1$-adrenoceptor with little or no affinity for the uptake site; (3) indirectly acting sympathomimetic amines, such as tyramine and hydroxyamphetamine, have affinities only for the uptake site but none for post-junctional alpha$_1$-adrenoceptors. Drugs belonging to the last group act indirectly: they are taken up by the noradrenaline uptake mechanism into the sympathetic nerve ending from which they release noradrenaline, which in turn can activate the post-junctional alpha$_1$-adrenoceptor.

Fig. 2 illustrates the mode of action of the three classes of adrenoceptor stimulants and also the ways in which uptake blockade and post-junctional alpha$_1$-adrenoceptor blockade by an antidepressant drug may influence the responses evoked by the three kinds of adrenoceptor stimulant. The *response to noradrenaline* would be potentiated as a result of uptake blockade and antagonised as a result of post-junctional alpha$_1$-adrenoceptor blockade, the net effect reflecting the relationship between these two opposing influences on the size of the tissue response. The *response to a directly acting synthetic*

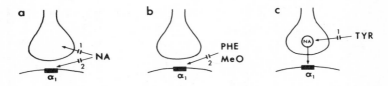

Fig. 2 — Modification of the effects of three classes of adrenoceptor stimulants by tricyclic antidepressants. (a) Natural transmitter: noradrenaline (NA). (b) Directly acting synthetic sympathomimetic amines, e.g. phenylephrine (PHE) and methoxamine (MeO). Indirectly acting sympathomimetic amine, e.g. (tyramine) (TYR). 1: blockade of noradrenaline uptake, 2: blockade of post-junctional alpha$_1$-adrenoceptors. The response to drug (a) will be either potentiated or antagonized depending on the relationship between 1 and 2; responses to drug (b) and (c) will be antagonized by an antidepressant which blocks both noradrenaline uptake and post-junctional alpha$_1$-adrenoceptors. (See text for details).

TABLE I

Changes in baseline autonomic functions and evoked tissue responses as the result of the blockade of muscarinic receptors, noradrenaline uptake, presynaptic alpha₂-adrenoceptors and postsynaptic alpha₁-adrenoceptors

Tissue function/response	Blockade of			
	muscarinic receptors	noradrenaline uptake	presynaptic α_2-adrenoceptors	postsynaptic α_1-adrenoceptors
Salivary glands				
Baseline salivation	decrease	no change	no change	decrease
Sweat glands				
Baseline sweating	decrease	no change[1]	no change[1]	decrease
Carbachol-evoked sweating	decrease	no change	no change	no change
Phenylephrine-evoked sweating	no change	no change	no change	decrease
Iris smooth muscle				
Resting pupil diameter	increase	increase	increase	decrease
Pilocarpine-evoked miosis	decrease	no change	no change	no change
Noradrenaline-evoked mydriasis	no change	increase	increase	decrease
Methoxamine-evoked mydriasis	no change	no change	no change	decrease
Phenylephrine-evoked mydriasis	no change	no change	no change	decrease
Tyramine-evoked mydriasis	no change	decrease	no change	decrease
Vascular smooth muscle				
Baseline blood pressure	no change[2]	increase	increase	decrease
Noradrenaline-evoked pressor response	no change	increase	increase	decrease
Phenylephrine-evoked pressor response	no change	no change	no change	decrease
Tyramine-evoked pressor response	no change	decrease	no change	decrease
Tyramine-evoked hand vein constriction	no change	decrease	no change	decrease
Cardiac muscle				
Resting heart rate	increase	increase	increase	no change[3]

[1] Assuming that sweat glands do not receive a significant adrenergic sympathetic innervation (see text: p. 199)
[2] See Weiner (1980a)

adrenoceptor agonist would be antagonised as a result of post-junctional alpha$_1$-adrenoceptor blockade. Finally, the *response to a directly acting adrenoceptor stimulant* would be antagonised as a result of uptake blockade, the response would be further attenuated as a result of post-junctional alpha$_1$-adrenoceptor blockade. Thus, by using adrenoceptor stimulants belonging to the three classes, it is possible to dissect the presynaptic and postsynaptic effects of antidepressants at the adrenergic synapse, uptake blockade being reflected in the potentiation of the effect of noradrenaline and antagonism of the effect of tyramine, and alpha$_1$-adrenoceptor blockade being reflected in the antagonism of the effects of phenylephrine and methoxamine.

Table I summarises how the four best-documented effects of antidepressants (blockade of muscarinic receptors, noradrenaline uptake, presynaptic alpha$_2$-adrenoceptors, postsynaptic alpha$_1$-adrenoceptors) are reflected in the results of commonly used pharmacodynamic tests in humans. It is noteworthy that, in general, the evoked responses are more specific than just recording changes in baseline functions. Thus, a properly chosen pharmacological challenge (e.g. methoxamine-evoked mydriasis) can be an incisive tool in pin-pointing an action (e.g. blockade of post-junctional alpha$_1$-adrenoceptors).

Effects of antidepressants on autonomically innervated peripheral tissues

Antidepressants have profound effects on most tissues which receive an autonomic innervation. This review is restricted to the discussion of those tissues whose activity has been studied quantitatively under both clinical and laboratory conditions (i.e. salivary and sweat glands, internal muscles of the eye, vascular smooth muscle, and cardiac muscle). So far as the effects of antidepressants on other tissues and organs (e.g. gastrointestinal tract, sexual organs, urinary bladder) are concerned, the reader is referred to the relevant reviews (e.g. van der Kolk *et al*, 1978; Baldessarini, 1980; Mitchell & Popkin, 1983).

Glandular tissue

Salivary glands

<u>Anatonomy and pharmacology</u>   The three pairs of salivary glands (parotid, submandibular and sublingual glands) receive a dual parasympathetic cholinergic/sympathetic adrenergic innervation. It is generally accepted that saliva produced by cholinergic stimulation is abundant and watery, whilst

saliva produced by adrenergic stimulation is of a lesser volume and has greater viscosity (see Brown, 1970). Thus both muscarinic receptor blockade and alpha$_1$-adrenoceptor blockade are expected to result in a reduction in salivary output.

Methods of assessment   There are three ways of measuring salivary output: (1) the salivary output from one gland, e.g. the parotid, can be measured using a suction cup over the opening of the duct of the gland in the oral cavity; (2) saliva collected from all the glands on the floor of the mouth can be removed by suction or by spitting into a measuring cylinder, and (3) saliva obtained from all the glands can be collected in some absorbent material, e.g. dental rolls, and can be removed from the mouth with the collecting material (for review see Brown, 1970; Turner, 1980). The most popular test seems to be the dental roll method originally described by Peck (1959). This method consists of placing three cotton-wool dental rolls in the mouth, two buccally and one sublingually, and measuring the increase in weight of the rolls over a set period of time.

Clinical relevance   The assessment of effects of antidepressant drugs on salivary gland activity is complicated by the fact that salivation is influenced by depressive illness itself. There is an impressive amount of information in the literature showing consistently that salivary output is reduced in depression (Strongin & Hinsie, 1938; Peck, 1959; Busfield et al, 1961; Busfield & Wechsler, 1961; Davies & Gurland, 1961; Gottlieb & Paulson, 1961; Busfield & Wechsler, 1962; Altschule, 1964; Davies & Palmai, 1964; Loew, 1965; Palmai et al, 1967; Noble & Lader, 1971; Bolwig & Rafaelsen, 1972; Toone & Lader, 1979). It has been shown that there is a good correlation between reduced salivation and retardation in depression (Noble & Lader, 1971) and that the physiological diurnal variation in salivary output (i.e. a gradual decrease in salivary output in the course of the day; see Brown, 1970) is reversed in depressed patients (Palmai & Blackwell, 1965). The mechanism underlying the reduction in salivary output in depression is unknown. It is likely that this feature of depressive illness is mainly of central origin since the salivary glands in depressed patients remain responsive to stimulation by systematically injected methacholine, a muscarinic receptor agonist (Davies & Palmai, 1964) and by the local application of citric acid, a directly acting salivary gland stimulant (Davies & Gurland, 1961). The reduction in salivation in depression is of clinical importance since the resultant xerostomia can increase the patient's discomfort and can contribute to the reduction in appetite (Toone & Lader, 1979).

It is well documented that antidepressant drugs reduce salivary output probably mainly by blocking muscarinic receptors on the gland cells but also partly by blocking post-junctional alpha$_1$-adrenoceptors. The resultant xerostomia is a troublesome side-effect of tricyclic antidepressants and probably the factor most commonly jeopardising patient compliance. The xerostomia resulting from the effect of the antidepressant is added to the xerostomia resulting from the depression itself and may further contribute to the patient's dysphoria and loss of appetite. Since tricyclic antidepressants are often administered over several months the long-standing xerostomia can result in an increased incidence of dental decay (Stevens & Wilkinson, 1971; Bertram *et al*, 1979).

Effects of antidepressants on baseline salivation   The effects of antidepressants on salivary output have been studied extensively under laboratory conditions, both in normal volunteers and in patients, mainly using Peck's dental roll technique. The standard protocol for these studies is to compare one or more antidepressants with an antidepressant with well-documented antimuscarinic properties (e.g. amitriptyline: positive control) and also with placebo (negative control). There are great variations in the dosage regimens used in the literature, and therefore comparison between different studies is difficult. However, some conclusions can be drawn (for summary, see Table II).

The results of the studies reviewed in Table II seem to be in good agreement with the reported muscarinic receptor blocking properties of the antidepressants (see Richelson & Nelson, 1984) and the results of other tests of muscarinic receptor blockade in human subjects (see Szabadi *et al*, 1980b). The general conclusion of these studies is that amitriptyline, which is the most potent antimuscarinic agent amongst the antidepressants, causes a considerable reduction in salivary output (a single dose of 100 mg reducing salivation by approximately 70%; see Blackwell *et al*, 1978; Szabadi *et al*, 1980b), followed by doxepin, imipramine, notrtriptyline and clomipramine. Desipramine is much less potent than any of these drugs, and some of the novel antidepressants (mianserin, nomifensine, zimelidine, binodaline, trazodone) are with little effect on salivary output. Reduction in salivary output seems to be a sensitive and reliable measure of peripheral muscarinic receptor blockade. However, it should be borne in mind that the reduction in salivation measured in the presence of an antidepressant is likely to be aggravated by peripheral $alpha_1$-adrenoceptor blockade in the case of antidepressants which have affinity for the $alpha_1$-adrenoceptor.

Sweat glands

Anatomy and pharmacology   Human eccrine sweat glands are innervated mainly by postganglionic cholinergic sympathetic fibres (Sato, 1977). Adrenergic nerve fibres have also been described in the vicinity of sweat glands (Uno, 1977); it is not clear, however, to what extent these fibres form synaptic contacts with the sweat glands themselves or with nearby blood vessels (Jenkinson *et al*, 1978). Sweat glands can be stimulated by both muscarinic cholinoceptor stimulants and by $alpha_1$-adrenoceptor stimulants

TABLE II

Effects of antidepressants on salivary output, resting pupil diameter and heart rate

Measure	Effect	Antidepressant	References
Salivary output	Marked decrease	Amitriptyline	Schubert (1973); Ghose et al (1976a); Blackwell et al (1978; 1980); Kopera (1978); Szabadi et al (1980b); Arnold et al (1981); Rafaelson et al (1981); Longmore et al (1985b; 1986)
		Doxepine	Peterson et al (1978); Blackwell et al (1980); Arnold et al (1981)
		Nortriptyline	Rafaelson et al (1981); Clemmesen et al (1984a; 1984b)
		Imipramine	Blackwell et al (1972; 1980); Sheth et al (1979); Knorring (1981); Rafaelson et al (1981); Clemmesen et al (1984a)
		Clomipramine	Rafaelson et al (1981)
		Maprotiline	Rafaelson et al (1981)
	Moderate decrease[1]	Desipramine	Ghose et al (1977); Blackwell et al (1978; 1980); Szabadi et al (1980b); Arnold et al (1981)
		Butriptyline	Ghose et al (1977)
		Dothiepine	Sheth et al (1979)
	Little/no effect	Mianserin	Kopera (1978); Elliott et al (1981)
		Zimelidine	Borg et al (1979); Rafaelson et al (1981); Knorring (1981); Clemmesen et al (1984a)
		Nomifensine	Rafaelson et al (1981); Clemmesen et al (1984a)
		Binodaline	Longmore et al (1985b)
		Trazodone	Longmore et al (1986)
Resting pupil diameter	Mydriasis	Imipramine	Lauber (1967); Tölle & Pörksen (1969)
		Desipramine	Szabadi et al (1980b); Shur & Checkley (1982); Kerr & Szabadi (1985)
		Amitriptyline	Tölle & Pörksen (1969); Szabadi et al (1975)
		Protriptyline	Tölle & Pörksen (1969); Langham & Carmel (1968)[2]; Kitazawa & Langham (1968)[2]
		Ciclazindol	Kerr & Szabadi (1985)
		Binodaline	Saletu et al (1980)[3]

continued

Measure	Effect	Antidepressant	References
Resting pupil diameter	Miosis	Amitriptyline	Lauber (1967); Lauber et al (1967); Kopera (1978); Peck et al (1979); Saletu et al (1980)
		Trazodone	Karniol et al (1976); Longmore et al (1986)
		Mianserin	Shur et al (1983)[4]
	No change	Amitriptyline	Ghose et al (1974; 1976); Kopera (1978); Szabadi et al (1980b); Longmere et al (1985b; 1986)
		Desipramine	Ghose et al (1977)[5]
		Nortriptyline	Bye et al (1979)
		Butriptyline	Ghose et al (1977)
		Binodaline	Saletu et al (1980); Longmore et al (1985b)
		Mianserin	Ghose et al (1976a)[6]
		Nomifensine	Hamilton et al (1983)
		Bupropion	Peck et al (1979); Hamilton et al (1983)
		Tranylcypromine	Sitaram et al (1983)
Heart rate	Tachycardia	Imipramine	Tölle (1970)
		Desipramine	Rudorfer & Young (1980); Szabadi et al (1980b); Arnold et al (1981)
		Amitriptyline	Tölle (1970); Ikeda et al (1982)
		Nortriptyline	Bye et al (1979)
		Protriptyline	Tölle (1970)
		Mianserin	Elliott et al (1981)
		Nomifensine	Hamilton et al (1983)
		Bupropion	Hamilton et al (1983)
	No change	Amitriptyline	Saletu et al (1980); Szabadi et al (1980b); Arnold et al (1981)
		Doxepine	Arnold et al (1981)
		Nomifensine	Ikeda et al (1982)
		Binodaline	Saletu et al (1980)

[1] less than after amitriptyline or imipramine
[2] topical application
[3] high doses only
[4] 90 mg/day
[5] single dose of 50 mg
[6] 60 mg/day

(Szabadi *et al*, 1980a); the alpha$_1$-adrenoceptors may respond mainly to circulating catecholamines.

Methods of assessment   Numerous methods have been devised to measure the activity of human sweat glands. It is possible to measure evaporation over a circumscribed area of the skin (Foster & Weiner, 1967), to measure electric conductance in the skin (Thomas & Korr, 1957) or to visualise active sweat glands using water soluble or plastic paints. The use of water soluble paints is based on dissolving a substance in the sweat secreted and producing a chemical reaction which results in the staining of the area of skin where sweat glands are active (e.g. the iodine/starch test [Chalmers & Keele, 1951], or the ferric chloride/tannic acid test [Silverman & Powell, 1944]). The plastic paint technique (Thomson & Sutarman, 1953; MacKinnon, 1963) involves coating an area of skin with a water repellent plastic paint in which active sweat glands appear as negative impressions. The layer of paint can then be peeled off the skin and active sweat glands can be counted using a microscope or by projecting the layer of paint onto a screen. This technique has been further developed by Clubley *et al* (1978) for the study of the effects of intradermally injected drugs. Using this method it is possible to measure both the baseline activity of sweat glands and the activation of sweat glands by intradermally injected cholinoceptor and adrenoceptor stimulants. The response to a drug is defined as an increase in the number of active sweat glands, and a full dose-response curve consisting of six data points can be constructed in one experimental session (Clubley *et al*, 1978; Szabadi *et al*, 1980a).

Clinical relevance   There are some indications that depressive illness itself can result in a reduction in sweat gland activity. Thus a reduction in skin conductance and in spontaneous fluctuations in skin conductance (Lader & Wing, 1969; Noble & Lader, 1972), and a decrease in palmar finger sweating (Bagg & Crookes, 1966) have been reported in depressed patients.

It is expected that both the blockade of muscarinic receptors and of alpha$_1$-adrenoceptors by tricyclic antidepressants would result in a decrease in sweating. Although there are reports of decreased sweating in depressed patients treated with tricyclic antidepressants, increased perspiration has also been reported as a side-effect of these drugs (van der Kolk *et al*, 1978; Ziegler *et al*, 1978). The mechanism underlying the increase in sweating is unknown; it is possible that this is due to a central rather than to a peripheral effect of the antidepressants.

Effects of antidepressants on baseline and evoked sweating   A reduction in palmar sweat gland activity has been reported following the administration of amitriptyline, doxepin and trazodone; in the case of the first two drugs this was attributed to the blockade of muscarinic receptors (Arnold *et al*, 1981; Ikeda *et al*, 1982), whereas in the case of trazodone, a drug with little affinity for muscarinic receptors, to general sedation (Karniol *et al*, 1976).

A more sensitive and specific measure of the ability of antidepressant drugs to block muscarinic receptors is the antagonism of carbachol-evoked sweating by these drugs. It has been reported that single doses of both amitriptyline and desipramine can antagonise carbachol-evoked sweating (Szabadi *et al*, 1980b; Longmore *et al*, 1985b); this effect can be detected when there is little change in the baseline activity of sweat glands. A reduction in carbachol-evoked sweating by amitriptyline may be caused partly by the blockade of muscarinic receptors on the sweat glands themselves, but also partly by the blockade of ganglionic muscarinic receptors. Ganglionic blockade would result in a reduction in the activity of sympathetic fibres which in turn could result in a decrease in the pharmacological sensitivity of sweat glands to carbachol (Longmore *et al*, 1985a). Phenylephrine-evoked sweating can be used as a measure of alpha$_1$-adrenoceptor activation. It has been shown that antidepressants with alpha$_1$-adrenoceptor blocking properties (amitriptyline, binodaline, trazodone) reduce phenylephrine-evoked sweating (Longmore *et al*, 1985a; and unpublished observations in our laboratory).

Smooth muscle tissues

Internal muscles of the eye

Anatomy and pharmacology   The internal smooth muscles of the eye (iris, ciliary body) receive a dual sympathetic/parasympathetic innervation. Pupil diameter is controlled by the physiological antagonism between contractions of the sphincter pupillae muscle (which receives mainly a parasympathetic cholinergic innervation linked to post-junctional muscarinic receptors) and of the dilator pupillae muscle (which receives predominantly a sympathetic adrenergic innervation coupled to post-junctional alpha$_1$-adrenoceptors). The ciliary muscle, which is responsible for accommodation, receives mainly parasympathetic cholinergic fibres linked to muscarinic receptors. (For details of anatomy and innervation, see Lowenstein & Loewenfeld, 1962; Havener, 1983).

Methods of assessment   Both pupil diameter and accommodation can be measured under laboratory conditions. Numerous methods have been developed for the measurement of pupil diameter; the two currently used reliable methods are pupil photography (Sneddon & Turner, 1969) and infrared television pupillometry (Lowenstein & Loewenfeld, 1958) (for recent reviews of these methods, see Turner, 1980; Sitaram *et al*, 1983). The assessment of accommodation consists of the determination of the visual near and far points (see Turner, 1980; Gilmartin *et al*, 1984).

Clinical relevance   There is only little information available about possible changes in pupil size in depressive illness. Tölle & Pörksen (1969) and Tölle (1970) compared pupil diameters of a group of depressed patients and a group of non-depressed control subjects: no significant difference was found. These authors thought that there was a relationship between reduction of depressive symptomatology and the development of mydriasis during treatment with tricyclic antidepressant drugs (imipramine, amitriptyline and protriptyline); it is more likely, however, that the mydriasis reflected only the presence of the drugs in the body (cf. Szabadi *et al*, 1975; Shur & Checkley, 1982).

Blurred vision is a well-recognised side-effect of all antidepressants which block muscarinic receptors: this symptom is related to the loss of accommodation resulting from cycloplegia (van der Kolk *et al*, 1978; Baldessarini, 1980). While blurred vision is troublesome it is rarely dangerous. A more serious side-effect is the precipitation of an attack of glaucoma; this propensity of antidepressants is related not so much to muscarinic receptor blockade per se, but to mydriasis, the development of which is influenced not only by cholinergic but also by adrenergic mechanisms (see below).

Effects of antidepressants on resting pupil size and accommodation The original generalisation that neuroleptics constrict and antidepressants dilate the pupil ('thymoleptic mydriasis': Tölle & Pörksen, 1969) has not been borne out by subsequent experimental observation: in fact, antidepressants do not have a uniform effect on resting pupil size, increases, decreases, and no changes having been reported following the administration of different antidepressants (see Table II).

While resting pupil diameter reflects the interplay between mutually antagonistic andrenergic and cholinergic mechanisms, and is also influenced by the level of arousal (see below) accommodation width is controlled mainly by a parasympathetic cholinergic mechanism (see Turner, 1980), and thus drug-induced reductions in this measure yield a relatively uncontaminated index of muscarinic receptor blockade. There is a paucity of quantitative reports on the effects of antidepressants on accommodation; it has been shown that both imipramine and zimelidine impair accommodation, imipramine being the more potent drug (Knorring, 1981), and that small single doses of mortriptyline are without any effect (Bye *et al*, 1979).

Effects of antidepressants on evoked pupillary responses The muscarinic cholinoceptors in the sphincter pupillae muscle can be activated experimentally either by acetylcholine released from nerve terminals via activation of the light reflex, or by topically applied cholinoceptor stimulants, such as pilocarpine (see p. 194). There is only little information on the effects of antidepressants on the light reflex; it has been reported that nortriptyline does not affect the light reflex, while more potent antimuscarinic drugs, such as atropine and procyclidine, reduce it (Bye *et al*, 1979). *Pilocarpine-evoked miosis* has been shown to be antagonised by amitriptyline (Szabadi *et al*, 1980b), unaffected by desipramine (Szabadi *et al*, 1980b), mianserin (Shur *et al*, 1983), and tranylcypromine (Sitaram *et al*, 1983), and potentiated by chronic administration of desipramine (Shur & Checkley, 1982; Kerr & Szabadi, 1985). The mechanism underlying the potentiation is not clearly understood: although it may be, to some extent, related to the increase in resting pupil diameter (Shur & Checkley, 1982), this is unlikely to be the full explanation (see Kerr & Szabadi, 1985).

The alpha$_1$-adrenoceptors in the dilator pupillae muscle can be stimulated experimentally by topically applied agonists (see p. 195). Noradrenaline, the natural transmitter, is a very weak dilator due to the poor penetration of this drug through the cornea (Owe-Larsson, 1956). However, the weak *noradrenaline-evoked mydriasis* can be potentiated by tricyclic antidepressants which block the uptake of noradrenaline into presynaptic terminals, such as protriptyline (applied topically: Kitazawa & Langham, 1968), desipramine and amitriptyline (Szabadi *et al*, 1981). Desipramine has been reported to be approximately four times more potent than amitriptyline in potentiating noradrenaline-evoked mydriasis, probably reflecting the greater affinity of desipramine for the uptake mechanism (see Szabadi *et al*, 1981). The directly acting sympathomimetic amines phenylephrine and methoxamine are effective mydriatics: the responses to these drugs are antagonised by alpha$_1$-adrenoceptor blocking drugs (see p. 195). *Phenylephrine-evoked mydriasis* has been shown to be antagonized by desipramine (Shur & Checkley, 1982), unaffected by mianserin (Shur *et al*, 1983), and some monoamine oxidase inhibitors (iproniazid, isocarboxazid, clorgyline: Bevan-Jones & Lind, 1971), but potentiated by the monoamine oxidase inhibitor tranylcypromine (Sitaram *et al*, 1983). *Methoxamine-evoked mydriasis* has been reported to be antagonised by desipramine (Szabadi *et al*, 1981; Kerr & Szabadi, 1985), amitriptyline (Szabadi *et al*, 1981), and ciclazindol (Kerr & Szabadi, 1985). When the relative potencies of amitriptyline and desipramine in antagonising methoxamine-evoked mydriasis were compared, amitriptyline was twice as potent as desipramine (Szabadi *et al*, 1981). The indirectly acting sympathomimetic amines tyramine and hydroxyamphetamine are potent dilators of the pupil; the mydriatic responses to these drugs are antagonised by antidepressants which block noradrenaline uptake (see p. 195). *Tyramine-evoked mydriasis* has been shown to be antagonised by some tricyclic antidepressants, such as amitriptyline (Szabadi *et al*, 1975; Ghose, 1976; Ghose *et al*, 1976a), desipramine (Shur & Checkley, 1982; Kerr & Szabadi 1985) and ciclazindol (Ghose, 1976; Ghose *et al*, 1976a; Shur *et al*, 1983), and potentiated by some monoamine oxidase inhibitors (iproniazid, isocarboxazid, clorgyline: Bevan-Jones & Lind, 1971; benmoxine: Palm *et al*, 1971). *Hydroxyamphetamine-evoked mydriasis* has been reported to be antagonised by tyramine and unaffected by mianserin (Ghose, 1976).

Fig. 3 illustrates the effects of desipramine and amitriptyline on the mydriatic responses of the pupil to noradrenaline and methoxamine, in the

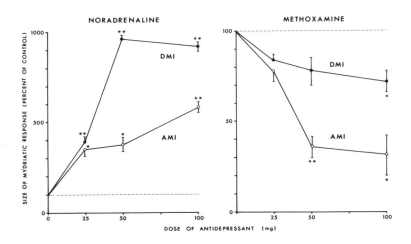

Fig. 3 — Changes in the sizes of mydriatic pupillary responses to noradrenaline and methoxamine in one female subject following the ingestion of single doses of desipramine (DMI) and amitriptyline (AMI). Ordinate: change in the size of the response expressed as a percentage of the placebo control; abscissa: oral dose of antidepressant. Horizontal dotted lines correspond to placebo controls. Each point is the mean of four measurements taken 40, 45, 50 and 55 min after the instillation of the eye-drops; vertical bars signify standard errors of the mean. Asterisks denote values that are significantly different from the placebo control; $*p < 0.05$; $**p < 0.001$ (Student's t-test; paired comparison). Note that both antidepressants potentiated the response to noradrenaline (order of potency: DMI > AMI), and antagonized the response to methoxamine (order of potency: AMI > DMI).
Data reproduced, with permission, from Szabadi *et al* (1981).

same subject: while the response to noradrenaline was potentiated, that to methoxamine was antagonized.

Interpretation of changes in resting pupil size   An antidepressant can produce one of these three effects: mydriasis, miosis, no change. *Mydriasis* can result from the antagonism of cholinergic pupil constriction (muscarinic receptor blockade) or potentiation of adrenergic pupil dilatation (noradrenaline uptake blockade, monoamine oxidase inhibition). *Miosis* can result from potentiation of cholinergic pupil constriction (increased parasympathetic tone resulting from central sedation) or antagonism of adrenergic pupil dilatation (blockade of alpha$_1$-adrenoceptors). *No change in pupil diameter* may reflect the lack of an interaction of the antidepressant with these mechanisms (e.g. in the case of nomifensine and lower doses of mianserin), or the balanced effect of the drug on the mutually antagonistic cholinergic and adrenergic mechanisms (e.g. in the case of amitriptyline, when mydriasis resulting from muscarinic receptor and noradrenaline uptake blockade is likely to be counteracted by miosis resulting from alpha$_1$-adrenoceptor blockade; see Szabadi *et al*, 1980b; 1981). Only by studying the individual mechanisms in isolation using selective pharmacological challenges (see p. 204), it is possible to unravel the pharmacological mechanisms which underly the change (or lack of change) in resting pupil diameter. There is evidence that the effect of an antidepressant on resting pupil size is influenced by such factors as the dosage used and the duration of treatment. Thus smaller doses of desipramine and binodaline have been reported to be without any effect on resting pupil size, whereas higher doses of the same drugs cause mydriasis (see Table II), suggesting that the low doses were probably sub-threshold for the effective blockade of noradrenaline uptake. Similarly, lower doses of mianserin have been shown to be without any effect on resting pupil size, whereas higher doses may cause miosis (see Table II); this has been related to the sedative effect of the drug at higher dose levels (Shur *et al*, 1983). Duration of treatment may be another important factor: amitriptyline has been reported to cause no change or a small miosis in acute experiments, but a small mydriasis during chronic administration (see Table II). It is possible that the mydriasis reflects the development of tolerance to the sedative effect of the drug during chronic treatment which allows the manifestation of the mydriasis resulting from muscarinic receptor and noradrenaline uptake blockade.

The study of the ocular pharmacology of antidepressants has important implications for the understanding of the relationship between anti-depressant medication and the risk of *glaucoma*. Although textbooks and data sheets on antidepressants warn the clinician of this risk, they either fail to give any guidance with respect to individual antidepressants, or implicate amitriptyline which has the highest affinity for muscarinic receptors. It should be borne in mind, however, that the risk of precipitating narrow angle glaucoma is not related to the blockade of muscarinic receptors per se, but to the degree of the resulting mydriasis (see van der Kolk *et al*, 1978). Therefore amitriptyline is unlikely to be associated with a high risk due to its minimal effect on resting pupil size. On the other hand desipramine, a drug with relatively low affinity for muscarinic receptors, is likely to carry a relatively high risk due to its marked mydriatic effect resulting presumably from noradrenaline uptake blockade (Szabadi *et al*, 1981). Therefore one cannot condone the advice given in a current authoritative textbook of pharmacology: 'The most rational choice of an antidepressant in such a case [i.e. elderly patients with narrow angle glaucoma] would be desipramine, due to its relatively low anti-cholinergic potency' (Baldessarini, 1980). We would suggest that when the risk of glaucoma is a relevant consideration, an antidepressant should be chosen that either does not affect or reduces resting pupil size (see Table II).

Vascular smooth muscle

In general, the activation of post-junctional $alpha_1$- and $alpha_2$-adrenoceptors is associated with vasoconstriction, whereas the activation of $beta_2$-adrenoceptors and muscarinic cholinoceptors results in vasodilatation (see Mayer, 1980; Vanhoutte & Flavahan, 1985).

Systemic blood pressure

Although systematic blood pressure can give some indication of the activity of resistance vessels, it is influenced by cardiac output, and is under the control of numerous regulatory mechanisms. Therefore changes in systemic blood pressure in the presence of an antidepressant are difficult to interpret. On the other hand, useful information has been provided by recording changes in the pressor or depressor responses to systemically administered vaso-active agents (see below).

Clinical relevance   Little is known about the effect of depression on systemic blood pressure. Tölle (1970) found no significant differences in resting blood pressure between a group of depressed patients and a group of control subjects; the orthostatic blood pressure rise was diminished in the depressed group. The depressor response to methacholine has been reported to be enhanced in depressed patients (Davies & Palmai, 1964). There have been contradictory reports on pressor responses to sympathomimetic amines in depressed patients: Prange *et al* (1967) described a reduced noradrenaline-evoked pressor response, and concluded that depression was associated with a diminished sensitivity of peripheral alpha-adrenoceptors, whereas Ghose *et al* (1975) and Coppen & Ghose (1978) found enhanced pressor responses to noradrenaline, phenylephrine and tyramine, and concluded that depression was accompanied by an increased sensitivity of alpha-adrenoceptors. Further work is needed to clarify the reasons for these discrepant findings.

Orthostatic hypotension can be a troublesome complication of treatment with tricyclic antidepressants (see Bigger *et al*, 1978; Baldessarini, 1980; Orme, 1984), some atypical antidepressants (e.g. trazodone: Al-Yassiri *et al*, 1981), and monoamine oxidase inhibitors (see Tyrer, 1979; Baldessarini, 1980; Orme, 1984). Severe hypotension can be observed following acute overdosage of tricyclic antidepressants (Bigger *et al*, 1978; Orme, 1984); there are, however, conflicting reports concerning the incidence of this complication (cf. Langou *et al*, 1980; Pedersen *et al*, 1982). The hypotensive effect of antidepressants is rather surprising since several actions of these drugs would be expected to raise blood pressure: adrenergic vasoconstriction could be potentiated as a result of noradrenaline uptake blockade, monoamine oxidase inhibition, and pre-junctional $alpha_2$-adrenoceptor blockade, and cholinergic vasodilatation could be antagonised as a result of muscarinic receptor blockade. The orthostatic hypotension may be only partly related to the blockade of vascular alpha$_1$-adrenoceptors; a decrease in cardiac output due to a direct action on the heart (Orme, 1984), the possibility of sympathetic ganglion blockade (see p. 194), or a possible central blood pressure lowering effect should also be considered. Monoamine oxidase inhibitors may lower blood pressure either due to sympathetic ganglion blockade (see p. 194), or via the synthesis of 'false transmitters' in the peripheral adrenergic nerve terminals, which would result in reduced noradrenergic transmission (see Weiner, 1980b).

Important drug interactions can manifest as changes in systemic blood pressure: monoamine oxidase inhibitors can provoke a severe hypertensive crisis by impeding the degradation of some pressor amines (e.g. tyramine ingested in food, phenylproponolamine administered in cold cures), and tricyclic antidepressants can reduce the effectiveness of some antihypertensive agents (adrenergic neurone blocking drugs: guanethidine, bethanedine, debrisoquine; centrally acting antihypertensives: alpha-methyl-DOPA, clonidine) (see: Bigger *et al*, 1978; Baldessarini, 1980; Orme, 1984).

Effects of antidepressants on baseline blood pressure   Although the hypotensive propensity of antidepressants is well known in the clinical situation (see above), single dose experiments with normal volunteers do not always reveal this effect. Thus relatively little changes in blood pressure have been reported after the administration of the following antidepressants: imipramine (DiMascio *et al*, 1964), desipramine (DiMascio *et al*, 1964; Arnold *et al*, 1981), amitriptyline (Kopera, 1978; Saletu *et al*, 1980; Arnold *et al*, 1981), mianserin (Kopera, 1978; Elliott *et al*, 1981), binodaline (Saletu *et al*, 1980), doxepine (Arnold *et al*, 1981), nomifensine (Hamilton *et al*, 1983), bupropion (Hamilton *et al*, 1983). Therefore acute volunteer experiments do not seem to be good predictors of changes in blood pressure in the course of chronic treatment with antidepressants.

Effects of antidepressants on pressor responses to sympathomimetic drugs The intravenous infusion of noradrenaline, phenylephrine and tyramine results in a rise in blood ('pressor response': for review of methodology, see Ghose, 1980c); the effects of antidepressants on these responses have been studied extensively. The *noradrenaline-evoked pressor response* has been reported to be potentiated by some antidepressants but not by others (see Table III). In general, these observations are in good agreement with the known effectiveness of these drugs on noradrenaline uptake: all the antidepressants which enhance the pressor response to noradrenaline are effective blockers of noradrenaline uptake, whereas the ineffective drugs have only low affinities for the uptake site (see Richelson & Pfenning, 1984). The only exception seems to be maprotiline whose uptake blocking property is well documented (Richelson & Pfenning, 1984). It should be noted, however, that maprotiline effectively blocked the pressor response to tyramine in the same subjects (see below), suggesting that the decrease in the tyramine-evoked

TABLE III

Effects of antidepressants on pressor responses to sympathomimetic drugs

Challenge	Effect of antidepressant	Antidepressant	References
Noradrenaline	Potentiation	Imipramine	Prange et al (1964; 1967); Larochelle et al (1979); Borg et al (1979)
		Desipramine	Mitchell et al (1970)
		Clomipramine	Borg et al (1979)[1]
		Amitriptyline	Prange et al (1967); Coppen & Ghose (1978); Ghose et al (1978); Ghose (1980b)
	No effect	Doxepin	Fann et al (1971)
		Ciclazindol	Ghose et al (1978); Ghose (1980b)
		Trazodone	Larochelle et al (1979)
		Mianserin	Ghose (1977); Ghose et al (1980b)
		Iprindole	Fann et al (1972)
		Zimelidine	Borg et al (1979)
		Maprotiline	Briant & George (1974)
Phenylephrine	Antagonism	Amitriptyline	Coppen & Ghose (1978); Ghose et al (1978); Ghose (1980b)
		Ciclazindol	Ghose et al (1978)[1]
	No effect	Mianserin	Ghose (1980b)
Tyramine	Antagonism	Imipramine	Ghose et al (1976c); Larochelle et al (1979)
		Desipramine	Mitchell et al (1970); Ghose et al (1976b; 1977); Ehsanullah et al (1977a; 1977b); McEwen (1977)
		Amitriptyline	Ghose (1976); Ghose et al (1976a); Ghose & Coppen (1977); Coppen & Ghose (1978); Ghose et al (1978); Ghose (1980a; 1980b); Hassan et al (1985)
		Nortriptyline	Freyschuss et al (1970)
		Maprotiline	Briant & George (1974)
		Nomifensine	McEwen (1977)
		Ciclazindol	Ehsanullah et al (1977b); Ghose et al (1977)

continued

Challenge	Effect of antidepressant	Antidepressant	References
Tyramine	Antagonism	Tandamine	Ehsanullah *et al* (1977a)
		Viloxazine	Ghose *et al* (1976c)
		Doxepin	Fann *et al* (1971)
	No effect	Trazodone	Larochelle *et al* (1979)
		Mianserin	Ghose *et al* (1976a); Ghose (1980b)
		Butriptyline	Ghose *et al* (1977)
		Iprindole	Fann *et al* (1972)
		Paroxetine	Hassan *et al* (1985)

[1] weak effect

pressor response is probably a more sensitive index of noradrenaline uptake blockade. The *phenylephrine-evoked pressor response* has been shown to be antagonized by amitriptyline (Coppen & Ghose, 1978; Ghose *et al*, 1978; Ghose, 1980b), only slightly reduced by ciclazindol (Ghose *et al*, 1978), and unaffected by mianserin (Ghose, 1980b), revealing the degree of alpha$_1$-adrenoceptor blockade by these drugs. The *tyramine-evoked pressor response* has been reported to be antagonised by some antidepressants but not affected by others (see Table III). The effectiveness of antidepressants in antagonising the tyramine-evoked pressor response is in good agreement with their ability to block noradrenaline uptake (see Richelson & Pfenning, 1984).

Fig. 4 illustrates how pressor responses to noradrenaline, phenylephrine and tyramine were modified by amitriptyline, in the same patient: while the response to noradrenaline was potentiated, responses to phenylephrine and tyramine were antagonised.

Dorsal vein of hand

Since systemic blood pressure is subject to numerous regulatory mechanisms (see p. 208), there is great need for tests which enable the study of changes in isolated segments of the vascular bed. The dorsal vein of the hand seems to

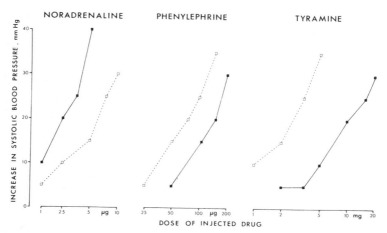

Fig. 4 — Dose-pressor response curves to noradrenaline, phenylephrine and tyramine obtained in one male patient before and during treatment with amitriptyline. Ordinate: increase in systolic blood pressure (mmHg), abscissa: dose of injected sympathomimetic amine. Open squares: values obtained before initiation of treatment; closed squares: values obtained after a fortnight's treatment with amitriptyline (150 mg daily). Note that the response to noradrenaline was potentiated, whereas responses to phenyleprrine and tyramine were antagonised.
Data reproduced, with permission, from Ghose (1980b).

offer such a possibility; drugs can be applied by local infusion, and constrictor and dilator responses can be recorded either optically as changes in the diameter of the vein, or manometrically as changes in venous pressure (for review, see Turner, 1980; Ghose, 1980c). It has been reported that desipramine antagonises the venoconstriction evoked by tyramine (Ghose *et al*, 1976b); this is consistent with the uptake blocking property of the antidepressant.

Cardiac muscle

Antidepressants can affect different aspects of cardiac function (e.g. heart rate, atrioventricular conduction, myocardial contractility) (for reviews, see Bigger *et al*, 1978; Baldessarini, 1980; Orme, 1984). Here we shall discuss only heart rate, for two reasons: firstly, heart rate is under a mutually antagonistic sympathetic/parasympathetic control and thus can be affected by drugs which interact with the adrenergic and cholinergic neuroeffector junctions in a predictable fashion (see p. 191), and secondly, this measure can easily be recorded under both clinical and laboratory conditions. While some antidepressants cause tachycardia, others have been reported not to change resting heart rate (see Table II). The following mechanisms may underly the antidepressant-evoked tachycardia: (1) antagonism of parasympathetic cardiodeceleration (muscarinic receptor blockade); (2) potentiation of sympathetic cardioacceleration (noradrenaline uptake blockade, pre-junctional alpha$_2$-adrenoceptor blockade, monoamine oxidase inhibition); (3) reflex tachycardia resulting from hypotension. These multiple sites of action explain why heart rate is not a reliable index of muscarinic receptor blockade by antidepressants: indeed, the most consistent cardioacceleration has been observed in association with desipramine, a drug with a relatively low affinity for muscarinic receptors, whereas amitriptyline, a more potent antimuscarinic agent, has only weak and inconsistent effects on heart rate (see Szabadi *et al*, 1980b).

Acknowledgement

The preparation of this paper was supported by the Sir Jules Thorn Charitable Trust.

References

ALTSCHULE, M. D. (1964) Salivary changes in emotional states. *Medical Science*, 15, 60–61.
AL-YASSIRI, M. M., ANKIER, S. I. & BRIDGES, P. K. (1981) Trazodone — a new antidepressant. *Life Sciences*, 28, 2449–2458.

ARIËNS, E. J. & SIMONIS, A. M. (1983) Physiological and pharmacological aspects of adrenergic receptor classification. *Biochemical Pharmacology*, **32**, 1539-1545.

ARNOLD, S. E., KAHN, R. J., FALDETTA, L. L., LAING, R. A. & MCNAIR, D. M. (1981) Tricylic antidepressants and peripheral anticholinergic activity. *Psychopharmacology*, **74**, 325-328.

ATKINSON, J. & LADINSKY, H. (1972) A quantitative study of the anticholinergic action of several tricyclic antidepressants on the rat isolated fundal strip. *British Journal of Pharmacology*, **45**, 519-524.

BAGG, C. E. & CROOKES, T. G. (1966) Palmar digital sweating in women suffering from depression. *British Journal of Psychiatry*, **112**, 1251-1255.

BALDESSARINI, R. J. (1980) Drugs and the treatment of psychiatric disorders. In *The Pharmacological Basis of Therapeutics*, Sixth Edition (ed. A. Goodman Gilman, L. S. Goodman & A. Gilman), pp. 391-447. New York: Macmillan.

BERTRAM, U., KRAGH-SØRENSEN, P., RAFAELSEN, O. J. & LARSEN, N.-E. (1979) Saliva secretion following long-term antidepressant treatment with nortriptyline controlled by plasma levels. *Scandinavian Journal of Dental Research*, **87**, 58-64.

BEVAN, P., BRADSHAW, C. M. & SZABADI, E. (1975) The effect of tricyclic antidepressants on cholinergic responses of single cortical neurones. *British Journal of Pharmacology*, **45**, 519-524.

BEVAN-JONES, B. & LIND, N. A. (1971) Interactions of monoamine oxidase inhibition and sympathomimetic amines on the human iris. *British Journal of Pharmacology*, **41**, 428P.

BIGGER, J. T. KANTOR, S. J., GLASSMAN, A. H. & PEREL, J. M. (1978) Cardiovascular effects of tricyclic antidepressant drugs. In *Psychopharmacology: A Generation of Progress* (ed. M. A. Lipton, A. DiMascio & K. F. Killam), pp. 1033-1046. New York: Raven Press.

BLACKWELL, B., LIPKIN, J. O., MEYER, J. H., KUZMA, R. & BOULTER, W. V. (1972) Dose responses and relationship between anticholinergic activity and mood with tricyclic antidepressants. *Psychopharmacologia*, **25**, 205-217.

—— PETERSON, G. R., KUZMA, R. J., HOSTETLER, R. M. & ADOLPHE, E. (1980) The effect of five tricyclic antidepressants on salivary flow and mood in healthy volunteers. *Communications in Psychopharmacology*, **4**, 255-261.

—— STEFOPOULOS, A., ENDERS, P., KUZMA, R. & ADOLPHE, A. (1978) Anticholinergic activity of two tricyclic antidepressants. *American Journal of Psychiatry*, **135**, 722-724.

BOLWIG, T. & RAFAELSEN, O. (1972) Salivation in affective disorders. *Psychological Medicine*, **2**, 232-238.

BORG, K.-O., JOHNSSON, G., JORDÖ, L., LUNDBERG, P., RÖHN, O. & WELIN-FOGELBERG, I. (1979) Interaction between three antidepressant drugs (zimelidine, imipramine and chlorimipramine) and noradrenaline in healthy volunteers and some pharmacokinetics of the drugs studied. *Acta pharmacologica et toxicologica*, **45**, 198-205.

BRIANT, R. H. & GEORGE, C. F. (1974) The assessment of potential drug interactions with a new tricyclic antidepressant drug. *British Journal of clinical Pharmacology*, **1**, 113-118.

BROWN, C. C. (1970) The parotid puzzle: a review of the literature on human salivation and its applications to psychophysiology. *Psychophysiology*, **7**, 66-85.

BROWN, D. A. & CAULFIELD, M. (1978) Adrenoceptors in sympathetic ganglia. In *Recent Advances in the Pharmacology of Adrenoceptors* (ed. E. Szabadi, C. M. Bradshaw, and P. Bevan), pp. 57-66. Amsterdam: Elsevier/North Holland.

BUSFIELD, B. L. & WECHSLER, H. (1961) Studies of salivation in depression. I. A comparison of salivation rates in depressed, schizoaffective depressed, non-depressed hospitalized patients, and in normal control. *Archives of general Psychiatry*, **4**, 10-15.

—— WECHSLER, H. (1962) Salivation rate: A physiologic correlate of improvement in hospitalized depressed patients treated with three anti-depressant medications. *Psychosomatic Medicine*, **24**, 337-342.

—— WECHSLER, R. H. & BARNUM, W. J. (1961) Studies of salivation in depression II. Physiological differentiation of reactive and endogenous depression. *Archives of General Psychiatry*, **5**, 472-477.

BYE, C. E., CLUBLEY, M., HENSON, T., PECK, A. W., SMITH, S. A. & SMITH, S. E. (1979) Changes in the human light reflex as a measure of the anticholinergic effects of drugs. A comparison with other measures. *European Journal of Clinical Pharmacology*, **15**, 21-25.

CAIRNCROSS, K. D., McCULLOCH, M. W., STORY, D. F. & TRINKER, F. (1967) Modification of synaptic transmission in the superior cervial ganglion by epinephrine, norepinephrine and nortriptyline. *International Journal of Neuropharmacology*, **6**, 293–300.

CHALMERS, T. M. & KEELE, C. A. (1951) Physiological significance of the sweat response to adrenaline in man. *Journal of Physiology*, **114**, 510–514.

CHARNEY, D. S., MENKES, D. B. & HENINGER, G. R. (1981) Receptor sensitivity and the mechanism of action of antidepressant treatment. *Archives of General Psychiatry*, **38**, 1160–1180.

CLEMMESEN, L., MIKELSEN, P. L., LUND, H., BOLWIG, T. G. & RAFAELSEN, O. J. (1984a) Assessment of the anticholinergic effects of antidepressants in a single-dose cross-over study of salivation and plasma levels. *Psychopharmacology*, **82**, 348–354.

—— JENSEN, E., MIN, S. K., BOLWIG, T. G. & RAFAELSEN, O. J. (1984b) Salivation after single-doses of the new antidepressants femoxoline, mianserin and citalopram. A cross-over study. *Pharmacopsychiatry*, **17**, 126–132.

CLUBLEY, M., BYE, C. E., HENSON, T., PECK, A. W. & RIDDINGTON, C. (1978) A technique for studying the effects of drugs on human sweat gland activity. *European Journal of Clinical Pharmacology*, **16**, 221–226.

COPPEN, A. & GHOSE, K. (1978) Peripheral alpha-adrenoceptor and central dopamine receptor activity in depressive patients. *Psychopharmacology*, **59**, 171–177.

DAVIES, B. M. & GURLAND, J. B. (1961) Salivary secretion in depressive illness. *Journal of Psychosomatic Research*, **5**, 269–271.

—— PALMAI, G. (1964) Salivary and blood pressure responses to methacholine in depressive illness. *British Journal of Psychiatry*, **110**, 594–598.

DiMASCIO, A., HENNINGER, G. & KLERMAN, G. L. (1964) Psychopharmacology of imipramine and desipramine. *Psychopharmacologia*, **5**, 361–371.

EHSANULLAH, R., GHOSE, K., KIRBY, M., WITT, D. & TURNER, P. (1977a) Clinical pharmacological studies of tandamine, a potential antidepressive drug. *Psychopharmacology*, **52**, 73–77.

—— KIRBY, M. J., LEIGHTON, M. & OH, V. M. S. (1977b) Some clinical pharmacological studies with ciclazindol hydrochloride. *British Journal of clinical Pharmacology*, **4**, 400P.

ELLIOTT, H. L., McLEAN, K., SUMMER, D. J. & REID, J. L. (1981) Pharmacodynamic studies on mianserin and its interaction with clonidine. *European Journal of Clinical Pharmacology*, **21**, 97–102.

FANN, W. E., CAVANAUGH, J. H., DAVIS, J. M., KAUFMANN, J. S., GRIFFITH, J. D. & OATES, J. A. (1971) Doxepin: effects on biogenic amine transport. *Psychopharmacologia*, **22**, 126–132.

—— DAVIS, J. M., JANOWSKY, D. S., KAUFMANN, J. S., GRIFFITH, J. D. & OATES, J. A. (1972) Effect of iprindole on amine uptake in man. *Archives of General Psychiatry*, **26**, 158–162.

FOSTER, K. G. & WEINER, J. S. (1967) The continuous monitoring of sweat secretion of man and cat using a ventilated capsule and an infrared analyser. *Journal of Physiology*, **191**, 1-2P.

FREYSCHUSS, A., SJÖQUIST, F. & TUCK, D. (1970) Tyramine pressor effects in man before and during treatment with nortriptyline and E.C.T: Correlation between plasma level and effect of nortriptyline. *Pharmacologia Clinica*, **2**, 72–78.

GHOSE, K. (1976) Correlation of pupil reactivity to tyramine or hydroxyamphetamine and tyramine pressor responses in patients treated with amitriptyline or mianserin. *British Journal of Clinical Pharmacology*, **3**, 666–667.

—— (1977) Studies on the interaction between mianserin and noradrenaline in patients suffering from depressive illness. *British Journal of Clinical Pharmacology*, **4**, 712–716.

—— (1980a) Decreased tyramine sensitivity after discontinuation of amitriptyline therapy — an index of pharmacodynamic half-life. *European Journal of Clinical Pharmacology*, **18**, 151–157.

—— (1980b) Assessment of peripheral adrenergic activity and its interactions with drugs in man. *European Journal of clinical Pharmacology*, **17**, 233–238.

—— (1980c) Biochemical assessment of antidepressive drugs. *British Journal of Clinical Pharmacology*, **10**, 539–550.

—— COPPEN, A. (1977) Noradrenaline, depressive illness and the action of amitriptyline. *Psychopharmacology*, **54**, 57–60.

—— COPPEN, A. & TURNER, P. (1976a) Autonomic actions and interactions of mianserin hydrochloride (Org. GB 94) and amitriptyline in patients with depressive illness. *Psychopharmacology*, **49**, 201–204.

——— DOBREE, C., TAYLOR, P. & TURNER, P. (1974) Interactions of amitriptyline with guanethidine and thymoxamine in the human iris. *British Journal of Clinical Pharmacology*, 1, 516–517.

——— GIFFORD, L. A., TURNER, P. & LEIGHTON, M. (1976b) Studies of the interaction of desmethylimipramine with tyramine after a single oral dose, and its correlation with plasma concentration. *British Journal of Clinical Pharmacology*, 3, 334–337.

——— HUSTON, G. J., KIRBY, M. J., WITTS, D. J. & TURNER, P. (1977) Some Clinical pharmacological studies with butriptyline, an antidepressant drug. *British Journal of Clinical Pharmacology*, 4, 91–93.

——— RAO, V. A. R., BAILEY, J. & COPPEN, A. (1978) Antidepressant activity and pharmacological interactions of ciclazindol. *Psychopharmacology*, 57, 109–114.

——— TURNER, P. & COPPEN, A. (1975) Intravenous tyramine pressor response in depression. *Lancet*, i, 1317–1318.

——— TURNER, P. & GRANT, I. N. (1976c) The assessment of interactions in man between tyramine and viloxazine hydrochloride, an antidepressant drug. *British Journal of Clinical Pharmacology*, 3, 668–671.

GILMARTIN, B., HOGAN, R. E. & THOMPSON, S. M. (1984) The effect of timolol maleate on tonic accommodation, tonic vergence, and pupil diameter. *Investigative Ophthalmology & Visual Science*, 25, 763–770.

GOTTLIEB, G. & PAULSON, G. (1961) Salivation in depressed patients. *Archives of General Psychiatry*, 5, 468–471.

GYERMEK, L. (1966) The pharmacology of imipramine and related antidepressants. *International Review of Neurobiology*, 9, 95–143.

HAMILTON, M. J., SMITH, P. R. & PECK, A. W. (1983) Effects of bupropion, nomifensine and dexamphetamine on performance, subjective feelings, autonomic variables and electroencephalogram in healthy volunteers. *British Journal of clinical Pharmacology*, 15, 367–374.

HASSAN, S. M., WAINSCOTT, G. & TURNER, P. (1985) A comparison of the effect of paroxetine and amitriptyline on the tyramine pressor response test. *British Journal of clinical Pharmacology*, 19, 705–706.

HAVENER, W. H. (1983) *Ocular Pharmacology*. Fifth Edition, Toronto: Mosby.

IKEDA, Y., NOMURA, S., SAWA, Y. & NAKAZAWA, (1982) The effects of antidepressants on the autonomic nervous system — a current investigation. *Journal of Neurotransmission*, 54, 65–73.

IVERSEN, L. L. & MACKAY, A. V. P. (1979) Pharmacodynamics of antidepressants and antimanic drugs. In *Psychopharmacology of Affective Disorder* (ed. E. S. Paykel and A. Coppen), pp. 60–90. Oxford: Oxford University Press.

KADZIELAWA, K., GAWECKA, I. & KADZIELAWA, R. (1968) The potentiating influence of imipramine on ganglionic effects of catecholamines. *International Journal of Neuropharmacology*, 7, 517–521.

KARNIOL, I. G., DALTON, J. & LADER, M. (1976) Comparative psychotropic effects of trazodone, imipramine and diazepam in normal subjects. *Current Therapeutic Research*, 20, 337–348.

KERR, F. A. & SZABADI, E. (1985) Comparison of the effects of chronic administration of ciclazindol and desipramine on pupillary responses to tyramine, methoxamine and pilocarpine in healthy volunteers. *British Journal of clinical Pharmacology*, 19, 639–647.

KITAZAWA, Y. & LANGHAM, M. E. (1968) Influence of an adrenergic potentiator on the ocular response to catecholamines in primates and man. *Nature*, 219, 1376–1378.

KNORRING, L. VON (1981) Changes in saliva secretion and accommodation width during short-term administration of imipramine and zimeledine in healthy volunteers. *International Pharmacopsychiatry*, 16, 69–78.

KOPERA, H. (1978) Anticholinergic and blood pressure effects of mianserin, amitriptyline and placebo. *British Journal of clinical Pharmacology*, 5, 29–34S.

LADER, M. H. & WING, L. (1969) Physiological measures in agitated and retarded depressed patients. *Journal of Psychiatric Research*, 7, 89–100.

LANGER, S. Z. & DUBOCOVICH, M. L. (1978) Physiological and pharmacological relevance of presynaptic beta-adrenoceptors in modulating transmitter release. In *Recent Advances in the Pharmacology of Adrenoceptors* (ed. E. Szabadi, C. M. Bradshaw and P. Bevan), pp. 181–190. Amsterdam: Elsevier/North Holland.

LANGHAM, M. E. & CARMEL, D. D. (1968) The action of protriptyline on adrenergic mechanisms in rabbit, primate and human eyes. *Journal of Pharmacology and Experimental Therapeutics*, **163**, 368–378.

LANGOU, R. A., VAN DYKE, C., TAHAN, S. R. & COHEN, L. S. (1980) Cardiovascular manifestations of tricyclic antidepressant overdose. *American Heart Journal*, **100**, 458–464.

LAROCHELLE, P., HAMET, P. & ENJALBERT, M. (1979) Responses to tyramine and norepinephrine after imipramine and trazodone. *Clinical Pharmacology and Therapeutics*, **26**, 24–30.

LAUBER, H. L. (1967) Pupillometrische Versuche bei Anwendung von Psychopharmaca. *Medizinische Welt*, **18**, 572–574.

—— HARTMAN, R. & HERRMANN, D. (1967) The effects of tranquillizers and thymoleptic drugs on the human pupil. *German Medical Monthly*, **12**, 232–234.

LOEW, D. (1965) Syndrom, Diagnose und Speichelsekretion bei depressiven Patienten. *Psychopharmacologia*, **7**, 339–348.

LONGMORE, J., BANJAR, W., SZABADI, E. & BRADSHAW, C. M. (1986) Effects of a new, controlled-release formulation of trazodone on psychomotor and autonomic functions in healthy volunteers. *British Journal of clinical Pharmacology*, in press.

—— BRADSHAW, C. M. & SZABADI, (1985a) Effects of locally and systemically administered cholinoceptor antagonists on the secretory response of human eccrine sweat glands to carbachol. *British Journal of clinical Pharmacology*, **20**, 1–7.

—— SZABADI, E. & BRADSHAW, C. M. (1985b) Comparison of the effects of binodaline and amitriptyline on peripheral autonomic functions in healthy volunteers. *British Journal of Clinical Pharmacology*, **19**, 295–300.

LOWENSTEIN, O. & LOEWENFELD, I. E. (1958) Electronic pupillography: A new instrument and some clinical applications. *Archives of Ophthalmology*, **59**, 352–362.

—— & LOEWENFELD, I. E. (1962) The pupil. In *The Eye, Volume 3: Muscular Mechanisms*. (ed. H. Davison), pp. 231–267. New York: Academic Press.

MACKINNON, P. C. B. (1963) Plastic paint and eccrine sweat glands. *Medical biological Illustration*, **14**, 13–16.

MAYER, S. E. (1980) Neurochemical transmission and the autonomic nervous system. In *The Pharmacological Basis of Therapeutics*, Sixth Edition (ed. A. Goodman Gilman, L. S. Goodman & A. Gilman), pp. 56–90. New York: Macmillan.

MCEWEN, J., JENKINSON, D., MONTGOMERY, I. & ELDER, H. Y. (1978) Studies on the nature of the peripheral sudomotor control mechanism. *Journal of Anatomy*, **125**, 625–639.

MCEWEN, J. (1977) Influence of nomifensine and desipramine on tyramine pressor responses in healthy volunteers. *British Journal of clinical Pharmacology*, **4**, 157–158.

MCGEER, P. L., ECCLES, J. C. & MCGEER, E. G. (1978) *Molecular Neurobiology of the Mammalian Brain*. New York: Plenum Press.

MINNEMAN, K. P., DIBNER, M. D., WOLFE, B. B. & MOLINOFF, P. B. (1979) Beta$_1$- and beta$_2$-adrenergic receptors in rat cerebral cortex are independently regulated. *Science*, **208**, 866–867.

MITCHELL, J. E. & POPKIN, M. K. (1983) Antidepressant drug therapy and sexual dysfunction in men: a review. *Journal of Clinical Psychopharmacology*, **3**, 76–79.

MITCHELL, J. R., CAVANAUGH, J. H., ARIAS, L. & OATES, J. A. (1970) Guanethidine and related agents: III. Antagonism by drugs which inhibit the norepinephrine pump in man. *Journal of Clinical Investigation*, **49**, 1596–1604.

NICKERSON, M. & RUEDY, J. (1975) Antihypertensive agents and the drug therapy of hypertension. In *The Pharmacological Basis of Therapeutics*, Fifth Edition. (ed. L. S. Goodman & A. Gilman), pp. 705–726. New York: Macmillan.

NOBLE, P. J. & LADER, M. H. (1971) Salivary secretion and depressive illness: a physiological and psychometric study. *Psychological Medicine*, **1**, 372–376.

—— LADER, M. H. (1972) A physiological comparison of 'endogenous' and 'reactive' depression. *British Journal of Psychiatry*, **120**, 541–542.

ORME, M. L'E. (1984) Antidepressants and heart disease. *British Medical Journal*, **289**, 1–2.

OWE-LARSSON, A. (1956) The local effect on the eye of noradrenaline. *Acta Ophthalmologica*, **34**, 27–34.

PALM, D., FENGLER, H.-J., GÜLLNER, H.-G., PLANZ, G., QUIRING, K., MAY, B., HEMSTAEDT, D., LEMMER, B., MOON, H. K. & HOLLER, C. (1971) Quantitation of irreversible inhibition of monoamine oxidase in man. *European Journal of Clinical Pharmacology*, 3, 82–92.

PALMAI, G. & BLACKWELL, B. (1965) The pattern of salivary flow in normal and depressed patients. *British Journal of Psychiatry*, 111, 334–338.

—— BLACKWELL, B., MAXWELL, E. & MORGENSTERN, F. (1967) Patterns of salivary flow in depressive illness and during treatment. *British Journal of Psychiatry*, 113, 1297–1308.

PAYKEL, E. S. & COPPEN, A. (1979) *Psychopharmacology of Affective Disorders*. Oxford: Oxford University Press.

PECK, A. W., CLUBLEY, M., HENSON, T., BYE, C. E. & RIDDINGTON, C. (1979) A comparison of bupropion hydrochloride with dexamphetamine and amitriptyline in healthy subjects. *British Journal of Clinical Pharmacology*, 7, 469–478.

PECK, R. E. (1959) The SHP test — an aid in the detection and measurement of depression. *Archives of General Psychiatry*, 1, 35–40.

PEDERSEN, O. L., GRAM, L. F., KRISTENSEN, C. B., MØLLER, M., THAYSSEN, P., BJERRE, M., KRAGH-SØRENSEN, P., KLITGAARD, N. A., SINDRUP, E., HOLE, P. & BRINKLØV, M. (1982) Overdosage of antidepressants Clinical and pharmacokinetic aspects. *European Journal of clinical Pharmacology*, 23, 513–521.

PETERSON, G. R., BLACKWELL, B., HOHTETLER, R. M., KUZMA, R. & ADOLPHE, A. (1978) Anticholinergic activity of the tricyclic antidepressants desipramine and doxepin in nondepressed volunteers. *Communications in Psychopharmacology*, 2, 145–150.

PRANGE, A. J., MCCURDY, R. L. & COCHRANE, C. M. (1967) The systolic blood pressure response of depressed patients to infused norepinephrine. *Journal of Psychiatric Research*, 5, 1–13.

—— PUSTROM, E. E. & COCHRANE, C. M. (1964) Imipramine enhancement of norepinephrine in normal humans. *Psychiatric Digest*, 25, 27–28.

RAFAELSEN, O. J., CLEMMESEN, L., LUND, H., MIKKELSEN, P. L. & BOLWIG, T. G. (1981) Comparison of peripheral anticholinergic effects of antidepressants: dry mouth. *Acta Psychiatrica Scandinavica*, 63, 364–369.

RICHELSON, E. & NELSON, A. (1984) Antagonism by antidepressants of neurotransmitter receptors of normal human brain *in vitro*. *Journal of Pharmacology and Experimental Therapeutics*, 230, 94–102.

—— PFENNING, M. (1984) Blockade by antidepressants and related compounds of biogenic amine uptake into rat brain synaptosomes: most antidepressants selectively block norepinephrine uptake. *European Journal of Pharmacology*, 104, 277–286.

RUDORFER, M. V. & YOUNG, R. C. (1980) Anticholinergic effects and plasma desipramine levels. *Clinical Pharmacology and Therapeutics*, 28, 703–705.

SALETU, B., GRÜNBERGER, J., LINZMAYER, L. & ANDERER, P. (1980) Classification and assessment of pharmacodynamics of SGD-SCHA1059 (binodaline) by quantitative EEG and psychometric analyses. *Advances in Biological Psychiatry*, 4, 140–166.

SATO, K. (1977) Physiology, pharmacology and biochemistry of the eccrine sweat gland. *Reviews of Physiology, Biochemistry and Pharmacology*, 79, 51–131.

SCHILDKRAUT, J. J. (1965) The catecholamine hypothesis of affective disorders: a review of the supporting evidence. *American Journal of Psychiatry*, 122, 509–514.

SCHUBERT, D. S. P. (1973) The effect of lithium and other antidepressant medications on the autonomic nervous system. *Current Therapeutic Research*, 15, 862–865.

SHETH, U. K., PAUL, T., DESAI, N. K. & PISPATI, P. K. (1979) Comparative effects of imipramine and dothiepin on salivary rate in normal volunteers. *British Journal of Clinical Pharmacology*, 8, 475–478.

SHUR, E. & CHECKLEY, S. (1982) Pupil studies in depressed patients: an investigation of the mechanism of action of desipramine. *British Journal of Psychiatry*, 140, 181–184.

—— CHECKLEY, S. & DELGADO, I. (1983) Failure of mianserin to affect autonomic function in the pupils of depressed patients. *Acta Psychiatrica Scandinavica*, 67, 50–55.

SILVERMAN, J. J. & POWELL, V. E. (1944) Studies on palmar sweating: I. A technique for the study of palmar sweating. *American Journal of Medical Science*, 208, 297–299.

SITARAM, N., JONES, D., KELWALA, S., BELL, J., STEVENSON, J. & GERSHON, S. (1983) Pharmacology of the human iris: development and use of challenge strategies in the study of antidepression response. *Progress in Neuro-Psychopharmacology & Biological Psychiatry*, 7, 273–286.

SNEDDON, J. M. & TURNER, P. (1969) The interactions of local guanethidine and sympathomimetic amines in the human eye. *Archives of Ophthalmology*, **81**, 622–627.

SNYDER, S. H. & YAMAMURA, H. I. (1977) Antidepressants and the muscarinic acetylcholine receptor. *Archives of general Psychiatry*, **34**, 236–239.

STARKE, K. (1978) Release-modulating alpha-adrenoceptors. In *Recent Advances in the Pharmacology of Adrenoceptors* (ed. E. Szabadi, C. M. Bradshaw and P. Bevan), pp. 173–180. Amsterdam: Elsevier/North Holland.

STEVENS, J. B. & WILKINSON, E. G. (1971) Drugs, dry mouth and dental disease. *Psychosomatics*, **12**, 310–312.

STRONGIN, E. I. & HINSIE, L. E. (1938) Parotid gland secretions in manic-depressive patients. *American Journal of Psychiatry*, **94**, 1459–1466.

SUGRE, M. F. (1983) Chronic antidepressant therapy and associated changes in central monoaminergic receptor functioning. *Pharmacology and Therapeutics*, **21**, 1–33.

SZABADI, E., BESSON, J. & BRADSHAW, C. M. (1975) Pupil responsiveness to tyramine in depressed patients treated with amitriptyline. *British Journal of clinical Pharmacology*, **2**, 362–363.

—— BRADSHAW, C. M. & BEVAN, P. (1978) *Recent Advances in the Pharmacology of Adrenoceptors*. Amsterdam: Elsevier/North Holland: Biological Press.

—— BRADSHAW, C. M. & NAHORSKI, S. R. (1985) *Pharmacology of Adrenoceptors*. Basingstoke: Macmillan.

—— GASZNER, P. & BRADSHAW, C. M. (1980a) Comparison of the effects of adrenoceptor and cholinoceptor agonists on sweat gland activity in man. *British Journal of Clinical Pharmacology*, **10**, 301–302.

—— GASZNER, P. & BRADSHAW, C. M. (1980b) The peripheral anticholinergic activity of tricyclic antidepressants: comparison of amitriptyline and desipramine in human volunteers. *British Journal of Psychiatry*, **137**, 433–439.

—— GASZNER, P. & BRADSHAW, C. M. (1981) Interaction of desipramine and amitriptyline with adrenergic mechanisms in the human iris in vivo. *European Journal of Clinical Pharmacology*, **19**, 403–408.

THOMAS, P. E. & KORR, I. M. (1957) Relationship between sweat gland activity and electrical resistance of the skin. *Journal of Applied Physiology*, **10**, 505–510.

THOMSON, M. L. & SUTARMAN (1953) The identification and enumeration of active sweat glands in man from plastic impression of the skin. *Transactions of the Royal Society of Tropical Medicine and Hygiene*, **47**, 412–417.

TÖLLE, R. (1970) Vegetative Effekte der Thymoleptika und ihre Beziehungen zur antidepressiven Wirksamkeit im Behandlungsverlauf. *Fortschritte der Neurologie, Psychiatrie und ihrer Grenzgebiete*, **38**, 1–20.

—— PÖRKSEN, N. (1969) Die thymoleptische Mydriasis im Behandlungsverlauf. *International Pharmacopsychiatry*, **2**, 86–98.

TOONE, B. K. & LADER, M. H. (1979) Salivary secretion in the affective disorders and schizophrenia. *Acta Psychiatrica Scandinavica*, **59**, 529–535.

TRENDELENBURG, U. (1972) Classification of sympathomimetic amines. In *Handbook of Experimental Pharmacology, Volume 33 Catecholamines*. (ed. H. Blaschko & E. Muscholl), pp. 336–362. Heidelberg: Springer.

TURNER, P. (1980) Tests of autonomic function in assessing centrally acting drugs. *British Journal of Clinical Pharmacology*, **10**, 93–99.

TYRER, P. (1979) Clinical use of monoamine oxidase inhibitors. In *Psychopharmacology of Affective Disorders* (ed. E. S. Paykel & A. Coppen), pp. 159–178. Oxford: Oxford University Press.

UNO, H. (1977) Sympathetic innervation of the sweat glands and piloerrector muscles of macaques and human beings. *Journal of Investigative Dermatology*, **69**, 112–120.

VAN DER KOLK, B. A., SHADER, R. I. & GREENBLATT, D. J. (1978) Autonomic effects of psychotropic drugs. In *Psychopharmacology: A Generation of Progress* (ed. M. A. Lipton, A. DiMascio and K. F. Killam), pp. 1009–1020. New York: Raven Press.

VANHOUTTE, P. M. & FLAVAHAN, N. A. (1985) The heterogeneity of adrenergic receptors. In *Pharmacology of Adrenoceptors* (ed. E. Szabadi, C. M. Bradshaw & S. R. Nahorski), pp. 43–46. Basingstoke: Macmillan.

VOLLE, R. L. & HANCOCK, J. C. (1970) Transmission in sympathetic ganglia. *Federation Proceedings*, **29**, 1913–1918.

WEINER, N. (1980a) Atropine, scopolamine, and related antimuscarinic drugs. In *The Pharmacological Basis of Therapeutics*, Sixth Edition (ed. A. Goodman Gilman, L. S. Goodman & A. Gilman), pp. 120–137. New York: Macmillan.

—— (1980b) Norepinephrine, epinephrine and the sympathomimetic amines. In *The Pharmacological Basis of Therapeutics*, Sixth Edition (ed. A. Goodman Gilman, L. S. Goodman & A. Gilman), pp. 138–175. New York: Macmilan.

ZIEGLER, V. E., TAYLOR, J. R., WETZEL, R. D. & BIGGS, J. T. (1978) Nortriptyline plasma levels and subjective side effects. *British Journal of Psychiatry*, **132**, 55–60.

Index

Acknowledgement

The book and the meeting were supported by an educational grant to the Royal College of Psychiatrists by E. Merck Ltd.